CW01083205

TYPE A4 PACIFIC EXPRESS LOCOMOTIVE No. 2510, " QUICKSILVER,"
LONDON AND NORTH EASTERN RAILWAY.

Mr. H. N. Gresley, C.B.E., Chief Mechanical Engineer.

Three cylinders, 18½ in. × 26 in.   Working pressure, 250 lb. per square inch.

STEAM
LOCOMOTIVE DESIGN:
DATA AND FORMULÆ

By
E. A. PHILLIPSON
Assoc.M.Inst.C.E., A.M.I.Mech.E., M.I.Loco.E.

1936

All rights reserved. No part of this publication may be reproduced, stored in a retrieval system, or transmitted in any form or by any means, electronic, mechanical, photocopying, recording or otherwise without prior permission in writing from the publishers.

British Library Cataloguing-in Publication-Data: a catalogue record of this book is held by the British Library.

First Printed in 1936 by The Locomotive Publishing Co. Ltd.

Second Printing 2004

ISBN No. 0-9536523-9-4

© 2004 the Estate of E.A. Phillipson & Camden Miniature Steam Services

Published in Great Britain by:

CAMDEN MINIATURE STEAM SERVICES
Barrow Farm, Rode, Frome, Somerset. BA11 6PS
www.camdenmin.co.uk

Reproduction by Salisbury Printing Co. Ltd.

Printed and Bound by Biddles Ltd., Guildford & Kings Lynn

Camden stock one of the widest selections of engineering, technical and transportation books to be found; contact them at the above address for a copy of their latest free Booklist

PREFACE.

THE technical literature available for the locomotive engineer comprises the many well-known works on the theory of heat engines, strength of materials, theory of structures, mechanics, mathematics and cognate subjects. It also includes much matter of a purely descriptive nature, of which *The Locomotive of To-day* may be cited as an excellent example. Between these two forms of publication there is a considerable hiatus, and the only apology which the author can offer for the present monograph is that it has been prepared with a view to bridging this gap by dealing with the application of pure technology, tempered, of course, by practice, to the design of the steam locomotive engine. Since it is avowedly of an intermediate nature, it has no pretensions to completeness as a treatise on the subject. Further, it has few, if any, claims to originality, as it is essentially a collection of data from various sources which, in the author's opinion, might conveniently be concentrated in one book; it is, in fact, merely a locomotive engineer's anthology.

Every endeavour has been made to include only the essential theory of heat engines and application of mechanics, and at the same time to avoid wearisome repetition of the most elementary principles on the one hand, and of abstruse academic theories, which have but limited application to everyday practice on the other. Historical details have been rigidly eschewed and descriptive passages avoided, except where they affect present-day considerations of design.

The author has attempted to treat the subject largely from the point of view of the running man. The latter is essentially a locomotive engineer, in the true sense of the term, and has the advantage over his colleague attached to the shops, who naturally inclines to be a general mechanical engineer, in that he knows precisely the conditions of operation and maintenance, what is demanded by them, and can forecast fairly closely the probable reaction thereto of any given form of design.

The divergence between theory and practice, being considerably more marked in the case of the locomotive than in many fields of engineering, has encouraged the growth of empirical formulæ. These have almost invariably a distinctly limited application, and the danger of their indiscriminate use cannot be over emphasised. The repeated application of such formulæ to the proportioning of details inevitably tends to hinder the natural progress of improvements in design. Again, many such formulæ have been evolved from data obtained on American test plants. The information thus obtained has been, and is, of considerable value, and the author would be the last to decry the researches of American workers. Nevertheless, the conclusions formed by them must not be too slavishly applied; conditions obtaining in America differ so widely from our own, and results from the test bed are obtained under constant conditions of operation, *i.e.*, not subject to the variables arising in actual traffic. On the other hand, the results of a purely comparative nature which have been obtained are of great value to the locomotive engineer, who is further indebted to such researches for data which could not otherwise be secured.

Many items of locomotive design involve controversial points which may be debated with equal force from entirely antipodean angles; the opinion formed by the individual engineer will be largely influenced by his previous experience and by the conditions peculiar to the system with which he is personally connected. In all such cases the author has endeavoured to present fairly both sides of the case. It is, however, very difficult to be strictly impartial unless one is completely detached from the locomotive engineering profession, and the author would take this opportunity of apologising for any personal bias which may have crept into the text.

Another difficulty which arises is the correct determination of the boundary between qualitative and quantitative data. Much information in the former category, although fundamentally necessary, is in itself of small intrinsic value, yet on the other hand, since each individual locomotive design is most emphatically a law unto itself, the application of quantitative data may be very misleading on occasion. The author can therefore only express the hope that he has succeeded in advancing the two forms of data in their appropriate proportions.

Lastly, locomotive design is largely a matter of compromise, the opposing factors usually being thermo-dynamic and mechanical considerations respectively. The relative importance attached to each is dictated by the experience and judgment of the individual designer, and the degree of success with which this proportioning is carried out in every detail will determine the ultimate commercial efficiency of the locomotive as a whole. In presenting both sides of such questions the author has necessarily been obliged to make statements which, when compared, appear to be contradictory, and he will leave it to the discretion of the reader as to which deserves primary consideration when the time for arbitration arrives.

Various references have been made to the Proceedings of the Institutions of Civil, Mechanical and Locomotive Engineers. Other information of a specialised nature has been requested, and willingly given, by firms in a position to do so. Similarly, the publication of dimensioned drawings has been made possible entirely by the kind permission, spontaneously granted, of the executives of the railway companies, locomotive builders and other manufacturing organisations. In all these cases the intention of the author has been to acknowledge the source of the data concerned where published. Should there be any omissions, the author would take this opportunity of proffering his apologies therefor. He must also acknowledge his indebtedness to Mr. A. E. English, B.Sc., of the L.N.E.R., for his careful checking of Chapters IX and X, and assistance in the preparation of the analysis of coupling rod and axlebox loadings.

CONTENTS

Chapter I.

EXTRANEOUS CONSIDERATIONS.

BEFORE commencing the design proper of the locomotive, consideration must be given to the external conditions obtaining. Typical examples of these conditions are given hereunder.

Climatic Conditions. The prevailing atmospheric humidity affects the permissible minimum factor of adhesion and also the efficiency of combustion. Ruling temperatures, if high, may dictate the use of hot water injectors. Suitable protection from the rays of the sun or other climatic extremes must be afforded the enginemen. Sanding gear, to take a random example, is an unnecessary refinement on engines which habitually work in arid desert areas. High altitudes may render difficult the use of the vacuum brake. Special measures must be taken to prevent the emission of sparks in those districts, especially when of an agricultural nature, or including numerous buildings of inflammable material, where the rainfall is limited. The bearing surfaces of engines working in sandy country must be protected as far as possible and suitably augmented; similarly, engines working in industrial areas and liable to foul heaps of clinker, ash, slag, spoil, etc., require generous vertical clearances.

Water. The maximum distance between water stations or troughs governs the minimum quantity of water which must be carried. The nature and extent of the work to be done between contiguous water stations obviously enters into the question also, and suitable allowance must be made for the enhanced consumptions occurring when the boiler is dirty or the engine is in poor condition mechanically and due for the shops.

The quality of the water available and the effects of mixture with those taken in other districts affect design to a considerable extent, e.g., number and location of wash-out plugs and mud doors, appropriate materials for boiler components, water space dimensions, etc.

1 gallon of water at 62° F. = 10 lb.
1 cu. ft. of water at 62° F. = 62.2786 lb.
1 gallon of water at 62° F. occupies 277.42 cubic inches at a
   barometric pressure of 30 inches of mercury.
The above information applies to the Imperial gallon.
   1 U.S.A. gallon = 0.833 Imperial gallon.

Fuel. As with water, the minimum quantity to be carried depends on the distance between adjacent fuelling stations, the nature and calorific value of the fuel used, nature and quantity of work done, efficiency of combustion, and other factors of a more variable nature, such as, for instance, prevailing weather conditions and the mechanical condition of the engine. Table I gives the storage space required, in cubic feet per ton, by various representative fuels together with their approximate calorific values in B.Th.U. per lb.

TABLE I.

APPROXIMATE STORAGE SPACE REQUIRED PER TON AND
CALORIFIC VALUES OF FUELS.

Fuel.	Cubic Feet required per Ton.	Calorific Value, B.Th.U. per lb.
Coal.		
Northumberland and Lancashire	45-46	11,500-14,700
Nottingham, Derbyshire, Staffordshire and Yorkshire ..	47-48	
Scotch	44-48	
Welsh Steam	40-43	14,500-15,500
Indian	43-46	11,000-13,000
South African	45-50	10,000-13,500
Australian	44-48	11,500-14,000
Coke	75-85	12,000-12,500
Timber.		
Hard woods	45-60	7,200-8,000
Soft woods	65-70	8,000-8,500
Liquid Fuel.		
American	33.8	18,700
Mexican	33.2	18,900
Russian	32.4	20,300
Texas	33.6	19,600
Borneo	34.5	19,600
Oil gas tar	35-36	18,500-19,000
Creosote oil	38	17,000

The calorific values of timber, as given above, apply only when the wood is thoroughly dry. Allowing for the moisture content, the calorific value of wood averages 6,000 B.Th.U. per lb.

American coal from Illinois has a calorific value of approximately 12,700 B.Th.U. per lb., the corresponding values for Pennsylvania and Kentucky coals ranging from 14,000 to 14,200.

The characteristics of the fuel available influence to a considerable extent the design of the grate and firebox generally.

Civil Engineering Limitations. These, chiefly dictated by the strength of underbridges, define the maximum permissible loads

    (a) per axle,
    (b) per foot run of rigid wheelbase,
    (c) per foot run of total wheelbase, and
    (d) per foot run over buffers or couplers.

It should be noted that permission to exceed the specified maxima, by an amount which in general ranges from 10% to 12%, may possibly be granted when the engine is provided with three or more cylinders in conjunction with a small proportion only of the reciprocating masses balanced, with a drive through gear reduction, or some other special feature likely to reduce the range of kinetic variation, above and below the static axle load, occurring with the two-cylinder engine of conventional design.

The empirical formula, applicable to average British chaired permanent way,

$$\frac{\text{Weight of rail (lb. per yard)}}{5} = \text{maximum permissible axle load (tons),}$$

may be used for rough approximations, but gives a low figure in so far as the special cases cited above are concerned.

The Baldwin Locomotive Works apply the following formula to spiked rail of 90 lb. per yard and over:—

Weight of rail (lb. per yard) × 700 = axle load (lb.).

Weight for weight, spiked rail is usually capable of withstanding a greater axle loading than chaired rail by reason of the closer spacing and relatively large dimensions of sleepers customarily adopted therewith.

Rail Gauge. The adoption of a narrow gauge tends to limit the maximum speed, due to the effects of centrifugal action on curves, but not necessarily the power of the locomotive. Train resistance is higher, owing to the smaller diameter of the wheels employed, but curve resistance is decreased on account of the reduced slip occurring. In many instances inside cylinders cannot be employed, and the adoption of outside frames may be unavoidable in extreme cases.

Loading Gauge. Determines all transverse and vertical dimensions of the locomotive. Care must be exercised that the locomotive clears the loading gauge when standing on the most severe curve it is required to traverse, and due attention must be paid to the effects of worn tyres, weakened springs, etc., on vertical clearances.

Gradients and Curves. Determine the maximum load hauled, rigid wheelbase, and also speed; they must be considered conjointly and the most detrimental combination taken as the criterion of the load hauling limit, with especial reference to the steaming capacity of the boiler. Gradients should further be regarded in conjunction with the approaches thereto, *i.e.*, whether a preceding favourable gradient will enable the train to gather sufficient momentum to "rush" the bank and, in this connection, the possible location of a station or stop signal at the commencement of an adverse gradient must also be taken into account.

Permanent Way. The type of track, *i.e.*, whether chaired or spiked, ballasting, sleepering and the general standard of maintenance prevailing affect locomotive design in so far as springs and the adoption or omission of compensating gear are concerned.

Mechanical Engineering Restrictions. The detail design, overall dimensions, and total weight of the locomotive may be limited by workshop facilities (*e.g.*, lifting capacity of cranes), lengths of pits and traversers, the availability of special tools and appliances, clearances in sheds and at coal stages and water cranes, and the maximum diameter of available turntables. With regard to the latter, the diameter must be sufficiently large, not merely to accommodate the total wheelbase of the engine, but also to enable the engine to be balanced on the table; the surrounding clearances must therefore not be neglected.

Due consideration must also be given to the methods of coal
ing adopted, and to the position of water cranes relative to
points and fixed signals.

Conditions imposed by the Traffic Department.   These
relate to the loads and type of stock to be hauled and speeds
attained.   They may also call for a specified rate of acceleration.

Legal Stipulations.   Government regulations are enforced in
certain countries and apply, for example, to the fitting or
various details such as boiler mountings, spark arresters, couplings and continuous brakes, and to the method and limitation
of the application of the welding process.

Chapter II.

TRACTIVE FORCE. POWER. ADHESION AND RESISTANCE.

The Tractive Force, or Tractive Effort, usually stated in pounds, is that force which the locomotive is capable of exerting at the treads of the coupled wheels. It is customary, when calculating it, to neglect the internal, or engine friction; the tractive force must therefore be of sufficient magnitude to overcome this frictional force in addition to the sum of the most adverse combination of resistances likely to be encountered in service.

Let D = cylinder diameter, inches,
S = piston stroke, inches,
p = mean effective pressure on piston, lb. per square inch,
W = diameter of driving wheels, inches, and
T = tractive force, lb.

Then, for a two-cylinder simple expansion engine,

$$T = \frac{D^2 S p}{W}$$

For a three-cylinder simple expansion engine,

$$T = 1.5 \left(\frac{D^2 S p}{W} \right)$$

And for a four-cylinder simple expansion engine,

$$T = 2 \left(\frac{D^2 S p}{W} \right)$$

Hence, as a general expression for simple locomotives,

$$T = \frac{N D^2 S p}{2W} \quad \dots \dots \dots \dots \dots \dots \dots \dots \dots \dots \dots \dots \quad (1)$$

where N = number of cylinders.

Based on the assumption that the work done in each cylinder is equal or, in other words, that the initial pressure in L.P.

cylinder equals the back pressure in H.P. cylinder (actually there is a pressure drop in the receiver, varying in extent according to the design), then,

for a two-cylinder compound expansion engine,

$$T = \frac{D_l^2 \, S p_i}{(R + 1) \, W} \quad \text{...} \quad (2)$$

and for a four-cylinder compound expansion engine,

$$T = \frac{2 \, D_l^2 \, S p_i}{(R + 1) \, W} \quad \text{.......................................} \quad (3)$$

where D_l = diameter of L.P. cylinder, inches,

R = ratio of areas of pistons, L.P.:H.P.

and p_i = initial pressure in L.P. cylinder, lb. per square inch.

Note.—If P_i be the initial pressure available in the H.P. cylinder, lb. per square inch, then $p_i = \dfrac{P_i}{R + 1}$. p_i is

conventionally assumed equal to (0.8 × boiler pressure).

According to von Borries, for a two-cylinder compound expansion engine,

$$T = \frac{D_l^2 \, S \, p_B}{4 \, W} \quad \text{...} \quad (4)$$

where p_B = boiler pressure, lb. per square inch.

It should be remembered that the tractive force formula is strictly limited in its application and therefore liable to abuse. For various reasons, which will be enumerated subsequently, the actual mean effective pressures are lower than those calculated by theory, the divergence increasing with the piston speed. The tractive force formula also presupposes the ability of the boiler to supply steam of sufficient volume at the specified pressure; the boiler output therefore determines the maximum power of the locomotive when running, and the tractive force, using the term with its customary limitation of application to starting, should consequently be regarded purely as an indication of the load the engine is capable of starting from rest. Even in this connection the numerical value obtained from the formula may be misleading, especially in those cases where the cut-off in full gear is restricted.

Pressure Drop from Boiler to Cylinders. The pressure available in the cylinders is lower than that generated in the boiler, this pressure drop being due to a variety of causes, such as condensation in, and radiation from pipes: friction at pipe bends, in the superheater, through the regulator, valves and ports: gland leakage, wiredrawing and cylinder condensation. It has been asserted that the reduction of pressure due to the passage of steam through the superheater, assuming efficient design, approximates to 5 lb. per square inch. This figure may be accepted as representative, but it should be noted that in favourable circumstances, *e.g.*, when running with a fully opened regulator and an early cut-off, the pressure drop is lower than this.

Experiments made on the Chemin de fer du Nord shewed that the pressure drop from boiler to steam chest ranged from 3% of the boiler pressure to nearly 6% at high speeds; trials carried out on the G.W.R. 4-6-0 engine *Caldicot Castle* in 1924 shewed that the average steam chest pressure was 92.6% of the boiler pressure for the inside cylinders and 93.6% for the outside cylinders. Every care must be exercised in designing to reduce this pressure drop to a minimum.

Preliminary calculation of the tractive force available when starting is usually effected by assuming the mean pressure available in the cylinder to be a certain proportion of the boiler pressure, in part to allow for the pressure drop mentioned previously. Originally this proportion ranged from 0.75 to 0.90, according to the opinion of the individual designer. As this variation rendered the resultant value useless for comparative purposes the proportion was standardised, in so far as British practice was concerned, at 0.85 of the boiler pressure. Since the innovation of this standard, however, locomotives have been introduced in which the maximum cut-off is restricted to 50% (U.S.A.) and 60 to 65% (Great Britain); in such cases it is obvious that the mean effective pressure actually attained, even at the lowest speeds, will be less than 85% of the boiler pressure. The tractive force of engines with limited cut-off in full gear, calculated on this basis, should therefore be accepted with reserve; the theoretical mean effective pressure for the given cut - off, preferably corrected with an agreed diagram factor, is a more reliable criterion. For comparative purposes the tractive force may be given in lb. for each lb. per square inch of the mean effective pressure. It should be remembered that the usual maximum cut-off at the time of the introduction of the 0.85 standard approximated to 75% or more, and it is doubtful whether it is actually valid for full gear cut-offs below 90%.

According to an American authority, with a maximum cut-off of 90%, the m.e.p. when starting = (0.85 × boiler pressure); of 80% = 0.75, and of 50% = (0.6 × boiler pressure). With a 50% cut-off in full gear and auxiliary ports in the valve bushes admitting steam up to 75% of the stroke when starting, the m.e.p. is assumed to be (0.75 × boiler pressure)

Mean effective Pressure. This is given, theoretically, by the formula

$$p_m = \frac{p_i}{r}(1 + log_e r) - p_b \dots\dots\dots\dots (5)$$

where p_m = mean effective pressure, lb. per sq. inch,
  p_i = initial pressure, lb. per sq. inch absolute,
  p_b = back pressure, lb. per sq. inch absolute, and
  r = ratio of expansion.*

*Where the clearance volume is known, r, to ensure accuracy, should be calculated on the *true* ratio of expansion, *i.e.*,

$$r_t = \frac{\text{volume of total piston displacement} + \text{clearance volume}}{\text{volume to point of cut-off} + \text{clearance volume}}$$

as opposed to the *apparent* ratio of expansion,

$$r_a = \frac{\text{volume of total piston displacement}}{\text{volume to point of cut-off}}$$

It will be seen that the true ratio of expansion is less than the apparent value.

In practice the mean effective pressure attained depends largely on the design and dimensions of the steam pipes, valves and ports, the relative immunity of the cylinders from heat loss, extent of regulator opening and characteristics of the valve gear employed; it is also influenced by the piston speed and point of cut-off.

When an engine is fitted with valves and valve gear of orthodox type, the decrease in m.e.p. occurring with rise of speed may be largely ascribed to:—

(a) Reduced opening of ports.

(b) Excessive compression at early cut-offs.

(c) Increased velocity of steam flow, one of the effects of which is to throttle the admission steam.

Causes (a) and (b) are both greatly reduced in their effects by the employment of "long travel" valves.

Mr. Lawford Fry (*Engineering*, Vol. XCV, p. 95), gave particulars of mean effective pressures obtaining with a locomotive having 16" × 24" cylinders with 7.6% clearance volume, and an average superheat of approximately 150° F. These are tabulated in Table II.

TABLE II.
MEAN EFFECTIVE PRESSURES ACTUALLY ATTAINED.

Boiler Pressure, lb. per sq. in.	Revs. per minute	Mean effective pressure, lb. per sq. in.					
		20 % cut-off		40 % cut-off		60 % cut-off	
		Saturated	Super-heated	Saturated	Super-heated	Saturated	Super-heated
120	60	36·4	33·2	68·6	68·9	87·0	101·0
120	180	24·4	22·2	50·0	50·2	66·7	77·6
120	300	12·4	11·3	31·2	31·4	46·5	54·2
180	60	61·8	57·9	108·0	109·0	130·0	149·0
180	180	42·2	39·5	78·0	79·0	96·8	111·0
180	300	22·6	21·2	47·5	48·1	64·3	73·9
240	60	90·6	86·0	154·0	155·0	179·0	199·0
240	180	62·3	59·2	110·0	111·0	132·0	147·0
240	300	34·2	32·4	66·4	66·7	79·6	88·4

It will be noted that at 20% cut-off a higher m.e.p. is obtained with saturated than with superheated steam, but that the reverse holds good when the cut-off is advanced to 40 and 60%. This may be regarded as a proof of the assertion that the harder a superheater engine is worked, the more efficient it becomes; on the other hand, it may be due to a characteristic of the steam distribution given by the valve gear of the particular engine under observation, *i.e.*, 20% cut-off was possibly premature in this case and gave rise to excessive compression.

Experience with locomotives of modern British design shews that the m.e.p. is not appreciably affected by the provision or otherwise of a superheater, as the rather more rapid drop evident in the expansion curve with superheated steam is compensated by improvements in the back pressure line and com-

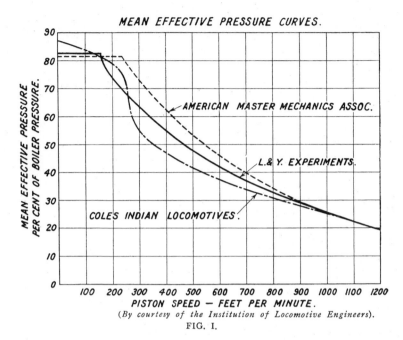

MEAN EFFECTIVE PRESSURE CURVES.

(By courtesy of the Institution of Locomotive Engineers).

FIG. I.

pression curves. In the author's experience, superheating tends to increase the m.e.p. at piston speeds in excess of 1,000

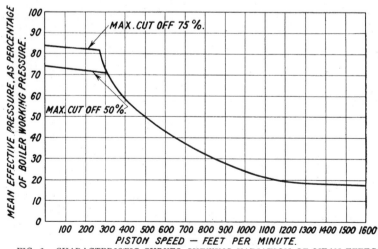

FIG. 2. CHARACTERISTIC CURVES SHEWING VARIATION OF MEAN EFFECTIVE PRESSURE WITH PISTON SPEED: SUPERHEATED STEAM.

ft. per minute. Fig. 1 (Gass, Proc. I. Loco. E., 1919) illus-
trates the drop occurring in m.e.p. with increase in piston speed,
and shews comparatively the results of observations carried
out independently under widely varying conditions. Fig. 2
shews graphically the results of investigations into this matter,
with exclusive reference to superheater engines of British
design, made by the author. It is hardly necessary to add
that in both cases a readjustment of the scale of ordinates will
enable the variation of tractive force with piston speed to be
read off from the same curves, except at the lowest speeds,
when the tractive force, as mentioned previously, depends
entirely upon the maximum cut-off available. It may be noted
that the straight line portion of the tractive force curve usually
falls on a gradient of approximately 1 in 12.

The ratio of actual to theoretical m.e.p. gives the *diagram
factor* for the locomotive. According to Inchley, whose estimates appear to be somewhat conservative, the diagram factor
for locomotives varies from approximately 0·8 at piston speeds
in the vicinity of 170 ft. per minute to 0·63 at 700-800 ft.
per minute.

The following are some of the points to which careful attention must be given, when designing, in order to secure the
nearest approach of the actual m.e.p. to that which is theoretically possible:—

The provision of a boiler of such dimensions that it is
able to supply the cylinders with a sufficient quantity of
steam at full working pressure under all conditions of
operation and at all speeds.

The cross-sectional areas of regulator valves, internal
steam pipe, superheater elements and ports respectively to be
so proportioned as to compensate for the increased friction
encountered in each stage of its path by the steam.

The provision of large steam chests or generously proportioned piston valve chambers.

Compensation by increased cross-sectional area at bends
in ports.

The elimination as far as possible of these bends. This
is facilitated by the use of a piston valve spindle of such
length that the valve heads reciprocate immediately over
the ends of the cylinder, or by the adoption of poppet valves,
which are also advantageous in that they ensure more rapid
and relatively greater port opening.

Sharp definition of valve events and care in the design of valves and valve gears generally.

Freedom of exhaust, with straight passages of ample area and the ability of each cylinder to exhaust without interference from that of the other cylinders in the blast pipe itself.

Effect of varying individual Factors in Tractive Force Formula.

(a) Cylinder Diameter and Stroke. The tractive force is directly proportional to the stroke of the cylinder and to the square of its diameter. Hence, it follows that where rapid acceleration is primarily essential, as for example in shunting and suburban passenger tank engines, the diameter should be relatively large in proportion to the stroke. The locomotive, however, in comparison with other types of reciprocating steam engine, is at a disadvantage in that the cylinders are more exposed, not only to the influence of atmospheric temperature, but also to that of air currents generated by the motion of the locomotive itself, with the result that cylinder condensation is appreciably greater in extent. It has been found that this condensation may be minimised by increasing the stroke, and therefore the piston speed for a given rate of revolution, the consequent reduction of the time element having a most beneficial effect.

The thermal loss due to condensation arises from the temperature difference between the steam and the metal comprising the mass of the cylinder respectively, and increases in extent as the area of metal in actual contact with the steam becomes greater. Callendar and Nicolson's law of condensation states that the rate at which steam condenses on a metal surface is proportional to the difference of temperature between the steam and that surface, and is independent of the pressure. It may be shewn that for a given volumetric piston displacement the cylinder of small diameter and long stroke has, at early cut-offs, the advantage over that of large diameter and short stroke ; for a concrete example readers are referred to p. 164 of Ripper's *Steam Engine Theory and Practice.* Cylinder condensation is further reduced by machining piston faces and the inner surfaces of the cylinder covers.

Cylinders of relatively small diameter and having a long stroke are also advantageous mechanically in that the distance between centres may be increased with given load gauge clearances. This permits of a longer crank pin journal with a correspondingly lower bearing stress. Axlebox thrust is at the same time reduced, as also is the clearance volume. On the other hand, the effects of inertia, angularity of the connecting rods and rubbing speeds of crankpins are all relatively increased.

Table III shews the ratio of cylinder diameter to stroke for various types of locomotives. It will be noted that the stroke is shorter, with relation to the diameter, in Continental and American practice than in British.

TABLE III.
TYPICAL RATIOS OF CYLINDER DIAMETER TO STROKE.

Type of Locomotive.	Ratio, Cylinder Diameter:Stroke
L.N.E.R., 0-4-0 shunting tank engine, Type Y4 ...	1 : 1.177
Austrian Federal Rys., 0-8-0 shunting engine, Series 478	1 : 1.073
S.R., 4-6-4 tank engine, No. 329B	1 : 1.127
G.W.R., 2-8-0 mixed traffic engine, No. 4700 ...	1 : 1.579
S.D.J.R., 2-8-0 goods engine, No. 86	1 : 1.33
Western Maryland R.R., 2-10-0 goods engine, No. 1112	1 : 1.067
L.M.S.R., 4-6-0 express engine, *Royal Scot* ...	1 : 1.445
Madrid, Saragossa and Alicante Ry., 4-8-2 express engine, Series 1,700	1 : 1.146

(b) Number and Disposition of Cylinders. If sufficient power can be obtained within the limits imposed by the loading gauge dimensions, two cylinders only should, for the sake of simplicity, be employed. If placed inside the frames, the following advantages accrue:—

1. By reason of the protection afforded, cylinder condensation is minimised.

2. Less exposure of moving parts to grit, dust, sand, etc., with reduced wear and liability to overheat in consequence.

3. Steadier running, tending to reduce wear of tyres, etc., due to the decreased arm of the couple, causing lateral disturbance, arising from the action of the steam on the pistons.

4. Number of castings reduced.

5. Greater transverse rigidity at the front end, and there-fore fewer stays required.

6. Simplified arrangement of steam and exhaust pipes and passages.

7. Cylinder castings less liable to damage.

8. Reduced hammer blow.

On the other hand, the advantages claimed for outside cylinders are:—

1. Shorter minimum wheelbase (unless cylinders are placed in rear of leading bogie or truck).

2. Longer connecting rods.

3. Elimination of the crank axle.

4. Greater accessibility for oiling, examination and repairs (partly lost by necessity for extended use of transverse stays). Alternatively, there is more clearance available for inside valve gear, if used.

6. Improved facilities for the accommodation of cylinders which are not inclined.

7. More space available for the firebox, brake cylinders and reservoirs, also for axleboxes and other major bearings.

8. Smaller horizontal thrust on the coupled axleboxes, unless compared with inside cylinder engines having coupling rods in phase with the adjacent main cranks; this latter arrangement is rarely adopted.

With regard to advantage 4, it should be pointed out that this superiority over the inside cylinder engine is largely nulli-fied when the latter is provided with outside motion and an indirect drive through a rocking lever, as exemplified, for in-stance, by the Beames gear on the L.M.S.R. *Prince of Wales* class of engine. Any arrangement of this kind at the same time improves crank axle design by the removal therefrom of eccentrics with their accompanying objectionable rigidity.

When power demands cannot be met by the maximum diameter obtainable with two cylinders, it then becomes neces-sary to adopt the multi-cylindered engine, the usual arrange-ments of which are:—

(*a*) 3 cylinders with cranks at 120°,

(*b*) 4 cylinders with cranks at 180°, and

(*c*) 4 cylinders with cranks at 135°.

With arrangements (*b*) and (*c*) the phase angle for the inside cranks is 90°.

Due to the greater number of working parts involved, and

the consequent increase of internal friction, both constructional and maintenance costs are somewhat enhanced in the case of the multi-cylindered engine. Against these, however, must be offset the following advantages over the two-cylinder locomotive:—

1. Greater power output within the limitations of a given loading gauge.
2. A "split" drive, facilitating equality of connecting rod length with a minimum rigid wheelbase, and effecting the distribution of driving forces over the frames, may be applied if desired.
3. More uniform torque, *i.e.*, the range of fluctuation is reduced. In consequence there is less liability both to slip when starting and to stop on dead centre, the running is freer, and the rate of acceleration increased.
4. As a corollary to 3, the limiting value of the factor of adhesion is reduced.
5. Steadier running at high speeds. The four-cylinder engine is better than the three-cylinder in this respect.
6. Increased mileage between repairs.
7. Decreased tyre wear.
8. If the crank phase angles are so arranged that there are more than four exhaust impulses per revolution, the range of draught fluctuation is reduced and degree of superheat increased, thereby reducing the fuel consumption, increasing the evaporation and reducing boiler repair costs. It follows that tendencies to throw sparks and pull holes in thin fires are also reduced.
9. Unless the monobloc cylinder casting is employed, a more satisfactory distribution of engine weight may be obtained.
10. Decreased weight of reciprocating parts per cylinder. This has a favourable effect on the balancing and also on the ease with which repairs may be executed in running sheds.
11. The proportion of the reciprocating masses to be balanced may be reduced.
12. Owing to the improvements possible in the balancing, the range of fluctuation above and below the normal static axle loading, due to hammer blow, may be reduced. For a given road the permissible axle load may therefore be increased.

13. Two valve gears may be arranged to actuate either three or four valves, thereby reducing the internal friction per cylinder.

14. More even drawbar pull. In spite of the greater internal friction involved, a sensible increase in the mean pull has been observed in some cases; this may possibly be attributed to reduced flange friction.

15. Increased bearing areas.

An additional advantage has been cited in that large cylinders are frequently found to be scored to a disproportionate extent by superheated steam.

Monobloc castings are employed in some instances, but are not to be recommended. They are not only expensive to replace in the event of a casting proving faulty or becoming damaged in service, but also lead to an undesirable concentration of weight, as mentioned above, and restrict unduly the lengths of the connecting rods. The application of a split drive is also rendered difficult.

(c) *Diameter of Coupled Wheels.* The tractive force exerted by the locomotive is in inverse proportion to the diameter of its coupled wheels. Although it is now generally recognised that this dimension has no great influence on the peak running speed attained, an empirical rule which states that the diameter of the coupled wheels at the tread, in inches, should equal the maximum speed at which the engine is required to run, in miles per hour, still finds acceptance in many quarters. This rule implies a maximum rotational speed of 336 revolutions per minute, and it is not desirable that this quantity be greatly exceeded, although for purposes of design a maximum speed of 360 r.p.m. is generally assumed; it should be mentioned that some Continental designs allow for the exceptional maximum of 420 r.p.m.

The employment of coupled wheels having a relatively small diameter involves the generation, for a given linear velocity, of larger stresses due to centrifugal action in the rotating masses of the engine, and therefore necessitates the employment of more substantial sections for these details, thus aggravating the balancing question. In this connection, however, it must be remembered that for a given tractive force the piston thrust is correspondingly reduced in the case of the wheel of small diameter. With small wheels, vertical clearances limit the piston stroke; with large wheels, the effects of the limit placed on the diameter of the boiler by the height of the loading gauge are felt acutely.

Whilst the engine having coupled wheels of large diameter is credited with freer running powers, which may be attributed to a decrease in internal resistance, due to the lower rubbing speeds of the bearings and to the reduced back pressure accompanying the lower rotational speeds, the moment of the shock side thrusts experienced when passing over gaps in the permanent way at crossings, etc., and transmitted to the axles, is increased. On the other hand, it follows that the bridging of gaps at points and crossovers is facilitated with a wheel of large diameter. It may be shewn that, in the event of an obstruction being encountered on the permanent way, the large diameter wheel is at a disadvantage in that there is a greater likelihood of derailment occurring than with a wheel of small diameter.

The general tendency in modern British design is to decrease the diameter of the coupled wheels for a given class of work. It is felt that the important thermal advantage accruing from high piston speeds is a factor of great importance, and that the accompanying disadvantages may be largely mitigated by careful attention to the design of ports and valve gears, bearings, reciprocating parts and other details concerned. Diameters of coupled wheels representative of modern British practice are given in Table IV.

TABLE IV.
DIAMETERS OF COUPLED WHEELS FOR VARIOUS CLASSES OF WORK: TYPICAL BRITISH STANDARD GAUGE PRACTICE.

Service.	Diameter of Coupled Wheels on Tread.		
Shunting	4'—0"	to	4'—6"
Suburban Passenger ...	4'—9"	to	5'—9"
Mineral	4'—6"	to	4'-10"
Goods	4'-10"	to	5'—3"
Mixed Traffic	5'—6"	to	5'—9"
Main Line Tanks	5'—9"	to	6'—9"
Express Passenger	6'—0"	to	6'—9"

Another factor influencing the extended employment of smaller coupled wheels is that, assuming two engines to exert an equal tractive effort, one provided with large wheels and cylinders and the other with small wheels and cylinders, the more frequent and lighter exhaust beats for a given linear velocity of the latter engine are undoubtedly responsible for a reduction in the fuel consumption. This is especially notice-able in local passenger, shunting and other engines which re-quire to make frequent starts from rest. It should be remembered, however, that the higher rotary speed of the small wheeled engine calls for especial care in the design of ports, valves and valve gears to prevent wiredrawing and excessive back pressure.

(d) *Pressure.* Prior to the advent of superheating, boiler pressures ranged up to approximately 200 lb. per square inch in this country. When superheaters were first fitted, the work-ing pressure was in many cases reduced and the cylinder dimensions at the same time correspondingly increased; pres-sure is, however, now shewing a decided upward movement. The present trend is in the direction of high working pressures in conjunction with a moderate degree of superheat, rather than moderate pressures with high degree superheaters. By this means the total heat of the steam is maintained at the desired number of thermal units whilst maintenance and lubrica-tion costs are kept within reasonable limits. This state of affairs must nevertheless be considered merely as an inter-mediate stage of evolution; as practical difficulties are over-come, the degree of superheat provided will indubitably be increased by a large amount.

Although the tractive force varies directly as the working pressure, and considerable thermal advantage is gained by the adoption of high steam pressure, with consequent reductions in steam and fuel consumptions per I.H.P.-hour, other factors affect the case from the economic point of view and must be considered. Increase in pressure not only necessitates larger overall dimensions of the boiler to meet the decreased specific volume of the steam, but also heavier sections of the compon-ents to withstand the increased stresses. Wear, and therefore maintenance costs, are augmented at a disproportionate rate; the theory has been advanced that the enhanced molecular activity of steam as it approaches the state of a perfect gas is responsible for this, and experience with superheated steam bears out this contention. A contributory factor, as regards costs, is the difficulty in keeping pipe and other joints tight when subjected to high pressures.

Cursory examination of steam tables will dispel the illusion that trouble due to expansion and contraction under an increased range of temperature may be attributed to high working pressures; the temperature of steam does not advance proportionately with the pressure at the higher values of the latter. Further, the decreased latent heat encourages fuel economy.

Pressures below 180 lb. per square inch are uncommon in modern British practice, and the number of engines working at 220-250 lb. per square inch is increasing rapidly. The latter pressure has frequently been exceeded for many years past on the Continent, and the introduction of water-tube fireboxes in the United States has led to the adoption of pressures of 350 lb. per square inch and over. The limiting working pressure with the conventional locomotive type boiler is probably in the region of 260 lb. per square inch. Although boilers of orthodox design, usually with nickel steel plates, have recently been introduced with working pressures of 275 and 300 lb. per square inch, they have not yet been sufficiently long in service to determine the ultimate success of the experiment.

Power of the Engine. The standard unit of the rate at which work is performed, the "horse-power," *i.e.*, 33,000 ft.-lb. per minute, has four applications in locomotive practice. These are:—

(1) *Indicated Horse Power* (I.H.P.). As in general steam engine practice, is the power actually developed by the steam in the cylinders and, for a locomotive of conventional design with double-acting cylinders, is given by

$$\Sigma \text{ I.H.P.} = N \left\{ \frac{(A_1 P_1 - A_2 p_1 + A_2 P_2 - A_1 p_2)LR}{33,000} \right\} \quad \text{...... (6)}$$

where N = number of cylinders,

A_1 = effective area of piston, front end, square inches,

= .7854 $(D^2 - d_2^2)$, where D is the diameter of the piston, inches, and d_2 is the diameter of the tail rod (if fitted), inches,

P_1 = mean pressure acting on piston during outward stroke, *i.e.*, towards driving axle, lb. per square inch,

A_2 = effective area of piston, back end, square inches,

$\qquad = .7854 \ (D^2 - d_1{}^2)$ where D is the piston diameter, as before, and d_1 is the diameter of the piston rod, inches,

$p_1 =$ mean back pressure acting on piston during outward stroke, lb. per square inch,

$P_2 =$ mean pressure acting on piston during inward stroke, lb. per square inch,

$p_2 =$ mean back pressure acting on piston during inward stroke, lb. per square inch,

$L =$ length of stroke, feet,

and $R =$ number of revolutions per minute.

In order to obtain accurate data, the I.H.P. developed in each cylinder must be calculated separately and the individual results then added together to give the total for the engine.

Equation (6) simplifies to

$$\Sigma \ \text{I.H.P.} = \frac{2 \, N \, P \, A \, L \, R}{33,000} = \frac{N \, P \, A \, S}{33,000} \ \dots\dots\dots\dots\dots \ (7)$$

where N, L and R have the same significance as in (6),

$P =$ mean pressure (average for both sides of piston), lb. per square inch,

$S =$ piston speed, feet per minute,

and $A =$ average effective area (one face) of piston, square inches.

Now, in the first of the two formulæ (7), for any given engine, $\dfrac{2 \, N \, A \, L}{33,000}$ has a constant numerical value. If C denotes this constant, this formula may then be written:—

$$\Sigma \ \text{I.H.P.} = C \times P \times R \ \dots\dots\dots\dots\dots\dots\dots\dots\dots \ (8)$$

The use of the *indicated horse power constant*, C, effects a considerable saving of time when the horse power has to be calculated from a series of indicator diagrams.

Tractive Force in Terms of I.H.P.

$$\Sigma \ \text{I.H.P.} = \frac{T V}{375} = \frac{R V}{375} \ \dots\dots\dots\dots\dots\dots\dots \ (9)$$

where $T =$ tractive force, lb.,

$V =$ velocity of train, miles per hour,

and $R =$ sum of total resistances of engine, tender and train, lb.

(2) *Rail Horse Power* (R.H.P.). Is the power developed at the rail, *i.e.*, the I.H.P. minus the power absorbed in overcoming the internal resistance of the engine mechanism. Internal resistance will be dealt with subsequently in this chapter. The calculation of R.H.P. is not often attempted as it involves the segregation of the power representing the resistance of the carrying wheels, the information usually available facilitating the deduction of

(3) *Drawbar Horse Power* (D.B.H.P. or D.H.P.). Is the nett power available for the haulage of the train at the tender drawbar and comprises the rail horse-power minus the power absorbed by the vehicular resistance of the engine and tender.

$$\text{D.B.H.P.} = 5.97\, PV \quad \dotfill \quad (10)$$

where P = drawbar pull, tons,

and V = velocity of train, miles per hour.

It may here be noted that $v = 88\, V$

where v = velocity of train, feet per minute.

The Mechanical Efficiency of a locomotive, expressed as a percentage, is given by $100 \left(\dfrac{\text{D.B.H.P.}}{\text{I.H.P.}} \right)$, and ranges in the case of a two-cylinder engine from 85% to 95% when starting. The G.W.R. four-cylinder engine *Caldicot Castle* gave an average mechanical efficiency of 74% on trial.

The mechanical efficiency of a two-cylinder engine is superior to that of the equivalent four-cylinder engine up to a speed of approximately 250 revolutions per minute.

(4) *Boiler Horse Power.* Is given theoretically by

$$\frac{\text{Total weight of water evaporated per hour, lb.}}{\text{Steam consumption, lb. per I.H.P.-hour}} \quad \dotfill \quad (11)$$

As the numerical values of both quantities are liable to considerable fluctuation owing to the influence of a number of variables, the result obtained is of little, if any, practical value, and the use of this formula for comparative purposes is to be deprecated; it has in fact been included merely for the sake of completeness. Further, the formula does not take into account the proportions of the individual items comprising the total heating surface, nor does it recognise their respective relative efficiencies. The assumptions made by investigators who have endeavoured to place this method of power rating on a comparable and comprehensive basis are so divergent that the generally unsatisfactory state of this matter has been further aggravated.

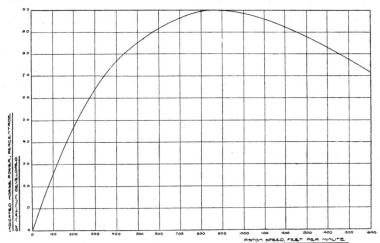

FIG. 3. CHARACTERISTIC CURVE FOR LOCOMOTIVES SHEWING VARIA-
TION OF I.H.P. DEVELOPED WITH PISTON SPEED.

It will be noted that the maximum I.H.P. is developed at a piston speed of
approximately 880 ft. per minute.

Piston Speed. The mean piston speed of a locomotive of orthodox design, *i.e.*, with direct drive, may be calculated from

$$S = \frac{672.27 \, V \, L}{W} \dots\dots\dots\dots\dots\dots\dots\dots\dots\dots\dots\dots\dots (12)$$

where S = mean piston speed, feet per minute,
V = speed of train, miles per hour,
L = piston stroke, feet,
and W = diameter of driving wheels, inches.

The normal maximum piston speed in modern locomotive work may approach 1,600 feet per minute, the average approximating to 1,000 feet per minute. To the best of the author's belief, the maximum recorded piston speed in this country is 1,890 feet per minute.

Fig. 3 is a characteristic curve for a locomotive shewing the variation of I.H.P. with piston speed.

Determination of Cylinder Diameter. For checking purposes, and as a rough approximation, cylinder diameter may be determined mathematically by inversion of the I. H. P. formula, thus:—

$$D = 205 \sqrt{\frac{\Sigma \text{ I.H.P.}}{N.P.S.}} \quad \dots\dots\dots\dots\dots\dots\dots\dots \quad (13)$$

The symbols used and units represented are as in equations (6), (7) and (12) respectively.

Adhesion. The values obtaining with various weather conditions, as quoted by Molesworth, are still usually accepted, and are given in Table V.

TABLE V.
VARIATION OF ADHESION WITH WEATHER CONDITIONS (MOLESWORTH).

Weather Conditions.	Adhesion, lb. per ton.	Corresponding Coefficient of Friction or Adhesion.
Rails very dry	600	0·268
Rails very wet	550	0·245
Ordinary English weather	450	0 2
Misty weather, rails greasy ..	300	0·13
Frosty or snowy weather	200	0·09

It will be noted that the variation in adhesion, with extremely wet and extremely dry rails respectively, is small.

The turning moment exerted by the locomotive fluctuates throughout the stroke, its maximum value, in the case of a two-cylinder simple engine, exceeding that deduced from the tractive force formula by 20—25%. Slipping will not occur if, assuming for the purposes of argument a co-efficient of friction of $\frac{1}{3.33}$,

(Tractive force × 3.33 × 1.25) < adhesive weight of the locomotive,

i.e.,

if the *factor of adhesion*, or ratio of adhesive weight to tractive force, is somewhat greater than 4.

Actually, the minimum desirable factor of adhesion approximates to 4.3, as allowance must be made for the increase in value of the tractive force occurring as the tyres wear, for the sensible diminution of adhesive weight and consequent slipping which takes place at high speeds owing to the centrifugal action

of the balance weights when on top centre, and for the considerable variation in pressure occurring during each stroke
when running at high speeds of revolution with an early cut-
off. The second phenomenon is an argument against the
balancing of a high percentage of the total reciprocating
weights, and the last favours the adoption of either three
cylinders at 120° or four at 135°. The very even torque developed by the multi-cylinder engine enables the adhesion
considerably to be reduced; the minimum value may be as
low as 3·5.

Tank engines, on the other hand, require a larger factor of
adhesion, as the adhesive weight varies with the quantity of
water in the tanks, and also with the weight of fuel, should
the bunker be so disposed as to affect the adhesive weight.
The minimum factor of adhesion should therefore be based
on empty tanks, and also on an empty bunker, should the
latter influence the result.

The number of axles requiring to be coupled in order to
secure the necessary adhesion is determined by the maximum
axle load allowed and is given by

$$X = \frac{T \times A}{2240 \times M} \quad\quad\quad\quad\quad\quad\quad\quad\quad (14)$$

where X = number of coupled axles required,
   T = tractive force, lb.,
   A = desired adhesion factor,
and M = maximum permissible load per axle, tons.

With regard to the value of X, any decimal in the numerical
result must obviously be treated as an additional integer.

Resistances. Ignoring the question of boiler power for the
moment, the tractive force of the locomotive must be sufficient
to overcome the summation of the most unfavourable combination of resistances likely to be encountered under any conditions which may arise in its intended service. These resistances
may be considered individually under the following headings:-

(1) Resistance of the engine and tender. Comprises air
resistance, the internal resistance, *i.e.*, the effects of inertia
forces in the engine mechanism and frictional resistance of
piston rings and packing, crosshead slides, connecting and
coupling rod bearings, driving axlebox bearings, valves, valve
spindle packing and valve motion, and the resistance of engine
and tender as a vehicle.

(2) Train resistances. Similarly to (1), includes journal and rolling friction and other resistances arising from various causes, *e.g.*, oscillation and wheel flange friction. The determination of air resistance to the motion of the train forms a somewhat complex problem which is, however, benefiting by the extended aerodynamic data now available.

(3) Resistance due to acceleration. Includes the rotary inertia effects of wheels and axles.

(4) Gradient resistance.

(5) Curve resistance.

(6) Natural wind resistance.

Information available on resistances in general is unfortunately vague and unsatisfactory. Since the earliest days of railways, engineers have devoted much time and thought to this interesting and important matter, but the data obtained, owing to the existence of variables not amenable to calculation (the presence during tests of accelerating forces, for example, is at times very difficult to detect) and outside the control of the innumerable experimentalists, lead to numerical results which are inconsistent and in no wise comparable. The author therefore wishes it to be clearly understood that many of the succeeding formulæ, which have been gathered from various sources, apply only within narrow limits and must therefore be used with discretion; he has, however, endeavoured to include formulæ which are applicable to modern British practice. Unless otherwise stated, R denotes resistance in lb. per ton of 2,240 lb., V, velocity in miles per hour, W, weight of vehicle in tons, and L, length of train in feet.

Calculated resistances are usually higher than those actually obtaining in practice, and in this connection it is strange that the majority of formulæ emanating from America, where conditions are not so favourable to low resistances as in this country, should give lower numerical values than those propounded by British experimentalists.

(1) *Resistance of Engine and Tender.* Various authorities hold widely divergent views on this matter. Some incline to the opinion that the internal resistance has a constant value at all speeds. Cole, the American engineer, gives it as 25 lb. per ton (of 2,000 lb.); this allowance applies only to oil lubricated locomotives running at speeds between 100 and 320 revolutions per minute.

According to Professor Goss,
Total internal resistance of engine (lb.) =

$$\frac{3.8 \times (\text{cylinder diameter})^2 \times \text{stroke}}{\text{Diameter of wheels}} \quad \dots\dots\dots\dots (15)$$

This formula was conceivably based on the results of experiments made by him with a small 4-4-0 engine not of recent design; its application should therefore be limited.

It is now generally conceded that the internal resistance is largely affected by the point of cut-off, which is ignored in formula (15). Further, it is considered by many that frictional resistance, assuming complete lubrication, increases proportionately with the speed (and therefore inversely as the diameter of the coupled wheels), and inertia forces, of course, with the square of that quantity. Again, the number of axles coupled, nature and amount of flexibility provided, number of cylinders employed, types of valve and valve gear provided, are all random examples of factors influencing the question.

Wellington, another American investigator, has estimated the internal resistance at from 5% to 8% of the indicated horse power developed, the latter figure being accepted by the Master Mechanics' Association. While 8% of the I.H.P. is, in the author's opinion, a fair allocation for power absorbed in overcoming the internal resistance of a two-cylinder engine when starting, it is extremely doubtful as to whether it is applicable at all speeds, having regard to the variables previously enumerated and to the fact that the I.H.P. commences to exhibit a falling tendency at quite a moderate piston speed (see Fig. 3).

Yet another American authority, Henderson, gives:—
Percentage of total I.H.P. absorbed by internal
friction $= 0.15\ V + C$ .... (16)
where C is a constant, having values of from 2 to 8, the latter being applicable to slow and heavy work.

Modern investigations into resistances, not only of engines and tenders, but also of trains, usually conform to the principles enunciated by Professor Carus-Wilson in a paper read by him before the Institution of Civil Engineers in 1907, and according to whom resistance equations take the general form
$$R = A + BV + CV^2 \quad \dots\dots\dots\dots\dots\dots\dots (17)$$
where A, B and C are constants which have to be determined for each individual case.

B

As far as engines and tenders are concerned, A is a symbol representing the frictional resistance of the bearings, rolling friction and track resistance; according to this authority it is independent of the speed, but its value applies only to a given point of cut-off and is affected both by the number of axles coupled and the steam pressure. With regard to the latter, A has an entirely different value when the regulator is shut. Coefficient B refers chiefly to flange action, which is accentuated in the case of the engine by nosing due to piston thrust, and varies directly as the speed. Coefficient C varies as the square of the speed, and therefore applies to all forms of air resistance and the effects of inertia.

The succeeding formulæ, (18) to (24) inclusive, are typical examples; they give reasonable results and may therefore be applied to estimates of tractive force for engines of the types specified. It is, however, possible that the results obtained are somewhat excessive for high values of V. Where estimates are concerned, this fault of course errs in the right direction.

Mr. Lawford H. Fry has published some formulæ (see *The Engineer*, Vol. CVII) which are based on European practice. These formulæ are comprehensive and embrace both internal resistance of the engine and vehicular resistance of engine and tender:—

Four coupled wheels, 79" diameter,
$$R = 8.5 + 0.0974\ V + 0.004\ V^2 \dots\dots\dots\dots (18)$$
Six coupled wheels, 79" diameter,
$$R = 10.08 + 0.126\ V + 0.004\ V^2 \dots\dots\dots\dots (19)$$
Eight coupled wheels, 56" diameter,
$$R = 13.34 + 0.48V + 0.004\ V^2 \dots\dots\dots\dots (20)$$

These formulæ compare very closely with those advanced by Mr. C. F. Dendy Marshall, *viz.*—

Four coupled wheels, 78" diameter,
$$R = 8.5 + 0.1\ V + 0.003\ V^2 \dots\dots\dots\dots (21)$$
Six coupled wheels, 78" diameter,
$$R = 9.5 + 0.13\ V + 0.003\ V^2 \dots\dots\dots\dots (22)$$

These formulæ again are in near agreement with two put forward by Professor Dalby:—

For 4-4-2 engine with coupled wheel diameter of 6.8 feet,
$$R = 8.8 + 0.1\ V + 0.004\ V^2 \dots\dots\dots\dots (23)$$
For 4-6-0 engine with coupled wheel diameter of 6.4 feet,
$$R = 10.8 + 0.15\ V + 0.004\ V^2 \dots\dots\dots\dots (24)$$

A formula for the determination of internal resistance which requires either knowledge or assumption of the vehicular resistance of the engine and tender is that propounded by Mr. Gass (Proc. I. Loco. E.):—

Internal resistance of engine, lb. per ton

$$= \frac{T - (D + R_v)}{W_e} \qquad \ldots\ldots\ldots\ldots\ldots\ldots\ (25)$$

where T = indicated tractive effort, lb.,
$\quad\quad D$ = drawbar pull, lb.,
$\quad\quad R_v$ = total vehicular resistance of engine and tender, lb.,
and W_e = weight of engine only, tons.

Formula (15), due to Professor Goss, has been amplified by him to include the vehicular resistance of engine and tender, and then becomes:—

Total resistance of engine and tender, lb.,

$$= \frac{3.8\ d^2\ l}{D} - w\left(2 + \frac{1}{6}V\right) - 0.11\ V^2 \ \ldots\ldots\ (26)$$

where d = piston diameter, inches,
$\quad\quad l$ = piston stroke, inches,
$\quad\quad D$ = diameter of coupled wheels, inches,
and w = total weight of engine and tender, less adhesive weight, in "short" tons of 2,000 lb.

It will be noted that no direct allowance is made in the above for the number of coupled axles.

When inclusive formulæ are not employed, *air resistance* may be calculated separately from Sir J. Aspinall's formula,

$$P = 0.003V^2 \ \ldots\ldots\ldots\ldots\ldots\ldots\ldots\ldots\ldots\ldots\ldots\ldots\ (27)$$

where P is the air pressure in lb. per square foot.

According to the American Locomotive Co.,

$$P = 0.002\ V^2 \ \ldots\ldots\ldots\ldots\ldots\ldots\ldots\ldots\ldots\ldots\ldots\ (28)$$

the area on which it acts being taken as 120 square feet.

Of these two formulæ (27) gives, in the author's opinion, the more reliable indication of the extent of this resistance. The area affected, according to Mr. Dendy Marshall, may be taken as $L\ (2\ H + W)$, the symbols representing the length, average height and average width, respectively, of the engine and tender, in feet. As allowances for side and top friction are included, the use of this expression gives higher values than are obtained when the usually accepted areas are taken as a basis.

(2) *Train Resistance.* (a) *Passenger Stock.* Several modern formulæ conform to the general expression given by (17), such as that propounded by Mr. Lawford Fry:—

$$R = 3.6 + .03 \ V + .0022 \ V^2 \ \dots\dots\dots (29)$$

Another formula of the same type has been advanced more recently by Mr. Johansen (*The Engineer*, February 10, 1928) and is applicable to trains of 500 tons weight and having a length of 400 feet:—

$$R = 3.5 + 0.1 \ V + 0.0015 \ V^2 \ \dots\dots\dots (30)$$

Mr. Dahlerus formulated an equation (Proc. I. Mech. E., 1925) which is limited in application to trains fitted with roller bearings,

$$R = \frac{2.6 + (V - 8)^{1.7}}{76.8} \ \dots\dots\dots (31)$$

A general formula which, although published several years ago, is still considered to hold good by many railway engineers, is that due to Sir J. Aspinall:—

$$R = 2.5 + \frac{V^{\frac{2}{3}}}{50.8 + 0.0278 \ L} \ \dots\dots\dots (32)$$

The formulæ evolved by D. K. Clark and other early investigators, although they may be regarded as classics, cannot be considered suitable for application to modern bogie stock and running conditions generally; they were the results of observations on the performance of engines and stock of light construction, having little or no side play and tyres of soft metal running on equally soft rails.

Two formulæ, due to Deeley and Wolff respectively, refer to bogie stock, but are by no means modern and can therefore only be used where the tare weight of the vehicle is low:—

$$\text{(Deeley)} \quad R = 3 + \frac{V^2}{290} \ \dots\dots\dots (33)$$

$$\text{(Wolff)} \quad R = 3 \left(\frac{V + 12}{V + 3} \right) + \frac{V^2}{300} \ \dots\dots\dots (34)$$

Equations (33) and (34) give results having high numerical values, and the author is of the opinion that (29), (30) and (32) give a more reliable indication of the conditions obtaining in modern operation.

The formula adopted by the American Locomotive Company is:—

$$R = 0.85 \left\{ \frac{100}{W} + 1.5 + \frac{V\,(V + 16)}{.100\,\sqrt{W}} \right\} \dots\dots\dots (35)$$

This applies to American cars and the ton units affecting R and W are of 2,000 lb., as also in the following table, which comprises the results obtained from trials made on the Illinois Central R.R.

Weight of Coach, tons of 2,000 lb.	R	
	35	75
$V = 10$	7·0	4·3
$V = 50$	11·2	6·6
$V = 75$	15·3	9·8

The starting resistance is considerably higher than that obtaining at low speeds, due to the fact that the establishment of an oil film between journal and bearing is not instantaneous, and has been variously estimated at from 14 to 19 lb. per ton of 2,240 lb. As a basis for calculation, 18 lb. per ton is a fair figure.

Resistance due to journal friction is inversely proportional to the diameter of the wheel and varies directly as the diameter of the journal. In this connection it may be noted that in the U.S.A. journals are relatively larger in diameter than in this country. According to Mr. Dendy Marshall, to whose book, *The Resistance of Express Trains*, published by *The Railway Engineer*, readers are referred for an analytical study of the resistance of engines and passenger vehicles, this resistance is constant when running conditions of lubrication are once established, and is of the order of 1.5 to 2.0 lb. per ton.

Flange resistance varies directly as the clearance between flange of wheel and rail.

The total resistance per ton of a vehicle decreases as its weight increases.

It has been estimated that lateral shocks, from the point of view of resistance, are equivalent to an increase of 55% in the journal load. According to the late Mr. Twinberrow (Proc. I.Mech.E., 1925), end thrust may be from 16 to 18% of the vertical load.

The provision of ball or roller bearings is a debatable point. They are unable to effect any reduction in air resistance or in those due to gradients, curves and flange action, and the first cost is considerably greater than that of a plain bearing. Trials made in this country on express services do not demonstrate any reduction in the resistance at high speeds when compared with plain bearings of good design, workmanship and materials; in fact, the reverse is the case. A justification can, however, be made out for the use of ball and roller bearings on vehicles working suburban and other services where stops, and therefore accelerations, are frequent, and the running speed is comparatively low.

(b) Freight Vehicles. In so far as British practice is concerned, very little information is available. As each loose coupled vehicle of the train is started individually, it is practically impossible to compute the starting resistance and, unless a train is made up especially for trial purposes, it is possible that a certain proportion of the journals will be grease lubricated; it is known that the journal resistance is approximately from 75% to 100% higher with grease than with oil.

Curves obtained from trials carried out on the quondam G.N.R. with 10 tons capacity wagons, having a gross weight of 16 tons and fitted with oil axleboxes, shew resistances of approximately 4.25 lb. per ton at 20 m.p.h., 5.2 at 30, and 8.2 at 40. There is a great disparity between these results and those obtained from tests made by the former L.Y.R. (Gass, Proc. I.Loco.E., 1919), according to which the resistance of wagons of similar capacity is 5 lb. per ton at 5 m.p.h., about 6.5 at 10, 10 at 20, 15 at 30 and over 20 lb. per ton at 40 m.p.h. Trials conducted on the old L.N.W.R. with similar wagons gave an average resistance of 6 lb. per ton at 16 m.p.h.

There are several formulæ available which are applicable to American practice.

Mr. Lawford Fry's formula for wagon resistance is

$$R = 1.5 + \frac{106 + 2V}{W + 1} + 0.001\ V^2 \quad\dots\dots\dots\dots (36)$$

A series deduced by A. M. Wellington is as follows:—

$$\text{For twenty loaded box cars, } R = 4 + \frac{V^2}{130} \quad\dots\dots (37)$$

For forty empty box cars, $R = 6 + \dfrac{V^2}{106}$ ...... (38)

For twenty loaded flat cars, $R = \dfrac{V^2}{113}$ ...... (39)

For forty empty flat cars, $R = \dfrac{V^2}{81}$ ...... (40)

The above formulæ are not intended for speeds greater than 30 miles per hour.

The *Engineering News* gives

$$R = 2 + \frac{V}{4} \quad \text{...} \quad (41)$$

and the Baldwin Co.,

$$R = 3 + \frac{V}{6} \quad \text{...} \quad (42)$$

Formula (36) should be used in preference to Nos. (37)—(40) inclusive, which are now more or less obsolete. (36) is not applicable to extra high capacity coal wagons. The following particulars apply to the latter, when running loaded at 10—15 m.p.h., and are quoted by the American Locomotive Company in their handbook:—

No. of Wheels.	Average Axle Load, lb.	R, lb. per ton (of 2,000 lb.)		
		Max.	Min.	Average.
8	40,555	3·55	2·76	3·13
8	49,235	3·34	2·77	3·05
12	40,373	3·36	2·90	3·17

For unloaded stock of this type the following information applies:—

No. of Wheels.	Light Weight (tons of 2,000 lb.)	R, lb. per ton (of 2,000 lb.)		
		Max.	Min.	Average.
12	30·15	7·85	6·75	7·27
8	25·40	6·01	4·11	5·04

Mr. Kimberley (Proc. I.Loco. E., 1921) has derived the following formula from observations made on B.A.P. Ry. freight trains:—

$$R = \left\{ \frac{V + 40 - 0.029\ W}{4.05 + 0.15\ W} \right\} + \left\{ 0.03\ (V - 5) \right\} \quad \ldots \ldots\ (43)$$

It should be noted that the unit of weight in equations (37) to (43) inclusive is the "short" American ton of 2,000 lb.

The effect of atmospheric temperature on resistance is shewn below, the authority quoted again being the American Locomotive Company.

Atmospheric Temperature, degrees Fahrenheit.	Increase over Summer Resistance, %
70	—
29	7·2
12	32·0

Resistance of Engine, Tender and Passenger Coaches. Some resistances of six - coupled express engines and bogie coaches have been put forward by Mr. Kelway Bamber, in a paper read by him before the Institution of Locomotive Engineers, as an indication of typical modern British practice. Table VI recapitulates them in tabular form. Although the numerical values are somewhat lower than those given by the accepted formulæ, they are probably a fair representation of the conditions actually obtaining.

TABLE VI.

RESISTANCES OF MODERN BRITISH SIX-COUPLED EXPRESS LOCOMOTIVE AND BOGIE COACHES (KELWAY BAMBER).

Speed, miles per hour.	Resistance, lb. per ton.	
	Engine and Tender.	Bogie Coaches.
10	10·57	3·68
20	12·80	4·55
30	15·75	5·82
40	19·41	7·50
50	23·85	9·58
60	28·93	12·05
70	34·78	15·05

(3) *Resistance due to Acceleration.*

Let V_1 = greater velocity, miles per hour,
   V_2 = lesser velocity, miles per hour,
   S = distance through which acceleration occurs, feet,
and t = period in which acceleration occurs, seconds.
Then, allowing for the rotary acceleration of wheels and axles, the resistance in lb. per ton of engine, tender and train, due to the specified acceleration, which must of course be stated in mile and hour units, is obtained either from

$$R = 82.3 \frac{(V_1{}^2 - V_2{}^2)}{S} \quad \dots\dots\dots\dots\dots\dots\dots \quad (44)$$

$$\text{or } R = 112.3 \frac{(V_1 - V_2)}{t} \quad \dots\dots\dots\dots\dots\dots\dots \quad (45)$$

The allowance made for the rotary acceleration of wheels and axles in these formulæ is 10%, and is applicable to rolling stock of British design. Where American practice (in which the wheels are of relatively small diameter and, for this and other reasons, form a considerably smaller proportion of the total weight of the vehicle) is concerned, this allowance may be reduced to 5%. Formulæ (44) and (45) then become, respectively,

$$R = 78.5 \frac{(V_1{}^2 - V_2{}^2)}{S} \quad \dots\dots\dots\dots\dots\dots\dots \quad (46)$$

$$R = 107.2 \frac{(V_1 - V_2)}{t} \quad \dots\dots\dots\dots\dots\dots\dots \quad (47)$$

(4) *Gradient Resistance.* This is simply a case of the inclined plane. Neglecting for the moment the resistances due to velocity and air, which may be calculated from the formulæ given previously, and must be added subsequently, the additional resistance incurred by ascending a gradient of 1 in x is given by:—

$$R = \frac{2240}{x} \text{ lb. per ton} \quad \dots\dots\dots\dots\dots\dots\dots \quad (48)$$

Table VII evaluates this resistance for various gradients. Gradient resistance obviously becomes a minus quantity when descending.

Applying the formula to Continental and American practice, in which gradients are customarily quoted as percentages,

$$y\ \% \ = \ \frac{y}{100} \ = \ \frac{1}{x},$$

whence $x = \dfrac{100}{y}$

<table>
<tr><td colspan="2" align="center">TABLE VII.
RESISTANCE DUE TO GRADIENTS.</td></tr>
<tr><td align="center">Gradient :
1 in</td><td align="center">Resistance of Engine, Tender and Train,
lb. per ton of 2,240 lb.</td></tr>
<tr><td align="center">30</td><td align="center">74·7</td></tr>
<tr><td align="center">40</td><td align="center">56·0</td></tr>
<tr><td align="center">50</td><td align="center">44·8</td></tr>
<tr><td align="center">60</td><td align="center">37·3</td></tr>
<tr><td align="center">70</td><td align="center">32·0</td></tr>
<tr><td align="center">80</td><td align="center">28·0</td></tr>
<tr><td align="center">90</td><td align="center">24·9</td></tr>
<tr><td align="center">100</td><td align="center">22·4</td></tr>
<tr><td align="center">150</td><td align="center">14·9</td></tr>
<tr><td align="center">200</td><td align="center">11·2</td></tr>
<tr><td align="center">250</td><td align="center">8·96</td></tr>
<tr><td align="center">300</td><td align="center">7·47</td></tr>
<tr><td align="center">350</td><td align="center">6·4</td></tr>
<tr><td align="center">400</td><td align="center">5·6</td></tr>
<tr><td align="center">450</td><td align="center">4·98</td></tr>
<tr><td align="center">500</td><td align="center">4·48</td></tr>
<tr><td align="center">600</td><td align="center">3·73</td></tr>
<tr><td align="center">700</td><td align="center">3·2</td></tr>
<tr><td align="center">800</td><td align="center">2·8</td></tr>
<tr><td align="center">900</td><td align="center">2·49</td></tr>
<tr><td align="center">1,000</td><td align="center">2·24</td></tr>
</table>

(5) *Curve Resistance.* In normal main - line working curve resistance is relatively immaterial as the additional resistance encountered is neutralised by the speed reduction occurring as the curve is traversed. The resistance due to curves of small radius is, however, high and materially reduces the hauling capacity of the engine, especially when found in combination with severe gradients.

Morison's formula (Proc. Inst. C.E., Vol. XXXI) is

$$R \ = \ 2240 \ \left(\frac{G + B}{2\,r} \right) f \ \dotfill \ (49)$$

where G =   gauge of rails, feet,
     B =   rigid wheelbase, feet,
     r =   radius of curve, feet,
and f =   coefficient of friction, varying from 0.1 to 0.27.

It is now many years since this formula was propounded and, for more recent examples, it is necessary to turn to American practice. Wellington gives curve resistances, varying according to the condition of the permanent way, of 0.33 to 1.5 lb. per "short" ton per degree of curvature, and these figures agree fairly closely with the Master Mechanics' Association, U.S.A., recommendations of 1.4 lb. per ton (of 2,000 lb.) per degree of curvature for locomotives and 0.7 for cars. F. J. Cole, of the American Locomotive Company, suggests 1.5 lb. per ton for Consolidation engines and 0.8 lb. per ton for cars, the ton in both cases being of 2,000 lb.

To convert n degrees of curvature to radius in feet or chains:—

$$n^\circ = \frac{5730}{\text{Radius of curve (feet)}} = \frac{86.8}{\text{Radius of curve (chains)}}$$

Converted to British units, the Master Mechanics' formula becomes:—

$$R = \frac{573}{r} \times c \quad \text{..............................} \quad (50)$$

where r =   radius of curve, feet,
and c =   constant.
Value for locomotives = 1.56.
For vehicles = 0.78.

Another formula of American origin for the computation of curve resistance is that due to A. J. Wood and, modified to suit British units, is given by:—

$$R = 0.45 + \frac{20.5 + 3.4B}{\text{Radius of curve (chains)}} \quad \text{...........} \quad (51)$$

where B is the bogie wheelbase in feet. This formula applies to vehicles only, but has been so modified by the American Locomotive Company as to be applicable to locomotives. (51) then reads:—

$$R = 0.45 + \frac{20.5 + 2.9B}{\text{Radius of curve (chains)}} \quad \text{...........} \quad (52)$$

It should be noted that B in this case represents the rigid wheelbase of the engine in feet.

It is necessary to emphasise the fact that although formulæ (50), (51) and (52) have been reduced to British units, they are of American origin and refer to the practice of that country. It will therefore be readily appreciated that, owing to the universal use there of central buffer couplings, the results will probably give lower results than those actually obtaining in this country, where the presence of side buffers undoubtedly exerts considerable influence on the question.

(6) *Natural Wind Resistance.* Actual information available on this point is both vague and disappointing in quantity. The effect of a direct head wind is of course capable of simple and direct solution. A very complete mathematical solution of the additional resistances set up by oblique winds is put forward by Mr. Dendy Marshall in *The Resistance of Express Trains*, to which work reference has previously been made.

In view of the variations in the units used in resistance formulæ generally, due to the varying national sources of their origin, it is suggested that much confusion would be avoided were the practice made uniform of giving resistances as, say, percentages of the tare, in preference to the somewhat ambiguous methods at present employed.

Chapter III.

DETERMINATION OF OTHER LEADING DIMENSIONS.

WITH general reference to the leading dimensions of the locomotive, too much importance cannot be attached to the care and discrimination which should be exercised in their determination and correlation ; they are interdependent and obviously the essence and basis of design. Therefore, should they be unsuitable in the first instance, mere excellence of detail design will not redeem the locomotive to which they are applied.

Heretofore attention has been confined entirely to the tractive effort of the locomotive, and the calculations made in connection therewith have in all cases been based on the assumption that this effort is exerted. It is now necessary to consider the question of providing a boiler of such proportions that it will generate sufficient steam, at the predetermined pressure, to maintain the tractive force at the required level under all conditions of working. Incidentally, it may be remarked that the decrease in m.e.p. evidenced as the piston speed is increased (see Figs. 1 and 2) is not entirely due to inherent faults in valves and valve gears, but is also attributable to characteristics of boiler performance, *e.g.*, the lowering of the evaporation with the decreased efficiency of combustion obtaining as the rate of firing is raised.

General Remarks, Definitions and Data.

The output of the boiler is basically influenced by the quality of the fuel, rate of firing, degree of completeness of combustion, efficiency of heat absorption by the heating surface, and radiation losses.

The decrease in boiler efficiency occurring as the rate of firing is increased is due not so much to the inability of the boiler to absorb the additional heat presented as to the less complete combustion obtaining and to the greater unburnt fuel loss. Other things being equal, a generous grate area combined with large firebox volume is therefore conducive to greater efficiency. It would appear that the rate of combustion per unit of firebox volume is a more reliable criterion of relative efficiency than the rate of firing per unit of grate area per hour. The latter has, however, usually been taken as the basis of calculation, and its continued use is justified by the facts that completeness of combustion and the rate of firing are interdependent and that the ratio of firebox volume (cubic feet) to grate area (square feet) is, owing to dimensional restrictions, sensibly constant, this ratio having an average value of about 6 or 7 to 1 in the case of an orthodox " narrow " firebox designed to meet typical British conditions.

The efficiency of absorption of heat is practically independent of the rates of combustion and of evaporation, is constant for any given ratio of heating surface to grate area, and is determined by the relation of the firebox heating surface to the tube heating surface and to the grate area, and by the length, diameter and pitching of the tubes. Mr. Lawford Fry (Proc. I. Mech.E., 1908) stated that the heating surface absorbs 81% of the heat produced by combustion; this probably represents the maximum efficiency attainable.

The maximum steam output is governed by the total cross sectional area of the tubes and flues, and approximates to 7,000 pounds of superheated steam per square foot per hour.

The difference between firebox and smokebox temperatures is fairly constant for all rates of firing, due to the constant efficiency of heat absorption, but according to Mr. Fry *(ibid.)*, the proportion of the heat carried away in the smokebox gases to the total heat generated is lowered as the rate of firing increases, since the consequent fall in the efficiency of combustion results in a decreased weight of gas produced per pound of coal burnt. In support of this contention he cites an instance of the rate of firing being increased from 30 to 130 lb. per square foot of grate area per hour, with the result that the corresponding weights of the products of combustion were reduced from 18 to 8.5 lb. per lb. coal fired.

The efficiency of firebox heating surface is about seven times as great as that of the tubes (Bryan Donkin). F.J. Cole gives the value as 5.5. Experiments made by Goss indicated values of 7.6 and 6.15 for oil fuel and coal respectively. The test boiler had a total heating surface of 3,000 sq. ft., of which

206 sq. ft. represented firebox surface; the grate area was 58 sq. ft. and the $2\frac{1}{4}''$ tubes were 18'–2" in length.

The ratio of tube length to diameter should be so proportioned that the minimum smokebox temperature exceeds that specified for the steam when superheated.

For purposes of calculation, *evaporative heating surface* is computed as follows:—

Firebox. The area of the outside, *i.e.*, " water contact," surface of the inner firebox plates is taken. The areas of the surfaces covered by the foundation ring and by the firehole door ring are excluded. The total cross-sectional area of all tube holes is deducted. If the firehole is of the flanged plate type, the area within the junction of the plates is excluded. No deductions are made for side, roof or tubeplate stays.

Where water (arch) tubes are fitted in the firebox, the inside or "water contact" surface of the tubes is taken, and the area of the holes made in the firebox for their reception is deducted; these stipulations also apply to thermic syphons.

Tubes, small and flue. The area of the outside, *i.e.*, "water contact," surface of the tubes is taken and in both instances is calculated on uniform diameters. The length to be considered effective is that between tube plates.

Grate Area. Is measured between the firebox sides at the level of the upper face of the firebars. No deduction is made for rounded corners or plate flange at the foundation ring.

Smokebox Tube Plate. The area of this plate is not included.

The *Superheater Surface* is computed as follows:—

Elements. The area of the inside, *i.e.*, " steam contact," surface of the elements is taken. Their effective length is from and to the smokebox end of the large flue tube.

The above practice is in accordance with the recommendations of the Locomotive Railway Engineers' Association.

The *equivalent heating surface* is that of a superheater engine in terms of a saturated steam engine, and is given by:—

Equivalent heating surface =
Total evaporative heating surface + x (superheater surface) .... (53)

The unit of area is, of course, the square foot.

The value of x is taken as 1.33 by some engineers and as

1.5 by others and, until this unfortunate lack of uniformity is removed, the value actually adopted must be definitely stated whenever this expression is used.

For rough approximations only, the *evaporative heating surface required per indicated horse-power developed* may be taken as:—

With saturated steam:
    Two-cylinder simple   ...   From 2.33 to 2.67 sq. ft.
    Two-cylinder compound ...   2.0   ,,

With superheated steam:
    Two-cylinder simple   ...   2.0   ,,
    Three-cylinder simple ...   1.7   ,,
    Four-cylinder compound   1.6   ,,

The foregoing are generous estimates and may therefore be applied to I.H.P. computed on the basis of maximum, and not average, value.

Equivalent evaporation from and at 212°F. To allow of equitable comparison, the actual evaporation of the boiler is usually converted to an equivalent evaporation based on the assumption that the feed water is delivered at the arbitrary temperature of 212 degrees Fahrenheit. This equivalent evaporation is given, sufficiently accurately for all practical purposes, by

$$W_e = \frac{W_a(H-t + 32)}{966} \quad\dots\dots\dots\dots\dots\dots\dots\dots\dots\dots\dots\dots \quad (54)$$

where W_e = equivalent evaporation, lb. water per lb. fuel, from and at 212 degrees Fahrenheit,
        W_a = actual evaporation, lb. water per lb. fuel,
        H = total heat in 1 lb. steam, as produced, above that in water at 32 degrees Fahrenheit,
and t = initial temperature of feed water, degrees Fahrenheit.

The *boiler efficiency* is given by

$$E_B = \frac{\text{total heat of steam generated per lb. fuel} \times 100}{\text{calorific value of 1 lb. fuel as fired}} \quad \dots \quad (55)$$

where E_B is the efficiency expressed as a percentage. For a well designed modern boiler of conventional type, the average value of E_B should approach 80% with a rate of firing of 65-70 lb. fuel per square foot of grate area per hour.

Mr. Lawford Fry propounds the formula

$$E_B = \frac{b}{1 + aG} \quad\quad\quad (56)$$

where G = weight of coal fired, lb. per square foot of grate area per hour, and a and b are constants depending on the quality of coal and design of the boiler. In some tests carried out at St. Louis the value of a was 0.0085, and of b, 89. In other trials made at Altoona, in which the coal had a tendency to coke, the value of a fell to 0.0042, that of b being 89 as before.

According to the American engineer, Mr. C. A. Brandt, boiler efficiency varies from 75%—80% at rates of firing below 40 lb. per square foot of grate area per hour to 40%—45% at 200 lb., the unburnt fuel loss ranging from 15%—20% at 60 lb. fuel per square foot of grate area per hour to 50% at 200 lb.

The *boiler demand factor* is given by

$$\frac{TW}{H_e} \quad\quad\quad (57)$$

where T = tractive force, lb.,
W = diameter of coupled wheels, inches,
and H_e = total evaporative heating surface, square feet.

In American practice the boiler demand factor has a lower value than in Great Britain, owing to the inferior grades of coal there available.

Engine Performance Data.

The following particulars have been abstracted from the published results of trials, largely in the proceedings of the Institutions of Mechanical and Locomotive Engineers respectively. The figures given are averages for the trials concerned.

Coal consumptions per drawbar horse-power hour.

L.M.S.R. three-cylinder 4-6-0, "Royal Scot" class	2.66 lb.
G.W.R. four-cylinder 4-6-0, "Castle" class	2.83 lb.
L.M.S.R. three-cylinder compound, 4-4-0	3.78 lb.
L.Y. Section, L.M.S.R., four-cylinder 4-6-0	3.924 lb.
N.E. Section, L.N.E.R., three-cylinder 4-4-2	4.60 lb.
G.N. Section, L.N.E.R., three-cylinder 2-8-0	4.79 lb.
G.N. Section, L.N.E.R., two-cylinder 2-8-0	5.25 lb.
N.E. Section, L.N.E.R., two-cylinder 4-4-2	6.15 lb.
L.Y. Section, L.M.S.R., two-cylinder 0-8-0 .... From	3.24 lb.
at 5 miles per hour to 7.21 lb. at 35 miles per hour.	

Coal consumptions per indicated horse-power hour.

P.L.M. compound, 4-6-2 .... about 2 lb.
G.W.R. four-cylinder 4-6-0, "Castle" class 2.10 lb.
N.E. Section, L.N.E.R., three-cylinder 4-4-2 2.62 lb. (calculated)
L.Y. Section, L.M.S.R., four-cylinder 4-6-0 2.64 lb. ,,
N.E. Section, L.N.E.R., two-cylinder 4-4-2 3.51 lb. ,,
G.N. Section, L.N.E.R., three-cylinder 2-8-0 3.74 lb. ,,
G.N. Section, L.N.E.R., two-cylinder 2-8-0 4.11 lb. ,,

Typical American values are 3.25 lb. with superheated and 4.0 lb. with saturated steam.

Coal consumptions per ton-mile.

L.M.S.R. three-cylinder 4-6-0, "Royal Scot" class .... 0.07 lb.
L.M.S.R. three-cylinder compound, 4-4-0 .... 0.0866 lb.
L.M.S.R. four-cylinder 4-6-0, modified "Claughton" class 0.0915 lb.
G.W.R. four-cylinder 4-6-0, "Castle" class .... 0.101 lb.

When working main-line stopping trains, the consumption may rise to 0.15 or 0.17 lb. per ton-mile. On heavy suburban services with frequent stops, the consumption may be as much as 0.3 lb. per ton-mile. The maximum for local goods work approximates to the same value. For goods trains running long distances without intermediate stops, the consumption varies from 0.13 to 0.16 lb. per ton-mile.

Water consumptions per drawbar horse-power hour.

L.M.S.R. three-cylinder 4-6-0, "Royal Scot" class .... 22.3 lb.
G.W.R. four-cylinder 4-6-0, "Castle" class .... 28.1 lb.
G.N. Section, L.N.E.R., three-cylinder 2-8-0 .... 28.15 lb.
G.N. Section, L.N.E.R., two-cylinder 2-8-0 .... 31.95 lb.
N.E. Section, L.N.E.R., three-cylinder 4-4-2 .... 38.44 lb.
N.E. Section, L.N.E.R., two-cylinder 4-4-2 .... 44.6 lb.

Water consumptions per indicated horse-power hour.

L.M.S.R. three-cylinder compound, 4-4-0 ... 19.1 lb.
G.W.R. four-cylinder 4-6-0, "Castle" class ... 20.9 lb.
N.E. Section, L.N.E.R., three-cylinder 4-4-2 21.9 lb. (calculated)
G.N. Section, L.N.E.R., three-cylinder 2-8-0 22.0 lb. ,,
G.N. Section, L.N.E.R., two-cylinder 2-8-0 25.0 lb. ,,
N.E. Section, L.N.E.R., two-cylinder 4-4-2 25.4 lb. ,,

The influence of piston speed on steam consumption is shewn by the following results of investigations made on the erstwhile L.Y.R.:—

Piston Speed (feet per minute)	Water Consumption (lb. per I.H.P. hour)
200	30
400	26
600	25
800	26
1,000	30

Water consumptions quoted by Cole as representative of American practice are 20.8 lb. with superheated and 27 lb. with saturated steam, including allowances for consumption by auxiliaries.

Passenger locomotives of recent American design, with 300°F. superheat, fitted with feed-water heaters and working at pressures of 225-275 lb. per square inch. are using only 15-16 lb. steam per I.H.P.-hour. Mr. Brandt suggests that, in such instances, 17½ lb. steam per I.H.P.-hour be taken as a basis for calculation, inclusive of an allowance for steam requirements of auxiliaries.

The steam used for auxiliaries in the U.S.A. ranges from 1½ to 3 lb. per I.H.P.-hour.

The recorded total steam consumption of an American 2-8-4 engine on heavy freight working was nearly 23 lb. per I.H.P.-hour.

Equivalent evaporation, from and at 212°F., per lb. coal.

G.W.R. four-cylinder 4-6-0, "Castle" class	12.2 lb.
N.E. Section, L.N.E.R., three-cylinder 4-4-2	10.72 lb.
N.E. Section, L.N.E.R., two-cylinder 4-4-2	9.22 lb.
G.N. Section, L.N.E.R., two-cylinder 2-8-0	7.91 lb.
G.N. Section, L.N.E.R., three-cylinder 2-8-0	7.76 lb.

The effect of varying rates of combustion on the evaporation is shewn by the following information, quoted by A. E. Johnson in *The Engineer* of 29th August, 1913.

I b. Coal per sq. ft. of Grate Area per hour.	Lb. Water evaporated, from and at 212° F., per lb. Coal.
200	6·1
180	6·3
160	6·5
140	6·8
120	7·1
100	7·5
80	8·1
60	9·0

Actual evaporation per lb. coal.

L.M.S.R. three-cylinder 4-6-0, "Royal Scot" class	8.4 lb.
G.N. Section, L.N.E.R., two-cylinder 2-8-0	6.79 lb.

A saturated steam yard shunting engine will give an average actual evaporation of slightly over 5 lb. per lb. coal. A representative figure for superheated engines on goods work is 6.2 lb. per lb.. and on main-line passenger service, 6.75-7.25 lb. per lb. The basis used for calculation in American practice is an evaporation of 6.75 lb. water per lb. coal.

Average efficiency of boiler.

G.W.R. four-cylinder 4-6-0, "Castle" class	79.8 %
N.E. Section, L.N.E.R., three-cylinder 4-4-2	74.0 %
N.E. Section, L.N.E.R., two-cylinder 4-4-2	63.6 %
G.N. Section, L.N.E.R., two-cylinder 2-8-0	54.6 %
G.N. Section, L.N.E.R., three-cylinder 2-8-0	53.6 %

Thermal efficiency of engine (indicated horse-power basis).

G.W.R. four-cylinder 4-6-0, "Castle" class	8.22 %
N.E. Section, L.N.E.R., three-cylinder 4-4-2	6.93 %
L.Y. Section, L.M.S.R., four-cylinder 4-6-0	6.88 %
N.E. Section, L.N.E.R., two-cylinder 4-4-2	5.18 %
G.N. Section, L.N.E.R., three-cylinder 2-8-0	4.86 %
G.N. Section, L.N.E.R., two-cylinder 2-8-0	4.42 %

Estimating Steam Consumptions.

Before the boiler dimensions can be determined it is necessary to investigate the probable steam consumption of the
proposed engine.   There are several methods of so doing, but
it must be borne in mind that each assumes ideal conditions of
working.   The missing quantity, leakage and other losses are
therefore neglected and the calculated result may represent only
50%-60% of the actual consumption, for which correction must
be made.   Since the missing quantity is reduced and wiredrawing increases as the piston speed rises, it is possible that
the percentages given here are somewhat high, but an error
of this description is, in these circumstances, defensible ;
calculated consumptions of superheated steam should in any
case be increased by at least 20%.   The extent of the missing
quantity decreases as the cylinder dimensions are increased;
this may be attributed to a reduction in cylinder condensation
and radiation losses occurring as the ratio of cylinder volume
to surface in contact with steam is augmented.

On at least one of the home railways it is the practice so to
dimension the boiler that it is capable of supplying steam to
the cylinders at a cut-off of 25% when working at the peak
rate of revolution.   Such a rule is, however, a somewhat too
sweeping assertion for general acceptance, and it is advisable
to consider each case individually with due regard to the
peculiar conditions applying.

Probably the most widely known method of estimating steam
consumptions is to take a hypothetical indicator diagram,
representative of the greatest demand on the boiler, then calculate the quantity of steam admitted to the cylinder per stroke
up to the point of cut-off and subtract the quantity trapped
at compression.

Professor Clayton gives the index of the expansion curve as

$$n = 0.805\ x + 0.463 \quad\dots\dots\dots\dots\dots\dots\dots\dots\dots\quad (58)$$

where x is the dryness fraction at cut-off.

Conversely,

$$x = 1.245\ n - 0.576 \quad\dots\dots\dots\dots\dots\dots\dots\dots\dots\quad (59)$$

According to Signor Caprotti, the expansion curve follows
the law $PV^{1.2} = C$, and the compression curve that of $PV^{1.3} = C$.

Let V = total piston displacement, cubic feet,

c = clearance volume,

v = volume swept through to point of cut-off,

x = volume from point of compression to end of stroke,

} expressed as decimals of V,

W_1 = weight of one cubic foot of steam at pressure of admission, lb.,

W_2 = weight of one cubic foot of steam at initial pressure of compression, lb.,

V_a = volume in cubic feet of 1 lb. steam at pressure of admission = $\dfrac{1}{W_1}$

V_c = volume in cubic feet of 1 lb. steam at initial pressure of compression = $\dfrac{1}{W_2}$

and R = number of revolutions per minute.

Then total indicated weight of steam consumed per cylinder per hour

$$= 120\,R\left\{(v + c)\,VW_1 - (x + c)\,VW_2\right\} \quad\dots\dots\dots\dots (60)$$

$$= 120\,R\left\{\frac{(v + c)\,V}{V_a} - \frac{(x + c)\,V}{V_c}\right\} \quad\dots\dots\dots (61)$$

The clearance volume varies approximately from 4% of the total piston displacement in the case of very large cylinders with poppet valves to 12% with small cylinders having piston valves. The clearance volume of piston valve cylinders usually ranges from 7% to 10%. With simple expansion, compression may be assumed to commence at a pressure of 19-20 lb. per square inch absolute.

Another method which, however, gives rather low results, is:

Total weight of steam consumed per cylinder per hour is determined in the first instance from:—

$$\left\{\frac{\text{Piston area (sq. ft.)} \times \text{piston speed (ft./min.)}}{\text{Ratio of expansion}}\right\} \times 60 \times W_1 \dots (62)$$

The value obtained from equation (62) is then increased by,

say, 5%–10% to allow for clearance volume, and the result finally multiplied by an appropriate factor which may be obtained from Table VIII (T. M. Naylor, *The Railway Engineer*, November, 1928).

TABLE VIII.
FACTORS FOR EQUATION (62).

Type of engine.	Factors							
	Cut off, %							
	5	10	15	20	25	30	40	50
Simple	1·72	1·51	1·40	1·35	1·31	1·28	1·22	1·16
Compound	—	1·35	1·31	1·28	1·25	1·22	1·17	1·13

The results given by formulæ (60), (61) and (62) must of course be divided by the I.H.P. developed per cylinder to give the steam consumption in I.H.P.-hour terms.

From experiments carried out on an engine having 16″ × 24″ cylinders, Mr. Lawford Fry deduced the formula,

Total volume of steam (cu. ft.) actually used per cylinder per stroke

$$= 1.1 S_i + \frac{0.13 \, V}{r^{\frac{2}{3}}} \quad \dots\dots\dots\dots\dots\dots\dots\dots\dots\dots (63)$$

in which S_i = volume of steam as shewn by indicator, *i.e.*, up to point of cut-off, inclusive of clearance, cu. ft.,

V = volume swept through in one stroke of piston, cu. ft.,

and r = number of revolutions per second.

Mr. Rowlands has modified this formula (Proc. I. Loco. E., 1927) to permit of application to cylinders of any given dimensions. It then becomes:—

Total steam actually used per cylinder =

$$S_i + \left\{ 6\left(d + \frac{2l}{dl} \right) \left(0.1 \, S_i + \frac{0.13}{r^{\frac{2}{3}}} \right) \right\} \quad \dots\dots\dots\dots (64)$$

where d = cylinder diameter, inches,
and l = cylinder stroke, inches.

The missing quantity is represented by the second term of the expression. It will be observed that a given missing quantity represents a smaller heat loss with superheated than with saturated steam.

Another formula due to Mr. Lawford Fry which may be interpolated here is that giving the theoretical work done per stroke in heat units (Proc. I. Mech.E., 1927):—

$$W = H_a - H_r + 0.1852 (P_r - P_e)V_r \quad\dots\dots\dots\dots (65)$$

where W = work developed, B.Th.U.,

H_a = total heat at admission, B.Th.U. per lb.,

H_r = total heat at release, B.Th.U. per lb.,

P_r = pressure at release, lb. per square inch absolute,

P_e = pressure during exhaust, lb. per square inch absolute,

and V_r = specific volume of steam at release, cubic feet per lb.

A method for the determination of the steam consumption which reverts to the use of the hypothetical indicator diagram requires the expansion curve to be produced to the end of the stroke, where the pressure is determined.

Then, steam consumption per cylinder per I.H.P.-hour =

$$\frac{\text{Piston displacement (cu. ft.)} \times R.P.M. \times W_e \times 120}{I.H.P. \times x} \quad\dots (66)$$

where W_e = weight of steam, at pressure determined by producing expansion curve to end of stroke, lb. per cubic foot,

and x = dryness fraction.

Mr. Naylor *(ante.)* suggests that x be taken as 0.65 for simple expansion and 0.74 for compound engines, and is of the opinion that very fair results are given by (66).

The *limiting condensation* in the cylinder, *i.e.*, the maximum condensation occurring under steady conditions when the amount of water re-evaporated equals the quantity of steam condensed in the cylinder, is given (Callendar and Nicolson) by

$$\pi D^2 (t_1 - t_2) \text{ lb. per hour} \quad\dots\dots\dots\dots\dots (67)$$

where D = cylinder diameter, feet,

t_1 = temperature of admission steam, degrees Fahrenheit,

and t_2 = temperature of exhaust steam, degrees Fahrenheit.

According to R. H. Thurston, the missing quantity is governed by the relation

$$\frac{M}{1-M} = \frac{30\sqrt{R}}{D\sqrt{N}} \quad \dots\dots\dots\dots\dots\dots\dots\dots\dots\dots \quad (68)$$

where M = missing quantity, lb.,
         R = ratio of expansion,
         D = diameter of cylinder, inches,
and N = number of revolutions per minute.

Calorific Value and Combustion of Fuel.

As these subjects are fully dealt with in most text books on the theory of heat engines, they will be only briefly reviewed here.

The *calorific value* of a fuel is the number of units of heat produced by the combustion of 1 lb. weight of that fuel and may be determined either by actual test in a calorimeter or by analysis. When the former method is employed, it must be remembered that calorimeters of the Bomb type are generally utilised. This implies the reduction of the fuel sample to powder in the first instance and combustion taking place in oxygen. Both factors conspire to a very complete combustion under ideal conditions which are impossible of attainment in actual locomotive practice, where the degree of completeness of combustion depends, *inter alia*, on the rate of firing, and the combustion takes place in air, which carries a varying proportion of moisture in suspension and contains, in addition to oxygen, a large proportion of nitrogen. The latter, which comprises about 77% of the mixture by weight, is of no use in the process of combustion and, further, carries away an appreciable quantity of heat in its passage through the firebox and tubes.

In accepting the calorific value of a fuel, care must be taken to differentiate between the *higher* and the *lower* value, as the former neglects to deduct the latent heat of the steam formed during combustion; this latter quantity, with average British coal, is of the order of 450 B.Th.U. per lb.

Analysis of a fuel may be either "ultimate" or "proximate," according to whether each element is treated individually or the constituents are grouped generically as moisture, volatile matter, fixed carbon and ash respectively. The analysis known, the calorific value is then found by formula, such as Dulong's:—

$$C.V. = 14{,}544 \left\{ C + 3.667 \left(H - \frac{O}{8} \right) + 0.275\ S \right\} \quad \text{....... (69)}$$

Inchley suggested, for average steam coals,

$$C.V. = 14{,}400\ C + 52{,}200\ H \quad \text{......................... (70)}$$

and for oil fuels,

$$C.V. = 13{,}500\ C + 52{,}200\ H \quad \text{......................... (71)}$$

In the preceding formulæ,

$C.V.$ = (lower) calorific value, B.Th.U. per lb.,

C = weight of carbon ⎫
H = ,, hydrogen ⎬ per lb. fuel, expressed as a deci-
O = ,, oxygen ⎪ mal of a pound.
and S = ,, sulphur ⎭

The actual calorific value of the fuel *as fired* is the value ultimately required by the locomotive engineer, and should in fairness be used as the true criterion of thermal efficiency. It is therefore necessary to allow for the effects of the temperature of the products of combustion not falling below that of the water in the boiler, for atmospheric moisture, and where coal is concerned, for deterioration of the basic C. V. due to a possible lengthy period in stack.

The minimum *theoretical quantity of air required for the complete combustion of* 1 *lb. fuel* is given by

$$\text{Air required (lb. per lb. fuel)} = (11.6 \times C) + (34.8 \times H) + (4.35 \times S) \quad \text{.................. (72)}$$

and for average British coal approximates to 12 lb. The symbols used have the same significance as previously.

The *actual* quantity of air required exceeds the theoretical quantity by 50%—100%.

Mr. Rowlands (Proc. I. Loco.E., 1919) suggests that the air supplied, lb. per lb. coal completely burnt, is given by

$$\frac{6200}{280 + F} \quad \text{.. (73)}$$

where F is the rate of firing in lb. fuel per square foot of grate area per hour.

Air comprises twenty-three parts by weight of oxygen and seventy-seven parts of nitrogen, whence the weight of air containing 1 lb. oxygen $= \dfrac{100}{23} = 4.35$ lb. The theoretical weight of air required for combustion is therefore 4.35 times that of the necessary weight of oxygen.

1 lb. air, at a temperature of 62°F. and under a pressure of 1 atmosphere, occupies 13.14 cubic feet, and at 32°F., 12.39 cubic feet.

The carbon value of a fuel is the number of pounds weight of carbon having the same calorific value as 1 pound of that fuel, and is therefore obtained by dividing the calorific value of the fuel by that of carbon.

The *theoretical evaporative power* of a fuel is given in lb. water evaporated from and at 212°F. per lb. fuel, and is obtained by dividing the calorific value of the fuel by 966. If the theoretical evaporative power be multiplied by the boiler efficiency (expressed as a decimal), the *actual evaporative power* is of course obtained.

Completeness of combustion in a locomotive boiler is given (Rowlands, Proc. I. Loco.E.) as a decimal by

$$\frac{28}{25.4 + KX} \quad \dots\dots\dots\dots\dots\dots\dots\dots\dots\dots\dots\dots\dots\dots\dots (74)$$

where K = ratio of firebox heating surface (square feet) to firebox volume (cubic feet),

and X = lb. coal fired per hour per cubic foot of firebox volume.

The *theoretical weight of the products of combustion* per lb. fuel is given by

$$A + C + H + S \quad \dots\dots\dots\dots\dots\dots\dots\dots\dots\dots\dots\dots\dots\dots (75)$$

where A is the theoretical quantity of air supplied, lb. per lb. fuel and the remaining symbols have the same interpretation as in formulæ (69)—(72) inclusive.

The *theoretical temperature of combustion* is given by

$$t = \frac{h}{sw} \quad \dots\dots\dots\dots\dots\dots\dots\dots\dots\dots\dots\dots\dots\dots\dots\dots\dots (76)$$

where t = temperature of furnace, degrees Fahrenheit,
   h = calorific value of 1 lb. fuel,
   w = weight of products of combustion, lb. per lb. fuel,
and s = mean specific heat of the products of combustion.

A representative value of s is 0.24.

Grate Area.

With reliable data available, the logical method of determining the requisite grate area is from the formula

$$x = \frac{S}{F\,E} \quad \text{..} \quad (77)$$

where x = grate area, square feet,
  S = calculated total steam consumption, lb. per hour,
  F = desirable rate of firing, lb. coal per square foot of grate area per hour,
and E = actual evaporation, lb. water per lb. coal.

Conservative values should be given to F and E. S may be determined by one of the methods previously mentioned in this chapter, the calculated result being increased to allow for the missing quantity and further additions made for continuous brakes, train heating, boiler feeding, and the maintenance of any other auxiliary services which may be installed, *e.g.*, mechanical stoker, booster, headlight dynamos, etc.; information on these points will be found in Chapter VI. F, for the purpose of calculation, should not be taken at a higher value than 60 with average grades of British bituminous coal; the engine should be designed to supply the mean demand at this rate. In modern American design, the maximum value for F is taken as 80, the average being 40. Similarly, to allow for the effects of decreased efficiency as the mileage run becomes high, a low value should be assigned to E; 6·2 is applicable to British superheated steam practice and includes an ample margin for impaired performance, formation of clinker on long runs, etc.

A purely empirical method of determining the grate area is to take as a basis the total piston displacement. Typical allowances are shewn in Table IX. The chief objection to this method is that it disregards the increase in weight of steam per unit volume with rise of pressure.

The greater displacement allowances for shunting and local tank engines, due to the intermittent character of the steam demand, and for three- and four-cylinder engines, due to greater efficiency, will be noted. In the case of shunting engines, the grate area should be restricted in order to minimise stand-by losses. It should again be emphasised that the determination of grate area by this method, although approximately

TABLE IX.
PISTON DISPLACEMENT PER SQUARE FOOT OF GRATE AREA.

Type of Engine.	Total Piston Displacement (cubic inches) per square foot of grate area.	
	Average British coal.	Inferior coal.
Shunting engines	700—750	650
Local tank engines	650—700	600
Heavy tank engines—		
Two cylinders	650—700	650
Three or four cylinders ...	750	—
Goods engines	600—675	500—550
Passenger express engines ...	500—650	450—500

correct, is purely empirical. The true basis of calculation is the maximum steam demand, the only disadvantage being the inability to estimate the latter quantity with a satisfactory degree of accuracy.

Table X comprises some examples of the proportions of grate area and cylinder diameter, for engines burning inferior coal, quoted by Mr. Kyffin (Proc. I. Mech.E., 1922). Although not definitely stated, it may be inferred that this table applies only to two-cylinder engines. The apparent inconsistencies in the proportions could probably be explained were further

TABLE X.
PROPORTIONS OF GRATE AREA AND CYLINDER DIAMETER WITH INFERIOR COAL.
(Kyffin, Proc. I. Mech.E., 1922).

Grate area (square feet)	Cylinder diameter (inches)
19.3	15¾
25.0	17
34.8	18
26.0	18½
28.0	19
27.5	20
29.8	21
48.0	21½

particulars of the engines concerned available, *e.g.*, length of stroke, class of work for which designed and normal mileage run between fire cleanings.

Mr. F. J. Cole, the consulting engineer to the American Locomotive Company, recommends the determination of grate area on the H.P. basis, and suggests:—

$$\text{Grate area} = \frac{\text{H.P.}}{36\cdot9} \text{ for superheated engines } \dots\dots\dots (78)$$

$$= \frac{\text{H.P.}}{30} \text{ for saturated steam engines } \dots\dots (79)$$

These formulæ are based on the assumption that the maximum rate of firing is 120 lb. per square foot of grate area per hour and are applicable to American bituminous coal. For hard coal, Mr. Cole gives the appropriate rate of firing as 55 to 70 lb. and in this case the grate area, as determined above, must be proportionately increased.

In American practice the ratio of rated tractive force (lb.) to grate area (square feet) has a value of from 600 to 700.

Firebox Heating Surface.

The ideal firebox possesses the maximum volume per unit of grate area, the majority of authorities inclining to the view that this should be in combination with the minimum surface per unit of volume.

In British practice the firebox heating surface is generally from 5 to 6·5 times the grate area, the firebox volume to surface ratio approximating to 1·1:1. The firebox heating surface to grate area ratio is rather less in foreign practice, due to the more shallow grates provided for the combustion of inferior fuels, and ranges from roughly 3:1 to 5·25:1. In the U.S.A., however, the ratios at present accepted are from 5·25:1 to 6·5:1, it being stipulated that the ratio shall have a value of not less than 4:1.

The quantity of *heat radiating to the firebox heating surface* may be calculated from Stefan's formula which, as adapted by Rowlands, is:—

$$H_r = \frac{16\ T^4}{10^{10}} - 875 \dots\dots\dots\dots\dots\dots\dots\dots (80)$$

where H_r = total heat radiated per square foot of firebox
heating surface per hour, B.Th.U.,
     and T = absolute furnace temperature, degrees Fahrenheit.

It is usual to determine the quantity of heat radiated on the total firebox heating surface provided, and not on a proportion thereof.

As a rough practical guide, Table XI gives approximate furnace temperatures as indicated by the colour of the fire (*Locomotive Running Shed Management,* Paterson and Webster).   For the purposes of approximation, the average temperature of a coal fire may be taken at 1900°F., and for liquid fuel, 2400°F.   With a mechanical stoker the average firebox temperature is of the order of 2600°F.

It will be noted that these temperatures, and also those given in the table, are actual and not absolute.

TABLE XI.
APPROXIMATE FURNACE TEMPERATURE AS INDICATED BY THE COLOUR OF THE FIRE (PATERSON AND WEBSTER).

Colour of Fire.	Approximate Temperature, degrees Fahrenheit.
Red (just showing)	1,000
Red (dull)	1,300
Red (bright)	1,800
Orange (deep)	2,000
Orange (bright)	2,200
Yellow	2,400
White	2,600
White (intense)	2,800

Tests carried out in the U.S.A. demonstrated an evaporation of 54·8 lb. water per hour per square foot of firebox heating surface.

Tube Heating Surface.

It would be utterly misleading to quote any ratios for guidance in the matter of providing suitable tube heating surface.   This latter quantity is in part determined by extraneous factors, such as the wheelbase and wheel arrangement, which limit the length of the boiler barrel, and is also directly affected by the proportion of superheater flues to small tubes.   Further, it is in many instances only too easy to provide an extent of heating surface in a boiler of quite moderate dimensions which appears, in theory, to be eminently satisfactory, but which, in practice, causes endless trouble for the running shed boilermakers by the formation of inaccessible scale and, fundamentally, gives a more than dubious efficiency of heat transmission.

For reasons such as these, departures from the ratios frequently seen stated as desirable for the proportion of tube heating surface to grate area are so numerous and so divergent that the following data may be accepted as a more reliable basis for calculation:—

The total cross sectional area of the tubes available for the passage of the gases of combustion usually varies from 0·185 to 0·25 of the grate area. The greater the value of this proportion, the less will be the draught, and consequently the power loss due to back pressure, necessary for the generation of steam.

The steam raising capacity of the boiler is directly proportional to the cross sectional area of the tubes and the maximum output, as previously stated, approximates to 7,000 lb. superheated steam per square foot per hour.

In order to secure the maximum gas area, American engineers frequently restrict the bridge between the tubes to $\frac{3}{4}''$. It is, however, recommended for British practice that the small tubes be so pitched, in standard and broad-gauge engines, that the minimum bridge, or thickness of metal between adjacent tubes, is 1″ at the firebox tubeplate. The adoption of this minimum dimension not only tends to increase the efficiency of heat transmission but also offers resistance to distortion arising in practice from continued use of the tube expander.

Excessive length of tube is another factor tending to increase the minimum value of the required draught. This, together with the facts that the efficiency of heat transmission for tubes is much inferior to that obtaining in the firebox and that the smokebox temperature must be greater than that of the steam when superheated, limits the maximum effective length of tube to approximately 16 feet, although practical considerations sometimes cause this dimension to be exceeded. Such additional length may with advantage be taken up by the extension of the firebox into a combustion chamber. The use of the latter has reduced the tube lengths of American Mallet articulated engines from 24 feet or 25 feet to 22 feet, which is the maximum now considered advisable in the U.S.A.

The ratio of length between tubeplates to the outside diameter of the small tubes is approximately 70 or 80 to 1 in normal British practice, rising to 90 to 1 for express engines; with inferior grades of slack coal, ratios of from 90 to 110 to 1 are permissible.

The considerations affecting tube design will be detailed more fully in Chapter V. Meanwhile, attention is drawn to Fig. 4, whence the length of tube appropriate to any required final steam temperature may be found. This figure is published in the Locomotive Engineers' Pocket Book, from which the data embodied in Table XII have also been extracted.

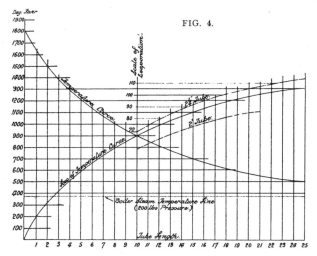

FIG. 4.

The *efficiency of heat absorption by the tubes* is given (Rowlands, Proc. I. Loco.E.) by

$$\frac{56 + l}{35d + 56 + l} \qquad \qquad (81)$$

where l = length of tube, inches,
and d = inside diameter of tube, inches.

Superheater flues must be considered separately. Mr. L. Fry has evolved a method of reducing them to a basis comparable with small tubes, assuming that the resistance to gas flow in a tube of any given section is proportional to its mean hydraulic depth (*i.e.*, ratio of cross sectional area to perimeter).

The calculation can best be illustrated by an actual example

TABLE XII.

RATED EVAPORATIONS FROM TUBES.

Length of tube, feet	10	12	14	16	18	20
2″ tubes, with ¾″ water space						
Evapn. per sq. ft., lb.	12·08	11·13	10·36	9·6	8·95	8·32
Evapn. per tube, lb.	63·25	70·24	75·94	80·43	84·35	87·03
2″ tubes with 1″ water space						
Evapn. per sq. ft., lb.	13·12	12·13	11·24	10·44	9·72	9·05
Evapn. per tube, lb.	68·69	76·21	82·38	87·46	91·61	94·77

Length of tube, feet	10	12	14	16	18	20	25
2¼″ tubes with ¾″ water space							
Evapn. per sq. ft., lb.	12·62	11·7	10·88	10·15	9·46	8·83	7·55
Evapn. per tube, lb.	74·33	82·7	89·72	95·66	100·27	104·03	111·18
2¼″ tubes with 1″ water space							
Evapn. per sq. ft., lb.	13·55	12·57	11·69	10·9	10·18	9·51	7·98
Evapn. per tube, lb.	79·81	88·85	96·4	102·73	107·91	112·04	117·51
5½″ tubes with 1″ water space							
Evapn. per sq. ft., lb.	14·08	13·15	12·3	11·52	10·82	10·22	8·9
Evapn. per tube, lb.	202·73	227·21	247·95	265·4	280·43	294·31	320·38

c

Assume a flue to have an internal diameter of 4.93" and house four elements each $1\frac{3}{8}"$ in diameter. The nett cross sectional area is

$$\left(\frac{\pi}{4} \times 4 \cdot 93^2\right) - \left(\frac{\pi}{4} \times 1 \cdot 375^2 \times 4\right) = 13 \cdot 16 \text{ sq. ins.,}$$

and the total perimeter is

$(\pi \times 4 \cdot 93) + (\pi \times 1 \cdot 375 \times 4) = 32.8"$

Then the mean hydraulic depth $= \dfrac{13 \cdot 16}{32 \cdot 8} = 0 \cdot 402$

$$= \frac{\text{diameter of equivalent small tube (ins.)}}{4}$$

Whence the equivalent diameter (*i.e.*, of a small tube) $= 4 \times \text{m.h.d.} = 4 \times 0 \cdot 402 = 1.608"$.

According to Mr. Rowlands (Proc. I. Loco.E.), the heat carried away by gases and solid matter in the products of combustion entering the tubes is

$$W \left\{ 0 \cdot 23 + 0 \cdot 000015 \ (T + t) \right\} \ (T - t) \ \dots\dots\dots\dots \ (82)$$

where W = weight of gases per lb. coal, lb.,

$\qquad t$ = absolute temperature of atmosphere and coal, degrees Fahrenheit,

and T = absolute temperature of firebox gases, degrees Fahrenheit.

The unburnt fuel loss may represent up to 40% of the total heat produced at maximum boiler output, and that in the gases ejected from the smokebox, 15% of this quantity (Diamond, Pro. I. Mech.E., 1925).

Superheater Surface.

As with small tube heating surface, it is impossible to give any ratios for reliable guidance in the matter of allocating the extent of superheater surface. The latter quantity is immediately affected, *inter alia*, by considerations of policy, *e.g.*, whether high boiler pressure and moderate degree of superheat or the converse are adopted. Other representative governing factors are the diameter of the barrel, length between tubeplates, and the presence of exhaust steam injectors or other forms of feed water heaters. Readers are therefore referred to Chapter VII, where superheating is considered at length.

With low degree superheat the superheater surface usually approximates to 1/7 or 1/8 of the evaporative heating surface, rising to 1/4 or 1/5 for high degree superheat. These proportions apply to British practice ; in America, and on the Continent, high degree superheater surface ranges from 1/4 to 1/2.5 of the evaporative heating surface, a representative value being 1/3.

The Leading Dimensions and Design Ratios of various engines have been tabulated as follows:—

Table XIII.   Tank engines.
Table XIV.   Goods engines.
Table XV.   Mixed traffic engines.
Table XVI.   Passenger express engines.

Compound engines are considered separately in Chapter XI.

Chapter IV.

CARDINAL POINTS OF DESIGN.

THE ultimate, or economic, efficiency of the steam locomotive involves many factors other than the minimisation of the quantities of fuel, lubricants and water consumed in the performance of a given amount of work. The unit in which the traffic officer is most likely to express this efficiency is the work done per engine hour, whereas the locomotive engineer takes as his criterion the number of hours in steam attained per annum. Irrespective of the point of view, and both must receive consideration, a common and decisive point in any engine is its vulnerability, or degree of susceptibility to repair.

It usually follows that an engine which is light on fuel is also economical as regards maintenance, but none the less there is a danger that the importance of fuel economy may be over-emphasised, especially by engineers. Although fuel costs in this country represent roughly 75% of the total running cost of a locomotive (the remaining 25% covering repairs), they form but a small proportion of the total working expenses of a railway—*The Engineer* suggested 7%-8% as a representative figure—and the introduction of complications to reduce the fuel consumption may involve additional capital charges to such an extent that the return thereon, if any, is not realised within a reasonable period of time. As previously stated, reliability is primarily essential. To ensure this characteristic, every detail must be so designed that it assumes the simplest form commensurate with the performance of its required duty. It must be rendered foolproof, especially when handled by un-intelligent or inexperienced staff. It must be as accessible for inspection and attention by the enginemen as it is for repair in shops and sheds. It must be sufficiently strong to with-stand the loads and forces to which it is subjected. In addi-tion, reasonable allowances must be made for any reduction in section likely to occur owing to wear and tear and to conse-quent re-machining, and the factor of safety must be further increased should there be any likelihood of increased stress due to forces of a more or less indeterminate nature, *e.g.*, occasional or intermittent impact and shocks. At the same time, no redundant material should be provided; unnecessary weight in reciprocating parts requiring to be balanced is a random case which may be cited. Any weight which is unproductive from the point of view of power output should be eliminated if possible or, if unavoidable, minimised.

As forces essentially act along straight lines it is preferable to arrange for material to surround those lines, where possible, throughout; every effort should be made to avoid excentric loadings.

Carried to excess, standardisation becomes a fetish and stifles development. On the other hand, departure from an existing standard involves expense, if not actually waste, and should not be made unless concrete advantages are likely to accrue thereby.

The individual detail must be considered not only with the outlook of the specialist, but also in relation to neighbouring parts as regards clearances, accessibility, etc., and to the design as a whole. A quality which, by reason of being commonplace and obvious, is liable to be overlooked on occasion, is that of "erectability." All components must be capable of being assembled in sequence; every dimension must be checked with this end in view and the necessary clearances provided. Attention must also be given to the relation of the individual detail to others in the vicinity, such that compliance with the requirements of rapid partial stripping for periodical examinations and repairs is ensured. For example, the breaking of the crosshead joint on inside cylinder engines is often an unnecessarily long and tedious process by reason of the inaccessible position of the cotter. The latter may be so located that it cannot be directly hammered out; withdrawal is consequently difficult to effect.

The design is bad in cases where numerous pipes have to be taken down before wheels and axles can be removed, or one or more steam-tight joints have to be broken in order to repair another which has commenced to blow. Again, steam pipe joints should be kept away from bearings so that, in the event of leakage, no water shall obtain access to lubricant reservoirs. Injectors are sometimes so located that it is impossible to remove the cones without taking down the complete injector.

Firebox side stays are frequently very inaccessible from the outside, especially on tank engines, where thorough attention cannot be given until the side tanks and cab sides have been removed; although admittedly benefitting by a larger loading gauge, most American and Continental designs shew a decided advantage over British practice in this respect. Engines have been designed which could not possibly be lifted at the trailing end without cutting away part of the cab. These are but a few of the many pitfalls which must be avoided.

Great care must be exercised in the location of details in the vicinity of the firebox and ashpan. When unfortunately but unavoidably close, main bearings must be suitably protected from heat and the possible intrusion of foreign matter. Continuous brake cylinders may suffer from the heat to which they would be subjected if placed at a short distance from the firebox. The placing of reversing rods, pipes, etc., under the boiler lagging is to be deprecated, and the use of splashers, especially when pipes are arranged to follow their contours, should be minimised or, preferably, eliminated entirely, thus improving the accessibility of outside rods and their bearings.

The location of wash-out plugs such that they are truly effective in practice, and the arrangement of the cab and other fittings for the greatest convenience of the enginemen and with the least obstruction to their range of vision, are further specimen items which will be dealt with at greater length under the appropriate headings.

For the purpose of making joints, Mr. Clayton (Proc. I. Loco.E.) gave in order of preference:—(1) bolts; (2) studs; (3) set screws. This is a rule which may be readily endorsed for general application.

It is well to remember that the strength of screwed sections subjected to alternating stresses is equivalent to only 70% of that of a plain bar having a diameter equal to that at the root of the thread.

Chapter V.

THE BOILER.

General Remarks.

Considered broadly, the most important rule to observe when designing the boiler is to make it as large as loading gauge clearances, height of centre of gravity of the engine, coupled wheel diameter and limiting axle loads will permit. It is almost impossible to over-boiler an engine and, for a given engine (unless intended for shunting work, in which instance the extent of grate is restricted, as previously stated, in order to minimise stand-by losses), it may be taken that the larger the boiler, with especial reference to grate and firebox dimensions and the gas area through the tubes, the lower will be both fuel and boiler maintenance costs. Where the question of securing appropriate adhesive weight arises, the provision of a large boiler having ample water capacity or, in other words, an adequate thermal storage reservoir, is infinitely preferable to the employment of otherwise unnecessarily heavy drag box castings and kindred clumsy devices. On the other hand, should loading limitations be severe, the attainment of sufficient grate area in conjunction with low boiler weight may be assisted by such measures as the adoption of a sloping back plate which, incidentally, also promotes the circulation of the convection currents.

Attention must be paid to the proportion of dissimilar metals present internally, the object being to minimise electrolytic action. Again, every effort must be made to avoid all undue concentration of metallic mass in the region of the firebox, *e.g.*, at the foundation ring and firehole ring (if fitted), as otherwise the water contact will be insufficient to conduct the heat away from the metal; wastage then occurs and trouble is experienced with leakage.

To permit of free circulation of the convection currents, and also to facilitate the removal of scale in the sheds, firebox water spaces should be as liberal as possible; 4″ should be regarded as a desirable dimension to arrange in the case of standard gauge engines.

Whilst adequate staying is essential, due consideration must at the same time be given to the "breathing" action of the firebox and a measure of flexibility provided therefor.

The longitudinal centre line of the boiler should be as high above rail level as possible, consistent with safety, so that, apart from other considerations, the greater portion of the firebox, if not its entirety, is above the frames, thus rendering the side stays accessible. In this connection, care must be exercised in locating the side tanks.

With a view to the elimination of priming and the attainment of a consistently high dryness fraction, the steam space and water area should both be as liberal as possible. To this end one should aim at a minimum vertical distance of 2'-0", for a standard gauge engine, between the crown of the inner firebox and the wrapper plate. It has been advocated that the minimum steam space shall be 16% of the total volumetric capacity of the boiler; in American practice, 20% is recommended. The minimum proportions accepted in Indian State Railways design are given by the ratio:—

Steam space in boiler: cylinder volume::8:1.

In French practice the steam space may comprise as much as 30%–35% of the total volumetric capacity of the boiler.

It should, however, be noted that the provision of ample water space is, relatively, far more important than that of steam space; in any case, the capacity of the latter is small when considered in terms of cylinder volumes.

To prevent priming as far as possible the number of internal steam pipes must be minimised and due consideration given to their location. With the exception of the main steam pipe, the majority may be submerged below water level for the greater part of their length, thus reducing possible turbulence of the steam.

Barrel.

Is now made practically exclusively of steel plate, acid open hearth being preferred in British practice and basic in American. It is usually found that the former, possibly due to its more uniform composition, is less susceptible to internal pitting. The use of pure iron plates may be considered in cases where the water is of an exceptionally corrosive nature.

In order to reduce the number of circumferential joints, the length of the individual plates should be as great as the capacity of the available plate rolls will permit ; there are boilers of considerable size in this country in which the barrel is formed from one plate only. Where more than one course is necessary in the barrel, with consequent variations in diameter of the latter, they should be so arranged that the diameters increase from the smokebox end towards the firebox. There is then no risk of water being trapped in the barrel, and causing corrosion of the plates, when the boiler is emptied. Longitudinal joints should be located well above the normal maximum water level to lessen the effects of corrosion.

Coned barrels, although more expensive as regards first cost, offer several advantages over the parallel or telescopic ring types. The water space is less at the smokebox end, where the heat transmission through the tubes is at a minimum, and greater at the firebox end, where it is most needed. There is a saving of otherwise unproductive weight at the smokebox end which, in the case of passenger engines, would tend to fall on carrying rather than on coupled wheels. Further, the enginemen's range of vision is extended. Lastly, an advantage applying more particularly to narrow gauge practice is that the centre of gravity of the engine is lowered and the liability to roll at speed reduced.

The thickness of the barrel plates is determined by the well-known formula:—

$$t = \frac{pd}{2fe_l} \quad \dots \dots \dots \dots \dots \dots \dots \dots \dots \dots \dots \dots \dots \dots \dots \dots \dots \quad (83)$$

where t = thickness of plate, inches,

p = working pressure, lb. per square inch,

d = diameter of barrel, inches,

f = stipulated working tensile stress in plates, lb. per square inch,

and e_l = efficiency of longitudinal riveted joints, expressed as a decimal.

Also,

$$t = \frac{pd}{4fe_c} \quad \dots \dots \dots \dots \dots \dots \dots \dots \dots \dots \dots \dots \dots \dots \dots \dots \dots \quad (84)$$

where e_c = efficiency of circumferential riveted joints, expressed as a decimal,

and the other symbols have the same significance as previously.

It should be borne in mind that the value of t as given above applies only when the plates are new; an addition of at least $\frac{1}{16}''$ in normal cases, or $\frac{1}{8}''$ when the water is of bad quality or maintenance dubious, must therefore be made to the calculated result to allow for wastage arising in service. p is the gauge pressure; d is calculated on the internal diameter, the dimension for the largest course in the boiler being taken. $f = \dfrac{T}{S}$, where T is the ultimate tensile strength of the plate, lb. per square inch, and S the factor of safety; the usual minimum value of S is 5 in British practice and 4 or 4.5 in American.

The thickness of barrel plates usually ranges from $\frac{1}{2}''$ to $\frac{11}{16}''$ in standard practice, and may be as little as $\frac{1}{16}''$ or $\frac{3}{8}''$ for boilers of very small diameter working at low pressures.

Lap riveted joints, the use of which is customarily restricted to circumferential joints, are objectionable in that the paths of the tensile forces are not coincident and bending action, resulting in grooving, takes place in consequence. Where possible, butt joints with double cover plates should be used for preference; the rivets are then subjected purely to shear stress. All rivet holes in boiler work should be drilled and not punched.

Riveted Joints. Either single or double zig-zag riveted lap joints may be employed for the circumferential joints. Their efficiency, on the basis of the resistance of the plate to tearing, is given by:—

$$\eta_t = \frac{(p-d)}{p} \quad \dots\dots\dots\dots\dots\dots\dots\dots\dots\dots\dots\dots (85)$$

The efficiency, based on the shearing resistance of the rivets, is given by

$$\eta_s = \frac{N \times \pi \times d^2 \times f_s}{4 \times p \times t \times f_t} \quad \dots\dots\dots\dots\dots\dots\dots\dots (86)$$

In these formulæ,

p = maximum pitch of rivets, inches,

d = final diameter of rivets, inches,

t = thickness of plates, inches,

N = number of rivets in section of joint p inches wide,

t_s = ultimate shear strength of rivets, tons per square inch,

and f_t = ultimate tensile strength of plate, tons per square inch.

For steel plates and steel rivets, the ratio $\dfrac{f_s}{f_t}$ must be taken at 23/28 if compliance with Board of Trade regulations is involved; Unwin suggests 0·79 for rivets in single shear and 0·73 in double shear.

For longitudinal joints, a butt joint with cover straps of unequal width is usually employed, the two rows of zig-zag rivets nearest the plate edge passing through both cover plates their pitch being one-half that for the outer row, the latter passing through the wider cover plate only. In the event of two rows of rivets being arranged to pass through the wider cover strap (which is placed on the inner side of the barrel), the outermost row of rivets is usually pitched at twice the distance employed for the inner row, the pitch for the zig-zag rivets then becoming one quarter of the maximum.

Formulæ (85) and (86) are applicable to joints of this type with the following reservations:—

p is the pitch of the outermost row of rivets, i.e., the maximum pitch.

N is the number of rivets present on both sides of the butt in a section of joint p inches wide.

Rivets in double shear should be regarded as taking only (1·75 × load allowed for those in single shear), and not twice that load.

To reduce the weight of the boiler, the use of quintuple joints, having an efficiency of over 90%, may be recommended.

In determining the efficiency of any given joint, both η_t and η_s should be calculated, the lowest value obtained therefrom being inserted in formulæ (83) and (84). Before doing this, however, the design must be examined to ensure that the rivet bearing stress does not exceed a working value of 6 tons per square inch of projected area.

The minimum distance from centre line of rivet to edge of plate should be 1·5 d.

The thickness of cover straps may be $\frac{5}{8}$ t.

For a detailed study of riveted joints, readers may refer to such works as *Elements of Machine Design*, Part I (Unwin), *Mechanics applied to Engineering*, Volume I (Goodman), and *A Manual of Machine Drawing and Design* (Low and Bevis).

Firebox Plates.

The thickness of flat plates subjected to fluid pressure and stayed together may be determined approximately from

$$f = \frac{p\,a^2}{4\,t^2} \quad\quad\quad (87)$$

where f = maximum working fibre stress in plates, lb. per square inch.

p = working pressure, lb. per square inch,

a = pitch of stays, inches,

and t = thickness of plates, inches.

Steel plates for the wrapper or outside firebox are usually about $\frac{9}{16}''$ or $\frac{5}{8}''$ thick, the same thickness being employed for the sides and back sheets of the inner firebox, if of copper. The thickness of the inner firebox side plates is reduced in British practice to $\frac{1}{4}''$ or $\frac{5}{16}''$ when of steel, material up to $\frac{3}{8}''$ thick being utilised for the flanged plates. With the large fireboxes common to American practice, the usual thickness of the plates is $\frac{3}{8}''$.

The criterion of the thickness of the firebox plates is based not so much on their strength structurally as on the provision of sufficient bearing length for the threads of the stays and the inclusion of a generous allowance for wastage and erosion of the plates. The strength of copper commences to deteriorate at a temperature of 430°F., and that of steel at 700°F.

Rivets vary in diameter from about $\frac{3}{4}''$ to $1''$, pitched at from $1\frac{7}{8}''$ to $2\frac{1}{4}''$ centres. Yorkshire iron or steel rivets are usually preferred as giving better results, although some railways employ copper rivets in conjunction with a copper firebox on the grounds of uniform expansion and reduction of electrolytic action.

By sloping the firebox crown downwards towards the back, an ample covering with water is ensured, especially when running down gradients. Moreover, the firebox volume is greatest at the front end, where most needed for efficient combustion, and more space is rendered available for the location of a steam turret, etc., whilst the enginemen's range of vision is improved.

Relative Merits of Steel and Copper for Inner Fireboxes.

The use of copper for the inner firebox is practically universal in British practice and, in comparison with steel, offers the following advantages:—

Wear is less rapid as scale is not so likely to adhere, owing to the greater movement due to expansion, and the plates will not pit in the event of the water being of a corrosive nature. The structure of the metal is less affected by accumulations of scale and of oil which may be carried over in the feed water, by too rapid cooling for washing out, and by abuse generally. Copper is the more dependable material and is not so liable to develop a sudden defect as steel. Plates of the latter may crack, for instance, immediately above the foundation ring, especially at the corners, owing to wastage on the fire side occurring simultaneously with grooving on the water side. Further, copper is more amenable to patching than steel; with the latter, horizontal edges will invariably give trouble if in the vicinity of the fire, although this condition does not arise when the patches are welded.

Although the first cost is higher, the scrap value of copper is correspondingly high. At the same time, disposal difficulties may arise abroad, and the advantage is in part lost should the copper be purchased when ruling prices are high and, after bearing interest for several years, be sold as scrap when prices are low.

Owing to the greater thickness of metal employed, the condition of the stayheads is relatively less important.

Copper is superior to steel as regards conductivity.

Steel fireboxes, on the other hand, cost less in the first instance, and the interest charges to be met are correspondingly reduced. The range of cost fluctuation is considerably greater with copper than with steel, and the statement that the price of copper is from three to five times greater than that of steel must therefore be accepted only as a very approximate generalisation. The divergence is, however, further accentuated, owing to the disparity in weight, when further allowances have to be made for carriage and handling charges if shipped overseas for any great distance.

The steel plates, being of greater strength, are considerably thinner, a sensible reduction of weight being effected in consequence. This, assisted by the small and comparatively light steel side stays customarily used, has a favourable effect on the restrictions imposed by axle loading limitations.

Rivets may be more or less completely eliminated, joints being effected by welding, not only during construction, but also for half sides and patches. The joints of many modern steel fireboxes are welded throughout. Patches are unsatisfactory in any event; the double thickness of metal at the lap joint, and the screws with insufficient hold for the threads, invariably cause trouble by leakage which is accentuated rather than overcome by subsequent caulking.

The adoption of welding enables the complete inner firebox, even when of the narrow type, to be renewed without removing the back plate of the outer firebox. To accomplish this the inner firebox is assembled in five sections, *viz.*, crown plate, tubeplate, firehole plate and two side plates; this is general practice in the U.S.A. for entirely welded fireboxes. Savings in the cost of renewing fireboxes thus are effected in three directions:—

(*a*) The direct cost of the renewal. There is no stay drilling, rivet cutting and removing, or stripping of outer back plate as with a copper box of the deep, narrow type, and it is possible for the largest steel box to be removed and the stays cut, with an autogenous flame, in 8–10 hours.

(*b*) The carrying of spare boiler stock is unnecessary.

(*c*) Reduction in time lost from traffic by engine for this repair.

The tubes may be welded into the tubeplate, thus eliminating distortion of the latter by the use of the tube expander and also minimising leakage. As the question of variations in the expansion of ferrous and non-ferrous metals respectively does not arise, this cause of leakage is obviated.

It is claimed that the life of a steel box at least equals that of a copper box. Records kept by an American railway shew an average life of 11 years for the complete firebox, 6 for tubeplates, 8 for side sheets and 9 years for door sheets, the working pressure in some cases being as much as 300 lb. per square inch. As stated previously, there is no deterioration with copper on account of pitting or corrosion but, on the other hand, abrasion is extensive, notably on the lower portions of the side sheets and bottom of the tubeplate.

Galvanic action, arising from the presence of dissimilar

metals in the boiler, is non-existent with steel fireboxes; copper
fireboxes, however, cause pitting and corrosion of the steel
wrapper plates, especially at the water legs and throat plate.

Decreased movement due to expansion, in the case of the
steel box, reduces the extent of the bending stresses to which
the stays are subjected, thereby increasing the life of the latter.

Table XVII comprises a typical composition of steel suitable
for firebox plates.

TABLE XVII.

REPRESENTATIVE COMPOSITION OF STEEL FOR FIREBOX
PLATES.

Element.	Content.
Carbon	0.15% — 0.25%
Phosphorus	Not above 0.04%
Manganese	0.40% — 0.45%
Silicon	0.02% — 0.03%
Sulphur	Not above 0.04%

When designing the firebox in the first instance, and fitting
half plates subsequently, care must be exercised that no plate
edge is directly exposed to flame action. This fault will sometimes be encountered in older engines of American construction, in which the crown sheet, if not welded, is not integral
with the side sheets and the resulting joint is so arranged
that the crown plate edges are on the fire side of the side
sheets, and not disposed in the water spaces as they should be.

Wide versus Narrow Fireboxes.

With bituminous coal of good quality, such as is available
in this country, deep fireboxes of the narrow type usually give
the best results. Their contours in the transverse plane tend
inherently to counteract distortion arising from unequal expansion of the inner and outer fireboxes and, further, facilitate
the movement of convection currents. The deep firebox is less
sensitive to the effects of unskilful firing and usually requires
less cleaning, especially with inferior fuel, than the wide,
shallow grate; on the other hand, there is the danger that the
fuel consumption may rise as, with a thick fire, which in any
event is likely to be found at the back of a deep box with

sloping grate, the engine must be more heavily worked in order to draw the requisite air supply through the fire.

Due to the fact that a larger firebox volume: grate area ratio is usually obtainable with the narrow box, combustion is more efficient and therefore, for a given length of tube, the gases are discharged at a lower temperature; given reasonably skilful firing, fuel consumption is consequently reduced. Stay heads in the vicinity of the brick arch ends are usually more liable to burn on wide than on narrow boxes, and this may be attributed to the fact that the products of combustion and attendant particles of unburnt fuel have to accommodate themselves to a converging, as opposed to a diverging, space. Nevertheless, it must in fairness be observed that the result of extensive experience on the quondam G.N.R., on which system the wide firebox was introduced in this country, is that this type of box has a longer life and is more efficient generally than the narrow firebox. It may be conjectured that the excellent results obtained on this railway were due not so much to the particular type of firebox adopted as to the generous dimensions of the boilers relative to the steam demand on the classes of engine concerned.

With low grade fuels, the realisation of appropriate grate area can only be effected by recourse to the wide type of box, the chief advantage of which is that all side stays are above the frames and consequently extremely accessible. When load gauge clearances are limited, the compromise which must necessarily be observed in order to obtain adequate depths of water legs and plate frames respectively, together with the retention of a reasonable range of vision for the enginemen, militates against the general adoption of the wide type of box, which is further at a disadvantage in that it generally necessitates the provision of carrying wheels at the trailing end of the engine, whilst the satisfactory arrangement of the firebox supports and of the ashpan are more difficult of attainment than with the narrow box.

The selection of a suitable type of firebox is governed in part by the manner in which the engine is operated. When habitually worked with late cut-offs the draught is heavy and, unless the fire is thick, causes "holes in the fire" and increases the unburnt fuel loss to an appreciable extent. With early cut-offs, on the other hand, the available draught is not sufficient to draw the requisite quantity of air through a thick fire.

For a given draught and boiler output, it follows that the fire must be thinner as the grate area is increased, but, in this connection, it should be noted that with wide fireboxes having large grate areas the practical limit may be exceeded, so that it is impossible to maintain a sufficiently thin fire when working with early cut-offs.

The type of firebox finally adopted is largely influenced by the fuel available. As stated previously, the bituminous coal customarily used on the British railways usually gives the best results in a deep firebox of large volume with relatively small grate area. When run of mine and other small coals of comparatively poor quality, briquettes, or lignite are used, larger grates must be provided, thereby reducing the rate of combustion, and consequently the necessary force of the draught, in order to minimise the unburnt fuel losses. Anthracite coal, owing to its slow burning and characteristic tendency to disintegrate as combustion proceeds, must not be fired too thinly and requires a large grate; special attention must also be paid to the even distribution of the air supply, as anthracite coals offer less resistance to the passage of air through the fire than bituminous grades. Wood also needs a large grate area, together with a generous firebox volume. A long, narrow grate gives the best results with liquid fuels, the complete combustion of which calls also for ample firebox volume.

Although primarily adopted as an artifice for the attainment of the maximum grate area within the given dimensions of the firebox, the practice of inclining the grate must also be considered in conjunction with the standard of skill exhibited by the firemen. Generally speaking, it is easier to fire a sloping grate, the chief danger to avoid being the concentration of fuel under the tube-plate. A further advantage which may be claimed for this construction is that the foundation rings are usually inclined to correspond with the grate, thus facilitating the removal of scale when washing out. A horizontal grate, on the other hand, must only be fired round the sides of the box, as the vibration of the engine when running is sufficient to feed the centre of the grate; this type of grate also exhibits a more pronounced tendency to develop "holes in the fire."

Relative Merits of Belpaire and Round-Topped Fireboxes.

In comparison with the round-topped firebox, the Belpaire box offers the following advantages:—

1. Constant water area, irrespective of level of water in boiler, where the evaporation is greatest and most efficient.
2. Full threads in both inner and outer plates for stays, which are in all cases normal to the plates.
3. Increased steam and water spaces.
4. The effects of expansion on the crown sheet are less marked. The construction is altogether more flexible; there is therefore less stay breakage and a diminution of roof-stay trouble in service. With a round-topped box, the variations in the lengths of the direct stays lead to distortion of the crown.
5. Base of seatings for stay heads flat and not rounded, facilitating and cheapening fitting of stays.
6. More freedom for convection currents and no accumulation of inaccessible scale on the crown. (The latter point applies only in comparison with the girder-stayed box, the adoption of which is exceptional in modern practice).

On the other hand, the advantages of the round-topped box are:—

1. Lower first cost (the disparity in cost is less where bulk manufacture is concerned).
2. No expensive and difficult plate flanging. The difficulties are naturally lessened with experience; Belpaire throat-plates may be flanged and set to template in one heat.
3. Reduced weight (unless girder stayed); greater evaporative capacity may therefore be provided for a given axle load.
4. Reduced liability of rounded crown plates to burn when running with low water level on curves having considerable superelevation.

Firehole.

The use of the firehole ring, although simple to fit and eliminating flanging, is not to be recommended, either for copper or steel fireboxes, because:—

(a) A relatively large mass of metal is concentrated to an undesirable extent and, as its area in contact with water is small, heat is not transferred sufficiently rapidly, with detrimental results to the plates in the immediate vicinity; these burn and develop lap cracks. Also, the rivet heads shear off as the metal becomes brittle.

(b) The construction is too rigid and tends to restrict movement due to expansion.

(c) The length of the rivets used is unavoidably long; their total expansion is consequently great and renders the maintenance of steam tightness difficult.

The effects of (a) are especially pronounced with a steel firebox.

In order to avoid the ring, the plates of both the inner and outer fireboxes may be flanged outwards to form a joint. In doing so, however, attention must be paid to two points:—

1. Owing to the greater expansion of the inner box, its back plate should be flanged as little as possible, and to an easy radius.

2. The design should be such that no awkward corners or angles, likely to encourage the accumulation of scale, are presented. These corners cannot be entirely avoided, and form the weak point of this design; scale lodging there is difficult to remove and leads to overheating, followed by leakage of the mouthpiece rivets.

The first stipulation may be observed by bending the plate of the inner box to such an extent that it forms an angle of not less than 30° with the longitudinal centre line of the boiler, this procedure also making machine riveting practicable.

The flanged type of firehole is not always entirely successful when used in conjunction with a sliding firedoor, since the flanged joint is not so well protected from the heat as, for instance, with the Webb type (inward swinging) door, and leakage occurs in consequence. The provision of a washout plug immediately above the top of the firehole is most desirable with this construction.

A double-flanged ring obviates most of the disadvantages of the solid ring, but can only be employed in those rare instances where the water space is sufficiently wide to permit of the rivets being held up preparatory to closure.

A compromise may be effected by dishing the back plate of the inner firebox and using a ring of correspondingly reduced thickness therewith. A further advantage of this form of construction is that a measure of protection is afforded the rivet heads.

With steel boxes, a very general American practice is to flange the plates of both boxes through 90° and effect a joint with screws of about ¾″ diameter or by welding.   In the latter event, one of the plates is usually dished to prevent initial stressing of the material with high welding temperatures.

Firehole rivets may be from ¾″ to 1″ in diameter, the pitch varying from 1¾″ to 2″.   Circular fireholes have a diameter of about 1′-3″ or 1′-4″, the width of oval holes varying from 1′-3″ to 1′-7″, and the height from 1′-0″ to 1′-2″.

The lower half of the firehole should be protected from the direct action of the flames, and from damage by fire irons, by an easily and cheaply replaceable cast-iron plate.

Combustion Chambers.   Offer several advantages; firebox heating surface, which is by far the most efficient, is increased, as also is the firebox volume, with a corresponding improvement in the degree of completeness of combustion. Tube ends are removed from the direct action of flames, and the tubes themselves, which are in danger of becoming inordinately long on large engines, are shortened.

Although the combustion chamber tends to reduce tube leakage, it should be pointed out that its employment renders the tubeplate rather more inaccessible than would otherwise be the case.   It also has the effect of setting forward the centre of gravity of the boiler, and therefore, to a certain extent, that of the engine as a whole.

Thermic Syphons.   The Nicholson thermic syphon, invented by an Englishman of that name, was originally manufactured and applied by the Locomotive Firebox Company of Chicago; its adoption has now become so extensive as to necessitate its manufacture in this country also, and this is now being done at Manchester by Messrs. Beyer, Peacock & Co. Ltd.   Messrs. Whitelegg and Rogers, of Grand Buildings, Trafalgar Square, are the London representatives, and the author is indebted to them for the information which follows.

The thermic syphon is virtually a funnel of triangular form, and is constructed of special firebox steel plate; the latter has a thickness of ⅜″ and is entirely welded.   The parallel portion of the syphon, which provides a water space of about 3″, is stayed with steel stays in the same manner as the firebox; the diameter of the bulbous neck approximates to 6¼″.   It is usual to weld the syphon into the steel firebox, thus preserving a uniform thickness at the points of attachment; at the lower of these the tubeplate is belled to a generous radius.

The velocity of the water through the syphons is of the order of 4 lineal feet per second. The syphons are, however, so proportioned that the discharge area is about ten or twelve times greater than that of the neck, thus ensuring a quiet release of water over the crown sheet with, in consequence, no reduction in the dryness fraction of the steam.

The number of syphons which may be fitted to a given locomotive is governed by the dimensions of the firebox, and is as follows:—

Width at Foundation Ring.	*Number of Syphons.*
Up to 43″	One.
50″ to 80″	Two.
Over 80″	Three.

In cases of large boilers provided with a combustion chamber, two smaller additional syphons are fitted therein, making five in all.

The advantages claimed for the Nicholson thermic syphon are:—

1. Accelerated circulation of the water in the boiler, especially as regards the firebox water spaces, with consequent reductions in scale formation and in the range of water temperature throughout the boiler; as a corollary, boiler maintenance costs are reduced.

2. A considerable increase in the most efficient form of heating surface, *viz.*, that of the firebox.

3. The firebox crown receives additional support, the syphon acting as a strut. This, together with the mild fountain action of the syphon, minimises the extent of damage occurring in those instances, due either to mismanagement or to working on mountainous sections, when the water level is insufficiently high to cover the crown sheet.

4. Affords an excellent support for the brick arch, thus rendering arch tubes unnecessary.

5. Owing to improved circulation, the rate of evaporation is increased.

6. Fuel economy of about 8% achieved.

7. Reduction in time necessary for steam raising. The results of comparative tests shewed a time saving of 17·5% in conjunction with an economy of 10% in the quantity of fuel used for lighting-up.

The advantages of the syphon are emphasised in those cases where the heating surface of the engine is somewhat restricted with relation to the cylinder capacity.

Firehole Door. May be of $\frac{1}{4}''$ plate.   If hinged at the bottom, the fireman has to work against gravity every time he closes the door; the Webb pattern, hinged at the top and opening inwards, thus acting as a deflector plate, has a somewhat short life.   The type of door used in stationary practice, with a vertical hinge at one side, is better, but requires a spring catch to retain it in the fully open position when desired.   Trap doors have the advantage over the foregoing in that "top air" is admitted at a constant rate whilst running, but with very few designs is it possible to fire the whole area of the grate, unless it be self-feeding, without opening the large door, thereby invalidating the chief object of their adoption.   Further, they permit of a relatively unimpeded path for cold air in the direction of the tubeplate, dissipate heat and emit a disconcerting glare in darkness.   The use of an apron to overcome these latter disadvantages is objectionable, as additional labour is involved in disengaging and securing it whenever the fire is replenished.

Probably the most satisfactory type of door yet in service is that in which the door is in halves, opening outwards simultaneously by the action of a simple arrangement of levers. It might be improved, although complications are thereby involved, in the following directions:—

(a) The provision of louvres with adjustable apertures or other measures to deflect ingoing "top" air in a downwards direction when the door is closed.

(b) The location of the lever system above, and not, as is usual, below the door, to minimise the risk of jamming by small pieces of coal, etc.

(c) Operation of the lever system by a spring-loaded treadle, conveniently placed for the fireman, or by power, to minimise the time during which the door is open when the engine is running.   A catch would have to be provided for the treadle, or corresponding device for a power valve, to enable the door to remain in the fully open position while the fire is being cleaned or repairs executed in the firebox.

In addition to the various types of hand operated fire doors already described, many locomotives are equipped with power (air or steam) operated fire doors as outlined by the foregoing suggested improvement (c). It is obvious that with manually operated fire doors the firehole is exposed to cold air for a considerable aggregate period whilst the engine is running; it has in fact been computed that, in cases of engines working heavily, the proportion may represent as much as 50% of the total time. This has a deleterious effect upon the firebox and tubes, quite apart from the large quantity of heat given out on the footplate, a matter which assumes serious proportions in tropical countries.

A representative type of power operated door, designed to overcome these adverse conditions, is that known as the "Ajax" Patent Firedoor, manufactured in Great Britain by Messrs. Whitelegg and Rogers. It comprises two half or butterfly doors which are hung or pivoted to a main door frame, each half door having a toothed rack or sector at its upper end; these sectors gear together, thus transmitting any movement of one half door to the other. The doors are operated by a cylinder which is fitted on one side of the door frame, and provided with a trunk piston to which is attached a crosshead pin complete with guide blocks. The crosshead pin has a projecting end which engages in a slot on one of the half doors, so that any movement of the piston, either inward or outward, is transmitted to the half doors. At the outer end of the cylinder is fitted a valve box, having a spring-loaded valve which is operated through suitable levers by a foot pedal; the latter is placed in a convenient position adjacent to the footplate. These doors open and close very rapidly, but provision is made whereby all possibility of jarring is eliminated by cushioning.

The "Ajax" door can be operated equally well with either steam or air; in the case of the former, a reducing valve is provided in order that the boiler steam pressure may be reduced to 75 lb. per square inch. These doors are not limited in their application by the size or shape of the firehole, as the main fire door frame is made to suit any individual design.

Foundation Ring. Is subject to disabilities identical with those previously enumerated for the firehole ring. A similar compromise to counter them is sometimes effected by dishing the inside firebox plates, thus reducing the necessary width of ring. The minimum dimension thus obtained may approximate to $1\frac{3}{4}''$. In addition to shortening the rivets, their heads are more protected, but, on the other hand, this design affords an effective trap for scale.

Great care must be devoted to the selection of the material, the type of joint employed and workmanship applied thereto, as any defect in the material or the development of leakage at the foundation ring involves heavy repair work in the shed. Cast steel is largely used in American practice, but British designers do not consider castings altogether reliable, owing to the possible formation of blowholes, and prefer forgings.

The rings must be double riveted at the corners, at least, as leakage is most likely to occur there; in some designs, the rings are double (zig-zag) riveted throughout. The rivets may be $\frac{7}{8}''$ in diameter and pitched at $2''$ centres. Where single riveted, the minimum depth of ring should be approximately $2\frac{1}{2}''$.

Fusible Plug. Whether to provide this detail or not is still a somewhat controversial question. Some arguments raised against fitting are:—

1. The plug may melt prematurely or unnecessarily, owing to the presence of scale on the top of the filling (in which case lack of facilities for the transmission of heat may cause fusing in spite of a water covering), to momentary uncovering when a sudden stop, severe or reverse curvature of the permanent way, or track irregularity, causes the water in the boiler to surge, or to the decomposition of the filling by the continued action of the firebox gases.

2. The plug may not function if the melting point of the alloy is raised by oxidation of the zinc component. The least effects will then be a discoloured crown sheet and leaking roof stays.

3. Fusing of the plug does not necessarily prevent overheating of the crown sheet. At the same time, it must be admitted that the engine is forced to give up its train.

4. The lower portion of the filling may melt out before overheating of the crown actually occurs.

5. The moral effect of providing plugs is that the enginemen tend to become careless as regards boiler management.

The majority of these objections can be overruled by rigid adherence to the stipulated period of plug changing and by careful attention to design. The plug should not be placed at the back of, or allowed to project too far downwards into, the firebox, and the top of the fuse must be finished smooth to discourage the adherence of scale; care must be taken that the plug projects positively above the crown sheet. The latter requirement may be met by stipulating a parallel thread, which ensures a constant dimensional relationship between the top of the fuse and the crown sheet and also, it is claimed, owing to the necessity for a faced joint, careful fitting. Opinions on this point are, however, divided, and advocates of the taper thread which, to assist in the maintenance of steam tightness, is usually fine by comparison with that employed for the parallel shank, claim that wear may be taken up merely by tapping, thus eliminating the necessity for bushing.

Practice also varies as regards the filling; some engineers favour lead, others alloy, *e.g.*, nine parts lead, one part tin. The plug should in any case be tinned preparatory to filling.

To avoid multiplicity of details, standard mud plugs may be adapted for use as fusible plugs by drilling. The top of the core must be liberally countersunk to facilitate the pouring of the fusible metal and also to augment the area subjected to pressure, so that the resistance set up by any adherent scale which may be present is overcome in the event of a fuse. In some cases an intermediate chamber, of larger diameter than that ruling for the core, is bored out to assist in the retention, under normal conditions, of the filling.

Brick Arch. Assuming the projected length of the inner firebox, measured on a line drawn through the centre of the firebox, to be x, then the true length of the brick arch may be from $0.45\ x$ to $0.6\ x$, the angle of inclination to the tubeplate varying from 65° to 75°. The maximum transverse camber, or rise, is approximately 4″.

The practice on at least one railway is to incline the brick arch at an angle of 60° to the tubeplate, and to make it of such length that the crown of the arch at the trailing end intersects a line drawn horizontally from the top of the firehole. In some cases a few $2\frac{1}{2}$″ or 3″ spaces are left between the end of the arch and the tubeplate to prevent excessive formation of smoke and also the accumulation of ash on top of the arch. The actual length and inclination of the brick arch most suitable for any given class of engine can only be finally determined by experiment.

The supporting studs should be at about 9″ centres.

Deflector Plates. Should be so inclined that the line along which the air is deflected, if continued, would intersect the tube-plate at a point not higher than that at which the latter is met by the abutment of the brick arch.

The deflectors may be pressed from $\frac{1}{4}$″ plate; the effective length should be as great as possible (although wastage is thereby increased at a disproportionate rate), and may be as much as $0.3\ x$.

Firebars. The air space between the bars varies from $\frac{1}{16}$″ to $\frac{5}{8}$″. The actual distance is dictated, of course, by the nature of the fuel used; the most suitable dimension with British bituminous coals is from $\frac{3}{8}$″ to $\frac{5}{8}$″.

The ratio of air space to grate area varies in practice from 1 : 3 to 1 : 5. Influenced by trials involving the analysis of smokebox gases, there is at present a tendency in American practice to reduce the air space provided. This was originally from 40% to 50% of the total area, but is now only about 12% to 16%; it is claimed that the supply of excessive quantities of air is thereby prevented.

In order to facilitate ash disposal, the width of the firebar at the top should be about twice that at the bottom. If long, the bar should be thickened in the centre as well as at the ends, in order to preserve the requisite distance for air space.

Long firebars, however, are not to be encouraged. It is axiomatic that the shorter the bar, the longer is its life. If in a given grate it is possible to provide, say, three sets of bars, this should be done in preference to two sets of longer bars. Long bars are peculiarly liable to crack, and eventually fracture, at the ends, in the vicinity of the shoulder from which the thick portion is developed; they are also more prone to excessive transverse warping. The ideal overall length for bars is from 2′-0″ to 2′-6″, and they should be of robust dimensions as regards depth. The fish-bellied contour prevents sudden change of section and assists in the attainment of sound castings.

Since both the low tensile strength and the brittleness of pure cast iron are accentuated by exposure to high temperatures, the mixture from which the firebars are cast may with advantage include up to about 15% of scrap steel (shavings).

Firebar bearers should be attached to the ashpan rather than to the foundation ring.

Drop Grates. The chief features to be embodied in the design of the apparatus are:—

1. A positive lock must be provided for the trunnions.
2. Mechanism must be protected from direct heat and from the percolation of ash.
3. Provision must be made for the counteraction of any possible warping.

The observance of these three stipulations is essential.

Ashpan. The ashpan may be of $\frac{1}{4}''$ plate and flanged, or built up with $2'' \times 2'' \times \frac{5}{16}''$ angle, or in the event of clearances permitting detachment *en bloc*, welded. Should the ashpan be habitually flooded, either a greater thickness of plate or less corrosive material, *e.g.*, pure iron or stainless steel, must be employed. In America, cast-steel ashpans are now frequently used.

To prevent burning and warping of plates, the ashes may be intermittently damped down by a pet cock installed specifically for the purpose, by the water gauge blow-down, or by the steam brake cylinder exhaust. Whichever device is adopted, the final discharge should be so arranged as to take place transversely across the ashpan, thus minimising the risk of ash being blown into the bearings, motion, or big ends, if inside the frames.

The ashpan must be of sufficient capacity to accommodate the largest accumulation of ash likely to be deposited under extreme conditions of working, the storage being so arranged relatively to the dampers that the air intake is not at any time obstructed or restricted. The ashpan should preferably be capable of instant emptying by ejection to the pit through bottom doors, especially on those engines fitted with drop grates; otherwise, hot clinker will cause rapid wear and excessive warping, with the result that the ashpan will " draw air."

Dampers. May be of $\frac{1}{4}''$ or $\frac{5}{16}''$ plate, and should be hinged on the horizontal centre line rather than at the top, thus securing a more even distribution of the air admitted to the grate. At the same time, due consideration must be given to the provision of suitable clearance for the operation of the ashpan rake and, as mentioned above, arrangements also made that the air supply is not impeded by the accumulation of ashes. The latter proviso is met on some of the Argentine railways by fitting an additional damper in the bottom of the ashpan solely for cleaning purposes.

Additional horizontal dampers at the mid-length of the ash-pan are required for the complete combustion of liquid fuel.

The dampers may be controlled by $1\frac{1}{2}'' \times \frac{1}{2}''$ rod, the major dimension of course forming the depth; the rods should be protected as far as possible from direct heat in order to prevent warping. When the rod is arranged at the cab end in a more or less horizontal position, the teeth for the ratchet should be cut on the underside of the rod in preference to the top; the teeth are then less liable to clog with coal dust and oil drippings, the damper can be closed more quickly and with greater facility should emergency demand, and there is less likelihood of self movement occasioned by wear or vibration of the engine in running.

Researches carried out in America have shewn that 300 cubic feet of air are required per lb. coal consumed, and that the air openings should be 15% of the grate area. The air openings customarily provided in British practice are the equivalent of from 18% to 20% of the grate area. Restriction of the air openings leads to an undesirable increase in the draught necessary for the production of a given quantity of steam.

Tubeplates.   Smokebox tubeplates are of steel boiler plate and usually about $\frac{3}{4}''$ thick.   The lower portion should be protected where necessary against the corrosive action of the ash accumulating in the smokebox by easily renewable cast-iron plates.   The firebox tubeplate, if of copper, varies from $\frac{3}{4}''$ to $1\frac{3}{16}''$ in thickness in the tube zone, the stayed portion being reduced to $\frac{7}{16}''$ or $\frac{5}{8}''$. Although the staying effect of the tubes is indeterminate, excessive thickness of the tubeplate in the tube zone leads to objectionable rigidity; there is therefore no advantage in making the maximum plate thickness more than $\frac{7}{8}''$ or $1''$.   Such a dimension provides sufficient bearing area for the tubes.

Rigidity, together with the initial stresses set up by severity of flanging, may also be minimised by specifying a generous radius for the flange.   The outside radius of the flange in the smokebox plate should be at least $1\frac{1}{2}''$; at the firebox end, the usual dimension, about $3\frac{1}{2}''$, may with advantage be increased to approximately $6''$ where possible.

When steel fireboxes are used, the thicknesses of the tube plate are usually $\frac{1}{2}''$ in the tube area and either $\frac{1}{4}''$ or $\frac{5}{16}''$ below. In American practice the thickness of steel tubeplates is from $\frac{1}{2}''$ to $\frac{5}{8}''$.

Both tubeplates, in spite of the action of the steam pressure, tend almost invariably to bulge forwards. Pitting is greatest at points of maximum stress. Due to this, and to the fact that this form of construction lends itself more easily to the uniform distribution of the effects of expansion, the drumhead type of tubeplate is to be preferred. The radius of the smoke-box tubeplate especially should be as large as possible as, owing to the fact that the expansion of the tubes is greater than that of the barrel, this plate is very liable to groove.

Small Tubes. Before entering into purely theoretical considerations, the following generalisations may be regarded as practical axioms:—

The greater the diameter of the tube, the lighter is the draught required to induce gas flow; in other words, increased tube diameter reduces the necessary back pressure. On the other hand, excessive diameter tends to diminish the quantity of heat transferred. The longitudinal expansion increases proportionately with the length of tube; a long tube therefore has a greater tendency to leak.

Contributory factors to the determination of the ratio of tube length to diameter are grate area, firebox volume, and characteristics of the fuel used. The results of researches made at Altoona indicate that no advantage is obtained by allowing the tube length to exceed 100–120 internal diameters, as any further increase beyond this limit demands more steam for draught than is provided by any small increment of boiler efficiency due to increased tube length. With British fuel and conditions of working it would appear that the desirable value of this ratio is lower than that given above. Proceeding to more detailed consideration, Prof. Dalby estimated (Proc. I. Mech. E., 1909) that of the total temperature head between the hot gases in the tube and the water surrounding it, 97% is utilised to overcome the resistance of the gas film, 1% that of the metal and 2% that of the water film. Accepting this statement, it follows that the thickness of, and material comprising the tube are both unimportant as regards efficiency of heat transmission, and the problem resolves itself into one of destroying as far as possible the film of inert, non-conducting gas adhering to the surface of the tube. The simplest means of accomplishing this is to set up attrition with adjacent gaseous strata by increasing the velocity of flow (the gas flow, under extreme conditions, may attain a velocity of 400 ft. per second), *i.e.*, the diameter of the tube should be made as small as possible, subject to the practical limitations of immunity from "blocking up" and the desirable extent of draught utilised to induce the gas flow. Efficiency is further improved thereby in that an increase of flow velocity causes the gases to be exposed to a greater area of surface in a given time, and since the heat transferred per unit time is proportional to the surface exposed, it follows that an increased quantity of heat is transferred as the velocity of flow is increased. If the gases are stationary in the tube, heat transmission can only take place by radiation, owing to the low thermal conductivity of the gas.

The decision on the material to be specified for the tube calls for careful consideration. The steel tube is cheapest in first cost and lighter in weight than that of non-ferrous metal ; it does not require any special protective measures, *e.g.*, ferrules, at the firebox end, and is the only tube which can be used in conjunction with a steel box. On the other hand, copper or brass tubes have a longer life and higher scrap value, are less prone to leak and give more satisfactory results when the quality of the water is bad. Where a characteristic of the water is excessive scale formation, the relatively high expansion of the non-ferrous metals tends to make the tubes self-cleaning; again, they are immune from pitting by corrosive waters. If used with a copper tubeplate, there is less galvanic action at the joint of the tube with the plate, and they are also preferable for shunting and industrial work, where the great and rapid fluctuations of firebox temperature aggravate liability to leakage.

The usual mixtures for brass tubes are 70% copper and 30% zinc, or 67% and 33% respectively. For copper, the analysis should shew 99% pure copper and 0.35% to 0.55% arsenic.

On one of the home railways using copper tubes the practice is to equip the boilers with tubes of greater length than is required, and then, as burning occurs at the firebox end, to drive them up. The more usual custom, however, is to fit beaded ferrules, either of iron or steel, as a protective measure at the firebox end. At the same time, the burning of these ferrules cannot be entirely accepted as evidence of tube end protection; it is in part due to lack of water contact.

The thickness of the material in copper tubes may taper uniformly, to take a specific example, in a length of 15′-0″

from 11 W.G. at the firebox end to 13 W.G. at the smokebox, with an outside diameter of $2\frac{1}{4}''$ throughout, or may be stepped, thereby affecting a weight reduction. In the latter case, in a similar length there might be, for instance, 1'-6" run of 7 W.G. at the firebox end, tapering thence for 1'-0" to 11 W.G., which would be the constant thickness for the remainder of the tube, apart from 3" or 4" strengthened to 10 W.G. at the smokebox extremity.

With steel tubes the method of repair has considerable influence on the necessary thickness of the wall ; if repaired by piecing up, 13 W.G. is sufficient, with water of fair quality, for a tube of $1\frac{3}{4}''$ diameter to withstand a working pressure of 180 lb. per square inch. On the other hand, repair by stretching would call for a minimum thickness, in similar circumstances, of 12 W.G., if not 11 W.G. It must be remembered that the adoption of a heavier gauge, although it prevents sagging and results in a longer life, may increase the total weight of the boiler to an appreciable extent. The thickness of tube adopted also depends upon the length of tube, pressure to which subjected, and the quality of water used. Representative thicknesses adopted are:—

$1\frac{5}{8}''$ tubes, 13 S.W.G.
$1\frac{3}{4}''$,,   12 ,,
2" ,,   11 ,,
$2\frac{1}{4}''$,,   10 ,,

Steel tubes are frequently swaged down at the firebox end, the usual reduction in diameter being $\frac{1}{8}''$, so that, when ultimately beaded over, the tubes are virtually riveted into the tubeplate. At the same time the dimensions of the bridge are increased, as also is the velocity of the gas flow where most desirable.

The minimum bridge should preferably be 1" for standard gauge engines; this may be reduced to $\frac{7}{8}''$, if desired, for those running on gauges of 3'-0" to 3'-6". Should the tubes be spaced more closely, cracks will be very liable to develop in the tubeplate; also, the flow of convection currents in the boiler will be hindered. For the latter reason, in conjunction with the risk of making-up with scale and the effects of comparatively cold water entering if the feed is introduced at the side, the tubes should be spaced well away from the inner periphery of the barrel. They should in any case clear the radius of the tubeplate flange by at least one tube diameter;

otherwise, expansion will result in distortion of the plate and eventually cause cracks to form in the root of the flange. Some of the tubes should be of larger diameter than the remainder of the set, the holes drilled for them in the smokebox tube-plate facilitating the insertion and removal of the remainder. For the same reason the diameter of each individual tube should be slightly increased for a short distance at the smokebox end; an increment of $\tfrac{1}{16}''$ will suffice for this purpose.

With a view to allowing a certain amount of expansion with-out undue distortion of the tubeplate, tubes are sometimes put into the boiler with an initial camber.

It is generally conceded that, at the smokebox end, expand-ing alone is sufficient to secure the tube.   If beaded in addition, the tube becomes undesirably stiff and accentuates the effects of expansion; this beading has, however, been found necessary in certain cases abroad where exceptionally bad water causes excessive leakage.

The methods employed to secure the tube in the firebox tubeplate are legion, and depend to a certain extent on the respective materials employed. British Colonial practice, where steel tubes are used in conjunction with steel boxes, largely favours the interpolation of a copper bush between the tube and the plate before expanding and beading are carried out; this reduces the amount of expanding necessary to ensure steam tightness.   The bush should be about $\tfrac{1}{16}''$ or $3/32''$ thick with tubes of $2''$ outside diameter, and should preferably be shorter in length than the thickness of the tubeplate; should the bush project into the boiler, water contact and, in consequence, galvanic action, are increased.   The tube is some-times prossered to prevent the beading coming away from the face of the tubeplate when expansion takes place.

American engineers frequently resort to welding, the tubes being fitted with copper ferrules and beaded initially.   In-structions issued by the Pennsylvania R.R. include the follow-ing regulations:—

1. Tubeplate and tubes should be sandblasted after bead-ing over and prior to welding.
2. Tubes should be welded only when there is water in the boiler.
3. The welding should be from the bottom of the tube to the top.   (The usual procedure is to weld from the bottom of the tube upwards to the right, then from

the bottom to the left, lapping over the end of the first weld).

4. Working of the tube with a roller expanded in the tubeplate should, except in extremely difficult cases, be prohibited.

In Great Britain, steel tubes are generally used in conjunction with a copper tubeplate, and are expanded and beaded. The best results are obtained if:—

(1) The tubes are ground on the periphery at both ends where contact is made with the tubeplates.

(2) The holes in the firebox tubeplate are reamered out taper to correspond with that generated by the expander.

A clean metal-to-metal joint throughout the thickness of the plates is thus ensured and leakage reduced to a minimum. As previously mentioned, copper and brass tubes require ferrules at the firebox end as a protective measure.

Where leakage is excessive, a compromise is sometimes effected by the adoption of the copper-ended steel tube. The practice is, however, open to the objection that galvanic action is thereby accelerated, and failures due to this cause may be expected. Given reasonable workmanship, mechanical failures of the brazed joint are rare.

Table XVIII may be used, purely for preliminary approximations, when determining suitable dimensions for small tubes.

TABLE XVIII.
TYPICAL PROPORTIONS OF SMALL TUBES.

Effective length of tube, *i.e.*, distance between tubeplates.	Approximate outside diameter of tube.
9'-0" and under	$1\frac{1}{2}''$
9'-0" to 10'-6"	$1\frac{5}{8}''$
10'-6" to 13'-0"	
13'-0" to 15'-6"	$2''$
15'-6" and over	$2\frac{1}{4}''$

Large (Flue) Tubes. Are almost invariably of steel, having an outside diameter of 5" to $5\frac{1}{2}''$, the thickness being 8 W.G. Where copper is employed, the usual thickness is either 5 or 6 W.G. These tubes are usually swaged down to a diameter of from $4\frac{1}{8}''$ to $4\frac{1}{2}''$ for a length of about $1'\text{-}0''$ at the firebox end, the portion bearing in the tubeplate being either screwed (10 or 12 threads per inch) or grooved, and expanded and beaded in addition. The nominal tube diameter is usually increased by a small amount, up to about $\frac{1}{4}''$, at the smokebox end to facilitate insertion and removal. Rectangular or marine pitching is necessarily followed, the minimum pitch being approximately 1·3 times the outside diameter of the tube. This proportion is, of course, considerably exceeded in those instances where small tubes are interspersed with the large. The actual pitch of the flue tubes is determined by the type of superheater adopted, but should in any event be as great as possible, as these tubes are far more rigid than small tubes, with the result that the tubeplates are more likely to crack in their vicinity.

It is advisable to protect the firebox end of the tubes with a mild steel ferrule which is expanded and beaded over all, and finally caulked.

Tube Lay-out.   There are three forms of tube spacing: the vertical diamond, the horizontal diamond, and the marine or rectangular. These are shewn in Fig. 5 at (a), (b) and (c) respectively. Of these, the marine spacing (c), although providing the minimum nominal heating surface for a given area of tubeplate, is probably the most efficient from the point of view of heat transmission; it is also preferable to the other forms in that it offers the most direct path for the circulation of upward convection currents in conjunction with the least encouragement for the settlement of scale on the tubes themselves. Next in order of efficiency is the horizontal diamond formation (b).

With reference to Fig. 5, the minimum bridge is denoted in each case by x.

The normal *circulating path of convection currents in the boiler* is from the front towards the firebox, upwards through the tubes, down the sides and along the bottom of the barrel. It will therefore be appreciated that, short of adopting the marine tube pitching above recommended, the cancellation of one or more vertical rows of tubes may be decidedly advantageous when other forms of spacing are employed.

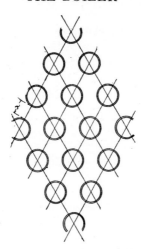

(a) Vertical Diamond.

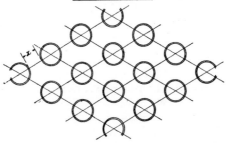

(b) Horizontal Diamond

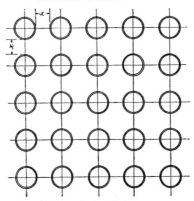

(c) Marine or Rectangular

FIG. 5.

Boiler Stays : General Formulæ.

(1) *Direct Stays.*

Let D = minimum diameter of stay, inches (where screwed throughout, the diameter taken should be that at the root of the thread),

f = working tensile stress in material of stay, lb. per square inch.

P = working pressure of boiler, lb. per square inch,

and A = area of plate supported by one stay, square inches.

Then
$$D = \sqrt{\frac{AP}{\cdot 7854 f}} \qquad \text{............................} \quad (88)$$

and
$$A = \frac{\cdot 7854\ D^2\ f}{P} \qquad \text{..................................} \quad (89)$$

whence
$$f = \frac{AP}{\cdot 7854\ D^2} \qquad \text{.......................................} \quad (90)$$

For copper stays, f = 5,000 to 6,000; if of steel, f = 9,000 to 10,000. For wrought-iron longitudinal stays, f should not greatly exceed 5,000, on account of welding.

(2) *Diagonal (Palm) Stays.*
$$f = \frac{x\ A\ P}{\cdot 7854\ D^2} \qquad \text{...} \quad (91)$$

where x = ratio of true to projected length of stay.

Formula (91) is based on the assumption that the stay is so constructed, *e.g.*, pin-jointed at both ends, that it is not subjected to bending stress As this condition is not realised in practice, f should not exceed 8,000 for steel, and 7,000 for iron, or 5,000 if welded.

(3) *Girder Stays.*
$$\text{Load per bolt} = \frac{P\ L\ D}{N}\ \text{lb. approximately} \quad \text{......} \quad (92)$$

Where L = span of girder, inches,

D = distance between centres of girders, inches,

and N = number of bolts per girder.

The maximum bending moment to which the girder is subjected approximates to:—

$$M_{max} = \frac{P\ L^2\ D}{8} \text{ lb.-inches} \quad \dots\dots\dots\dots\dots\dots \quad (93)$$

All flat surfaces in the boiler must be stayed.

Firebox Side Stays. Are subjected both to direct tensile and to bending stresses, the latter arising from the expansion of the inner firebox relative to the outer. The movement is naturally greater with a copper box than with steel, but in both cases attains its maximum value at the top rows of stays (where breakage is most likely to occur), since downward expansion is restricted by the foundation ring. As this bending action is of an indeterminate nature, the ideal arrangement would be one in which the stays were under purely tensile stress. The stays are further subjected to action by impurities in the water, to the effects of scale adhering to them, and to rough usage by washing-out rods; the heads or ends in the firebox have to withstand flame action and attrition by rapidly moving fuel particles.

The fact that stay breakage usually occurs at sections adjacent to the plates is an additional indication that flexibility in the stay is essential. There are several methods of securing this latter characteristic, many of them the subjects of patents, but one of the simplest and most effective is to turn down the centre portion plain to the diameter obtaining at the root of the thread. The abolition of the thread is further advantageous in that there is less encouragement for scale to adhere to the stay, but at the same time there is a possibility that the thread may break or partially fracture at the termination of the screwed portion. To eliminate this latter risk, some engineers prefer merely to reduce the thread on the centre portion, although by so doing some of the freedom from scale adherence is sacrificed. The thread should in any event be turned off at the fire end of the copper stays, as heads riveted from an initially plain shank are better able to resist the effects of flame action and attrition mentioned above.

In America, and other countries where steel fireboxes of large dimensions are customary, the lack of flexibility in the material and great expansion of the plates have necessitated the introduction of various types of flexible stay in order to obviate both breakage of top row stays and fracture of the firebox plates. The stay head is generally spherical and bedded in an appropriate socket. Whilst they are not merely justifiable, but essential under the conditions mentioned, and have the desired effect, these stays are comparatively costly and open to the objection that they present a large radiating surface.

In addition to the effects of expansion, another cause of top row breakage, frequently overlooked, lies in being over-generous, when actuated by a desire to provide sufficient fire-box flexibility, in the matter of the unstayed area between the top row of side stays and the outer row of roof stays. If this area be excessive, the wrapper plate bulges and the stays are overstressed by the consequent distortion.

Theoretically, staying action should depend entirely upon the threads, the fit of which in the plates is a matter of funda-mental importance ; the function of the head should be regarded as purely protective. For this reason the nuts on the fire end of steel stays should be of such a thickness that, when screwed home, only about two-thirds of that thickness is engaged with the stay. Nuts have an advantage over riveted heads in that they are easily replaceable when burnt out and, as a corollary, this renewal obviates that of the com-plete stay. As regards riveted copper stays, this disability is overcome on some railways by fitting special protective heads when the original head has worn down. The desired effect is obtained, but it is usually found that there is a tendency for the abrasion of the plate between the stays concerned to be increased.

Side stays are customarily screwed either 11 or 12 threads per inch. The latter pitch is preferable; the threads are finer and therefore more likely to remain steam tight, the effective cross sectional area of the stay is increased, and shop pro-cesses facilitated with an even number of threads per inch.

A tell-tale hole may be drilled concentrically, either partially or completely through the length of the stay, to give an indica-tion of the existence of any fracture which may occur, but is extremely likely to make up, and therefore fail to fulfil its intended function. Some such provision is, however, advis-able when firebox inspection is in the hands of comparatively unskilled staff.

Copper stays have usually a nominal diameter of $1''$ or $1\frac{1}{8}''$, and steel stays $\frac{5}{8}''$, the recommended working tensile stress being 5,500–6,000 lb. per square inch (copper), and 9,000–10,000 lb. per square inch (steel); pitch in both cases, $2\frac{3}{4}''$ to 4″, the latter being considered the maximum dimension advisable. Heads of copper stays should be at least $\frac{1}{2}''$ deep on the fire side and $\frac{5}{16}''$ at the other extremity; this latter dimension is ultimately limited, in the case of deep fireboxes, by the clearance, about $\frac{1}{2}''$ for standard gauge engines, between firebox and main frames. It has been found in some instances that copper stays under 1″ in diameter will not form sufficiently substantial heads to give a reasonable life. Steel side stays are not riveted, but caulked both ends and nutted on the fireside only. Advocates of the steel stay claim that as, for given conditions, it is of smaller diameter than the copper stay, the firebox plate is not weakened to such an extent and water circulation is less impeded.

A compromise has been effected in some instances by using nutted steel stays only in those areas where the effects of burning and attrition are greatest, and copper stays where expansion attains its maximum value; this arrangement is, however, open to the objections that trouble may arise owing to the difference in the expansions of the two metals and that galvanic action is aggravated.

Roof Stays. As the tubeplate expands vertically upwards, from two to four of the rows of roof stays immediately adjacent thereto are usually allowed a certain amount of play, up to about $\frac{3}{16}''$, to allow of free movement due to this expansion. In round-topped fireboxes the longitudinal outer rows of stays are also made flexible, as they are the most likely to break. Flexibility, however, is not always provided, even on large boilers, the arguments being that scale formation eventually prevents the articulations from functioning, and that additional upward movement of the tubeplate, set up by continued tube expanding, should be checked. Advocates of the flexible stay maintain that if the attempts of the tubeplate to expand are frustrated by a virtually rigid structure, the plate is liable to fracture in the radius of the flange.

Inclined work should be avoided in staying; direct stays should be so located, radially, that the threaded holes in the plates are normal to the stay centre line. Threads must be a tight fit to prevent leakage. Pins and cotters must be so located as to be easily erected; the number of pins should be restricted and ample bearing surface provided for them.

Wrought iron may be recommended in preference to steel for stays. It is less corrodible and better able to withstand shock stresses. The opinion has been expressed (Proc. I. Mech. E., 1923) that the chemical analysis is relatively unimportant, but correct and sufficient " working " of the material prior to manufacture is essential.

Unless the life of the snap-headed stay can confidently be anticipated to equal that of the firebox itself, stays should be nutted rather than snap headed on the fire side; the effects of ultimate burning can then be removed by renewing merely the nut and not the complete stay. The provision of washers on the fire side and nuts on the water side is not always followed, some engineers contending that these adjuncts are unnecessary, and that more satisfactory results are obtained in practice without them. Where used, the washers should be of copper and the nuts of iron.

Channel, tee or angle sections are sometimes employed to form a top anchorage for roof stays; although involving additional weight and cost, stripping is facilitated, the stays may be withdrawn intact when the firebox is dropped, and are therefore available for further use (if in suitable condition), and the effects both of the staying and of expansion are distributed over the plates concerned.

Direct stays facilitate washing out and do not unduly impede convection currents, and are infinitely preferable to the girder type. The excessive rigidity of the latter engenders the formation of longitudinal cracks between roof bolt holes in the crown sheet as it alternately expands and contracts, and the accumulation of inaccessible scale between the bosses of the girders leads to local overheating of the plates. Where used, girders should preferably be forged rather than cast in steel. Girders built up from two bars with distance pieces are less rigid, but offer difficulties to the renewal of bolts as the nuts are unavoidably inaccessible; this construction also encourages scale formation between the bars.

Longitudinal Staying.

As the tubes themselves possess staying properties, although to an indeterminate extent, and the area subject to pressure is relatively small, longitudinal staying between the two tubeplates is not usually considered necessary ; the use of stay tubes in locomotive practice is consequently restricted.

In general, longitudinal staying may be effected with either direct or palm stays. The former are to be preferred for both longitudinal and transverse staying; the diameter of the plain portion should not exceed that obtaining at the bottom of the thread where screwed.

Palm stays are liable to break, especially when attached to tubeplates, owing to movement of the latter. For this reason, and also to avoid overheating, they should be made as long as possible (3'-6" may be regarded as the minimum desirable distance of the anchorage from the plate supported by the stay) and should preferably be articulated.

Irrespective of the type of longitudinal stay adopted, Yorkshire iron is a more suitable material than steel.

Washing-out Facilities.

More care than is sometimes evident should be devoted to the extent of the washing-out facilities provided and their location. The firebox crown and water-legs, and the bottom of the barrel are the most vulnerable points as regards scale formation, and arrangements must be made for the most effective introduction of the washing-out water and, as far as possible, unrestricted use of rods at these points, together with measures for the complete evacuation of the dislodged scale and for subsequent inspection of the internal condition of the boiler. Traps of any shape or form in which scale may accumulate, resist the intended action of the washing-out water and give trouble subsequently, must be rigorously avoided. For example, the provision of a mud door or manhole in the bottom of the barrel, near the firebox tubeplate, enables scale which has been dislodged from the tubes to be removed without risk of the front water leg becoming further congested.

Plugs should be provided in the smokebox tubeplate near the top row of tubes, in the tube zone (displacing individual small tubes if necessary), or on the barrel in the immediate vicinity, and others arranged near the bottom of the barrel to enable the latter to be drained. The back and wrapper plates of the firebox should be equipped with plugs immediately above, and parallel with, the level of the crown sheet. Further plugs should be placed, approximately bisecting the height of the water legs, at all corners of the box, to permit of both transverse and longitudinal operation of rods, in order that the water legs may receive thorough attention; suitable discharge points should be located immediately contiguous to the foundation ring.   Additional plugs may be provided above the firehole door and in higher positions than those previously mentioned on the wrapper plate (in the case of a Belpaire box, at the top corners), thus enabling the crown and side water legs to be attacked from above, and on the upper part of the barrel to allow the water side of the firebox tubeplate to be cleaned.

Mud plugs are frequently preferred to mud - hole doors, especially where the quality of the available labour is dubious, as they are easier both to adjust and to maintain steam-tight. The usual type of plug, *i.e.*, a solid plug with a maximum diameter of about $1\frac{5}{8}''$, tapered 1 in 8 and screwed into a pad, with about 12 threads per inch, is, however, open to the objection that the threads tapped for it in the pad are liable to be damaged by the wash-out nozzles or rods.   This disadvantage may be eliminated by substituting a drilled boss, forming an integral part of a pad and threaded externally, with a screw cap.   The latter may be of hexagonal form externally, or alternative means for tightening it up satisfactorily may of course be adopted.

Where used, mud holes should be about $4\frac{3}{4}''$ × $2\frac{3}{4}''$. The door, which may be a drop stamping, should have a maximum thickness of approximately $1''$, with a $1''$ diameter shank. The bridge may be $1\frac{3}{4}''$ deep with a width of $1''$, the latter being increased to a maximum of about $2\frac{1}{8}''$ where required to form a seating for the nut on the shank of the door.

Dome.   To ensure freedom from priming and the maintenance of a satisfactorily high dryness fraction under all conditions of working, the dome should be of as generous dimensions, both as regards height and diameter, as clearances will allow.   The joint must be as low as possible so that, when broken, the regulator head, if located in the dome, is as completely exposed as possible for repair.   The dome should not be placed in the vicinity of the firebox, as ebullition is most violent there, and further, difficulty may be experienced, when running chimney first, in starting a heavy train from rest on a severe up gradient.   On the other hand, suburban, shunting and other engines making frequent stops of short duration will give trouble by priming if the dome is placed too near the smokebox, owing to the surging of water in the boiler.

As a general rule, the most favourable location for the dome is on the line bisecting the length of the tubes. On the other hand, when the regulator is placed in the dome, an excessive length of internal steam pipe is objectionable, not only because it is liable to corrode and is inaccessible for repair, but also on account of the large volume of steam accommodated between boiler and cylinders, especially with a superheater; there is therefore less flexibility of control in the event of the engine slipping or priming. This is one point in favour of placing the regulator between the superheater and the cylinders; the additional space then available in the dome may be utilised for the provision of a steam drier, if desired.

The dome may be secured to the barrel with two rows of $\frac{3}{4}''$ or $\frac{13}{16}''$ rivets pitched at about $2''$ centres; when of large diameter or subjected to high pressure, a third row of rivets may be provided, pitched at about $4''$ centres. An additional reinforcing plate is usually provided inside the barrel for the dome joint.

Strength of Joints for Domes, Manholes, etc. These joints may be designed from

$$D^2p = Nd^2f_t \quad \text{...................................} \quad (94)$$

where $D =$ diameter of aperture subjected to pressure, inches,

$p =$ working pressure, lb. per square inch,

$N =$ number of studs provided,

$d =$ diameter of studs at root of thread, inches, and

$f_t =$ working tensile stress in studs, lb. per square inch.

Pipes subjected to internal Pressure. The thickness may be determined from

$$t = \frac{pd}{k} + c \quad \text{...} \quad (95)$$

where $t =$ thickness of pipe wall, inches,

$p =$ internal pressure, lb. per square inch,

$d =$ internal diameter of pipe, inches,

and k and c are constants.

The values of these constants (D. A. Low) are as follows:—

		k	c
Cast iron steam pipes	...	4,000	0·3
Copper steam pipes	...	7,000	0·1
Solid drawn steel tubes	...	40,000	0·0

The thickness of solid drawn copper piping, when required to comply with Board of Trade regulations, is given by

$$t = \frac{pd}{6,000} + \frac{1''}{32} \quad\dots\dots\dots\dots\dots\dots\dots\dots\dots\dots\dots \quad (96)$$

For thick pipes (Lame),

$$t = \frac{d}{2}\left\{ \sqrt{\frac{3f + 2p_e}{3f - 4p_e}} - 1 \right\} \quad\dots\dots\dots\dots\dots\dots (97)$$

where f = safe tensile stress in material, lb. per sq. inch,
and p_e = excess of internal over external pressure, lb. per square inch.

Tubes subjected to external Pressure. The necessary thickness is given by

$$t = \frac{pd}{2f} \quad\dots\dots\dots\dots\dots\dots\dots\dots\dots\dots\dots\dots\dots \quad (98)$$

where t = thickness of tube wall, inches,
  p = excess of external over internal pressure, lb. per square inch,
  d = external diameter of tube, inches,
and f = working compressive strength of material, lb. per square inch.

A conservative value should be assigned to f.

Main (internal) Steampipe. In order to minimise pressure drop to cylinders, should be of as generous diameter as can conveniently be accommodated. To this end it is advantageous to provide a pipe having one square inch of cross-sectional area to every 21 or 22 square inches of the total piston area (two-cylinder engines) and up to about 35 square inches in cases where more than two cylinders are employed.

As sudden movement of the regulator may subject this pipe to shock stresses, it should preferably be reinforced with bands; these may be of steel, with a section of 2″ × ⅜″ or 2″ × ½″.

In British practice the internal steam pipe is usually of copper with brass flanges; in the United States, steel pipes are used in conjunction with cast iron or cast steel flanges. The use of ferrous materials engenders a risk of corrosion, especially near the smokebox tubeplate joint flange, and copper is further preferable in that it fastens more satisfactorily.

The total cross-sectional area of the subsidiary pipes taking steam to each cylinder, subsequent to superheating, should be about 2·4 times as great as that of the main steam pipe. According to Wilton, the cross-sectional area of branch pipes to the cylinders should be (0·05 × piston area), whilst that of the main steam pipe should be (0·66 × total cross-sectional area of branch pipes).

The preceding methods of determining the appropriate diameter of the steam pipe are purely empirical. In stationary practice the velocity of flow is taken as the basis of calculation, and the following information is quoted from a handbook published by Messrs. Babcock & Wilcox.

The flow of saturated steam through a pipe is given by

$$W = 87 \sqrt{\frac{D(p_1 - p_2)d^5}{L\left(1 + \dfrac{3·6}{d}\right)}} \quad\dotfill \quad (99)$$

where W = weight of steam flowing per minute, lb.,
$\quad d$ = pipe diameter, inches,
$\quad D$ = density of steam, lb. per cubic foot,
p_1 and p_2 = initial pressure and pressure at end of pipe respectively, lb. per square inch,
and L = length of pipe, feet.
Appropriate velocities of flow are:—

	For pipes up to and including 3″ diameter	For pipes from 3½″ to 9″ diameter inclusive.
Saturated steam ...	75 ft. per second	90 ft. per second
Superheated steam ...	100 ,, ,, ,,	120 ,, ,, ,,

In connection with the foregoing, the ratios of the volume of superheated to that of saturated steam are given as 1·15 to 1 for 100°F., 1·23 to 1 for 150°F., 1·30 to 1 for 200°F., 1·36 to 1 for 250°F., and 1·44 to 1 for 300°F. superheat respectively.

The resistance to flow at the pipe opening and at a valve of the globe type is stated to be equivalent to an additional pipe length of $\dfrac{114\,d}{1\ +\ \dfrac{3.6}{d}}$, and that at an elbow is equal to two-thirds of this quantity.

The collapsing pressure of lap-welded Bessemer steel tubes is given (R. T. Stewart) by:—

$$P\ =\ 1,000\left(1 - \sqrt{1 - 1,600\,\dfrac{t^2}{a^2}}\,\right) \quad\dots\dots\dots\dots\dots\dots \text{(100)}$$

$$\text{and}\ P\ =\ 86,670\,\dfrac{t}{d}\ -\ 1,386 \quad\dots\dots\dots\dots\dots \text{(100a)}$$

where P = collapsing pressure, lb. per square inch,
$\qquad d$ = outside diameter of tube, inches,
and t = thickness of tube wall, inches.

(100) is for values of P below 580 lb. per square inch, or for values of $\dfrac{t}{d}$ less than 0·023, whilst (100a) is for values greater than these.

A more general formula is

$$P\ =\ \dfrac{D^2 - d^2}{D^2 + d^2}\,f \quad\dots\dots\dots\dots\dots\dots\dots\dots\dots\dots \text{(101)}$$

where D and d are the external and internal diameters of the tube respectively, in inches.

Appropriate values of f for this formula (Kempe) are:—

Steel, at	60°F.	... ...	95,000
,, ,,	800°F.	... ...	28,800
Copper (rolled) at	60°F.	...	35,000
,, ,, ,,	640°F.	...	14,700
Brass (rolled) at 60°F.		...	30,000

Strength of flanged Pipe Joints. The tension on each bolt is given theoretically by

$$T\ =\ \dfrac{\pi\,D^2\,p}{4\,N} \quad\dots\dots\dots\dots\dots\dots\dots\dots\dots\dots\dots\dots \text{(102)}$$

where T = tensile force, lb.,
$\qquad p$ = internal pressure, lb. per square inch,
and N = number of bolts per joint.

Diameter D, in inches, is frequently taken as that of the pipe internally, but some engineers prefer to accept as a basis that of the bolt circle. N is customarily a multiple of 4.

In calculating the tensile stress f in each bolt, the nett area, *i.e.*, on diameter d at the bottom of the thread, should be taken. Then (Unwin),

$$f = 2,500 + 3,000\ d^2 \text{ lb. per square inch} \dots\dots\dots\dots (103)$$

British standard flanges are suitable for application to loco- motive practice.

Lagging. The efficiency of lagging is given as a percentage by:—

$$\frac{(\text{heat loss from bare pipe} - \text{loss from covered pipe})}{\text{heat loss from bare pipe}} \times 100 \dots\dots\dots\dots (104)$$

Lagging of boilers is now almost invariably effected either with mattresses, in most cases consisting largely of asbestos and stooled to prevent direct contact with the boiler, or with magnesia insulation, which may be applied either in the form of blocks or as a plastic composition. The following data, published by the courtesy of Messrs. J. W. Roberts, Ltd., of Armley, Leeds, may be accepted as representative of good modern practice.

(a) *Mattresses.* The usual thickness of the mattress is 1″, with $\frac{5}{8}$″ stools for the barrel (total thickness of insulation, $1\frac{5}{8}$″) and $\frac{7}{16}$″ stools for the firebox. Where covering riveted joints, a $\frac{1}{8}$″ stool is employed, the thickness of the mattress be- ing determined by the clearances available. The mattresses are laced together with 16 gauge wire.

The following particulars apply to "Limpet" mattresses:—

Weight per square foot, full 1″ thick, approximately	...	...	...	16 oz.	
Efficiency, full 1″ thick	...	...	86·21	%
,, $1\frac{1}{2}$″ ,,	...	...	87·88	,,
,, 2″ ,,	...	...	90·48	,,

It is claimed that the life of these mattresses is equal to that of the boiler.

For lagging pipes, asbestos webbing may be employed. The following widths are recommended:—

For train heating pipes ...	...	...	$2\frac{1}{2}$″ wide.
,, injector feed pipes ...	...	...	2″ ,,
,, steam sanding pipes...	...	...	1″ ,,
,, pressure gauge pipes...	...	...	1″ ,,

TABLE XIX.
LENGTH OF "LIMPET" WEBBING REQUIRED PER FOOT RUN OF PIPE LAGGED.
(Messrs. J. W. ROBERTS LTD.)

Width of Webbing.	Size of Pipe, Inside Diameter.						
	$\frac{3}{8}''$	$\frac{1}{2}''$	$\frac{3}{4}''$	$1''$	$1\frac{1}{4}''$	$1\frac{1}{2}''$	$2''$
$\frac{1}{2}''$	5' 0''	6' 0''	8' 0''	9' 0''	11' 0''	12' 1''	15' 0''
$1''$	2' 6''	3' 0''	4' 0''	4' 6''	5' 6''	6' 1''	7' 6''
$1\frac{1}{2}''$	1' 8''	2' 1''	2' 8''	3' 1''	3' 7''	4' 1''	5' 1''
$2''$				2' 4''	2' 8''	3' 0''	3' 9''
$3''$							2' 6''

(b) *Magnesia Plastic Composition and Blocks.* Newall's 85% magnesia may be applied in blocks or as a plastic composition. The desirable thickness is 2" and the corresponding efficiency, 93%-94%. It is not economical to exceed this thickness in locomotive practice, as the additional heat saving is not balanced by the extra cost of lagging incurred. The efficiencies which may be expected with various thicknesses, based on comparative experiments carried out with saturated steam at a pressure of 180 lb. per square inch, are:—

MATERIAL.	EFFICIENCY, %
Composition, 2" thick	74.69
Hair Felt	77.6
Pine Lagging	80.74
Ordinary Plastic Composition, 2" thick	82.0
Asbestos Felt, 1¾" thick	85.17
Aircell, 1½" thick	85.72
Newall's 85% Magnesia Plastic, or Newallite	
1" thick	88.4
1½" thick	90.7
2" thick	93.1

As regards the density, one ton of the Newall's composition will cover 2,400 square feet to a thickness of 1".

Lagging Plate and Bands. Plate having a thickness of 14 S.W.G. will suffice for both the plates and the bands. The usual width of the latter varies from 2" to 3".

It is customary to allow a minimum clearance of about 2" between boiler and lagging plate. The provision of a gap of, say, ¼" between the plates, where covered by the lagging band, facilitates erection. The hoops and stiffeners for the lagging may be of 2" × ¼" steel bar.

Chapter VI.

BOILER MOUNTINGS AND STEAM USING AUXILIARIES.

(a) BOILER MOUNTINGS.

Regulator. Opinions are somewhat divided as to whether the flat slide or piston (double beat) type is the easier to maintain steam-tight; it would appear that the former type is preferred, not only for this reason but also on account of the lower resistance offered to steam flow. Piston regulator valves, and also those comprising a battery of progressively opening mushroom, or poppet, valves, usually fitted integrally with the superheater header, are, however, increasingly used in modern practice as the flat valve, if of large dimensions, is difficult to operate with high pressures.

The steam area provided through the valve, when fully opened, should at least equal the cross sectional area of the main steam pipe, *i.e.*, about 1 square inch per 21 square inches of total cylinder area and, to allow for the effects of eddying, should preferably exceed this allowance. It has been suggested (Shields, Proc. I. Loco. E., 1930) that with flat valves the area of the pilot port should be one-fourth that of the main steam pipe, and the area of the main valve equal to ($0.9 \times$ main steam pipe area). The valve should be so designed that the increase in area of the opening to steam is gradual in relation to the movement of the regulator handle.

The prevailing wall thickness of the regulator head, if of cast iron, may be about $\frac{1}{2}''$ or $\frac{5}{8}''$.

There are three possible locations for the regulator:—

    (*a*) In the dome, the usual position.

    (*b*) In the smokebox, between the boiler and the superheater, and

    (*c*) In the smokebox, between the superheater header and the cylinders.

The advantages accruing from the adoption of position (*c*) are:—

1. Since the superheater is continuously under pressure, superheated steam is always available for the use of auxiliaries, *e.g.*, air brake pump, feed-water pump, blower, mechanical stoker, turbo-generator, etc. The total steam demand of such details may represent a large percentage of the total evaporation, and considerable economy in fuel may be effected by the supply of superheated steam thereto. It must be remembered, however, that auxiliaries at present made from non-ferrous materials, *e.g.*, ejectors, injectors, are not suitable for operation with superheated steam. The possibilities of substituting, say, alloy steel in these cases may therefore be considered.

2. The necessity for draught retarders, circulating steam or other devices for the protection of the superheater elements is removed.

3. The superheater functions as an adjunct to the evaporative heating surface when the regulator is shut.

4. The effective steam space in the boiler is sensibly augmented. In one particular instance the increase effected was 54·5% (with a full glass of water), and 26·8% with a half glass.

5. Quicker response of the engine to the regulator, due to reduction in volume of steam space between regulator and cylinders.

6. Reduced effect of priming on both control and performance of the engine.

Further advantages claimed particularly for the multiple poppet valve regulator, one of which, by the courtesy of the Superheater Company, is shewn in Fig. 6, are:—

1. Easier maintenance in steam-tight condition. The comparatively small size of each individual valve is less affected by high temperatures.

2. Simplicity. There are no bolts, pins, cotter-pins, rods, links, or other parts to work loose.

3. Practically complete balancing is ensured by the provision of a small pilot valve, and the regulator, owing to the very gradual successive movements of the valves, is most sensitive to any slight alteration made as regards the position of the regulator handle in its quadrant.

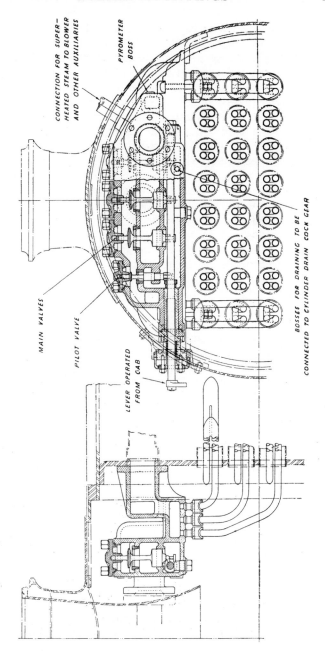

CONNECTION FOR SUPER-
HEATED STEAM TO BLOWER
AND OTHER AUXILIARIES

PYROMETER
BOSS

MAIN VALVES

PILOT VALVE

LEVER OPERATED
FROM CAB

BOSSES FOR DRAINING TO BE
CONNECTED TO CYLINDER DRAIN COCK GEAR

FIG. 6. MULTIPLE POPPET VALVE REGULATOR.

4. Accessibility of valves: by providing a removable plate in the smokebox wrapper, directly over the header, there is no necessity to open the smokebox door, should any repairs or examinations be necessary. By fitting an isolating valve at the entrance to the main steam pipe, the regulator may receive attention when the boiler is in steam. It should be mentioned that the provision of this valve entails the fitting of a safety valve to prevent the possible accumulation of excess pressure in the superheater whilst isolated.

5. Minimisation of number of joints in the smokebox. The fitting of the multiple valve type regulator, integral with the superheater header, does not add to the usual number of steam pipes leading from the header to the cylinders.

6. No dome joints are broken for the purpose of examining or repairing the regulator.

The pilot valve is generally 2″ in diameter, and each main valve, 4″. The usual practice of the Superheater Company is to provide one main valve to eight or nine superheater elements. Possible movement of the valves due to the longitudinal expansion of the boiler is prevented by fitting a compensating link intermediately in the length of the regulator rod. The chief objection which can be raised to this type of regulator is the difficulty of detecting the individual valve responsible in the event of leakage.

It is always advisable, in cases where the regulator is located between the header and cylinders, and the superheater is continuously under pressure in consequence, to provide a bye-pass valve whereby the superheater may be isolated, so that in the event of trouble arising, e.g., failure of an element, the engine may be worked to destination with saturated steam.

In view of the fact that the efficiency of the superheater depends largely on the initial dryness fraction of the steam with which it is supplied, the dome, if retained, may be used for the housing of a steam drier. So far, however, the performance of most existing forms of this detail has not been altogether satisfactory.

When a perforated pipe is used for the collection of steam, there is little or no advantage in providing a number of holes such that their total cross-sectional area greatly exceeds that of the regulator valve when fully open, as the bulk of the steam passes through the holes nearest the regulator. The holes provided should, however, be so located that the driest steam is likely to pass through them.

Regulator Handle. Must be so arranged that any possible self-movement, due to gravity or to vibration of the engine whilst running, tends to close the regulator, and that it may be manipulated by the driver without diverting his attention from the road. The latter stipulation is of especial importance when shunting, backing on to a train, etc.

Clamps or other positive locking devices are a potential source of danger and therefore to be discouraged.

The easiest method of opening the regulator, at the same time securing sensitive control, is by making use of the shoulder muscles. Handles working transversely across the backplate should therefore be arranged to open away from the driver; those working in the longitudinal plane should be opened by a "push," as opposed to a pulling movement. Transverse regulator handles in the lower quadrant involve a lifting movement which, with a stiff valve, leads to the risk of strain, and is therefore not altogether satisfactory. The repetition of the "push and pull" type of handle on the fireman's side, although useful on occasion when shunting, is a possible cause of injury and should be avoided.

For purposes of leverage calculation, the force which may be applied manually should not be taken at a higher value than 25-30 lb., the former amount being assumed for preference. In some cases the specified force is as small as 10 lb.; if the operation of the regulator be made too easy, however, the risk of unintentional opening, *e.g.*, by falling against the handle or by clumsy manipulation of the fireirons, is incurred.

The possibility of the regulator rod breaking, due to excessive corrosion in the vicinity of the stuffing box, is countered, on the L.M.S.R., by providing the rod with a brass sleeve.

Steam Pipe Connections to Mountings. The employment of internal steam pipes in the boiler is to be deprecated; external pipes, although subject to heat loss and therefore preferably lagged, offer the following advantages:—

1. Greater accessibility and less time required for shed repairs in consequence.
2. Pipes can be withdrawn or replaced without dropping steam in the boiler.

3. Repairs do not necessitate breakage and renewal of dome joint.

4. Reduced liability to make up, as the pipe is not receiving heat externally from steam in the boiler.

5. Firebox crown more accessible for rodding and washing out.

6. Risk of priming reduced (*vide* Chapter V).

The best method of minimising the number of internal steam pipes is to provide a **steam turret, manifold or fountain** which requires only one internal steam pipe from the dome or superheater, according to the position of the regulator relative to the superheater. It naturally follows that only one hole has to be cut in the boiler for the connection to the turret, thus increasing the mechanical strength of the boiler. The turret, to be satisfactory, should be fitted with an isolating cock so that repairs to the other cocks may be carried out whilst the boiler is in steam; additional bosses should be cast in to allow for any later additions which may be required. The turret is usually cast in gunmetal, with a wall thickness of $\frac{1}{2}''$ or $\frac{5}{8}''$; nickel steel is frequently adopted in the U.S.A. for this detail. When designing, the formation of undrained pockets must be avoided.

Thickness of cylindrical Castings (e.g., Steam Turrets). According to Lamé:—

$$ t = \frac{d}{2} \left\{ \sqrt{\frac{f + p}{f - p}} - 1 \right\} \quad \dots\dots\dots\dots\dots\dots\dots\dots\dots\dots\dots (105) $$

where t = wall thickness, inches,

d = internal diameter, inches,

f = maximum working stress in material, lb. per square inch,

and p = excess of internal over external pressure, lb. per square inch.

Small Steam Cocks. Unless adjustment is normally infrequent (as in the case of the pressure gauge isolating cock or the steam cock for a hydrostatic lubricator), or exceptional circumstances demand it, screw-down valves should be fitted in preference to plug cocks. The first cost is admittedly higher in the former case, but is more than balanced by the ease with which they are maintained steam-tight in the shed. If possible, the spindle thread should be so arranged that the maximum opening is obtained with less than a complete revolution of the handwheel, one spoke of which should be extended through the rim, as on injector steam cock handwheels. The enginemen can then note the relative amount of opening at a glance, and the necessity for "trying" the wheel, thereby upsetting a position previously adjusted to a nicety, does not arise.

With screw-down cocks the best results, from the point of view of maintenance costs, are those in which the valve proper is distinct from, *i.e.*, not integral with, or rigidly attached to, the spindle. The valve is then not subjected to hard rotary friction, causing surface abrasion, when screwed home.

Valve spindles are in some instances extended in order to facilitate the operation of the handwheel in locations where clearance is limited. This practice should not be followed unless unavoidable, and the spindle should then be supported by a bearing, placed near the handwheel, in order to minimise the liability of the spindle to bend.

The cross - sectional areas through the valve passages and valve (when the latter is fully open) must be larger than that of the pipe to which it is fitted, in order to compensate for losses by friction and eddying.

Blower Valve. Should take the form of a plug cock with direct pull and push control from the cab; although requiring adjustment frequently in service, and therefore liable to give more trouble as regards maintenance in steam-tight condition than a screw-down valve, opening can be effected far more quickly. Rapidity in operation is essential when emergencies, such as sudden back draughts, arise. Owing to the possible occurrence of the latter, the control, which must be conveniently placed for the driver, should be as far removed as possible from the firehole door and should be provided, for both mechanical and visual reasons, with positive stops for the fully open and shut positions respectively. When the valve is placed at the smokebox end of the boiler, this being the best position, the control rod may be conveniently located in a tubular handrail. Should the blower cock be placed on the backplate, a pipe is necessary thence to the dome, and another the full length of the boiler to the blower; such lengths of internal piping are both excessive and objectionable.

Blow-down Cock.   For a standard gauge engine a 2″ screw-down cock will suffice. The cock, to be really effective, should be as near the lowest level of the foundation ring as possible. Thus, for an engine with a sloping grate, the best location is in front of the firebox, on the centre line of the boiler, in which case provision must be made, by worm and key or other appropriate device, for operation from the footplate. On the score of accessibility, the cock may be placed at the side of fireboxes in which the grate is horizontal. The use of hot water washing-out plant may dictate to a certain extent the form of the lead away, but it should in any case be so arranged that, when operating the cock, there is no likelihood of grit from the ballast being blown up into the motion.

It has been computed that with average modern boiler pressures a 2″ cock discharges approximately 2,000 lb. water per minute, and a $1\frac{1}{2}$″ cock about 1,735 lb. per minute.

Safety Valves, "Pop" Type.   Valves of this pattern are almost invariably fitted in modern practice. The discharge capacity is directly proportional to the diameter of the valve, and not to its discharge area. The latter is of course given in square inches by πdl, where d is the valve diameter and l the lift, both in inches; d may obviously be varied as desired, but l, in locomotive practice, is very small and, with this type of valve, practically constant.

TABLE XX.

DIMENSIONS OF ROSS SAFETY VALVES RELATIVE TO GRATE AREA AND BOILER PRESSURE.

Grate Area (square feet)	Boiler Pressure (lb. per square inch gauge).	Number and Diameter (in inches) of Ross Safety Valves.
18	160	2×2
23	180	2×2
27	175	$2 \times 2\frac{1}{2}$
30	200	$2 \times 2\frac{1}{2}$
30	170	2×3
35	200	2×3
38	180	$2 \times 3\frac{1}{2}$
44	200	$2 \times 3\frac{1}{2}$
42	180	$3 \times 2\frac{1}{2}$
46	200	$3 \times 2\frac{1}{2}$
41	175	2×4
50	200	2×4
50	180	3×3
56	200	3×3

The appropriate size of valve is directly proportional to the grate area and varies inversely as the pressure, owing to the decrease in specific volume in conjunction with increased velocity of steam as its pressure rises, giving a correspondingly greater discharge per unit of time.

Table XX, for which the author is indebted to Messrs. R. L. Ross & Co. Ltd., gives suitable valve dimensions for boilers of varying capacity consuming British coal of good quality.

Applying the foregoing data to an equation of the form

$$A = \frac{x\,G}{P} \quad\dotfill\quad (106)$$

where $A =$ total area of "pop" valves provided, square inches,

$G =$ grate area of boiler, square feet, and

$P =$ pressure, lb. per square inch absolute,

the value of x varies from 53·3 to 116·4, the average being 86·5. Formulæ for the closer determination of safety valve capacity will be given later.

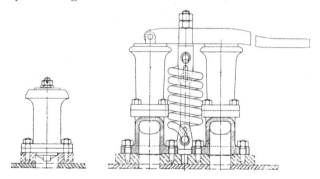

FIG. 7. COMPARISON OF A 3″ ROSS VALVE WITH TWO 3″ RAMSBOTTOM VALVES OF APPROXIMATELY THE SAME DISCHARGE CAPACITY.

The accompanying drawings are also published by the courtesy of Messrs. Ross. Fig. 7 affords an interesting comparison of a 3″ Ross valve with two 3″ Ramsbottom valves. The respective valves have appreciably the same discharge capacity; they are drawn to the same scale, and the difference in overall dimensions and weight will be noted.

Fig. 8 shews adapters for the application of Ross valves to existing seatings; these are designed to allow of the continued

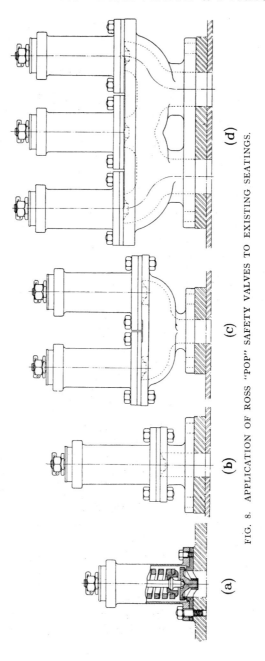

FIG. 8. APPLICATION OF ROSS "POP" SAFETY VALVES TO EXISTING SEATINGS.

use of standard details subsequent to the change over to "pop" safety valves from other types. It may be pointed out that in all four instances the Ross valves themselves, and their flanges, are identical, although the pads on the boilers vary considerably. The adapter shewn at *(b)* has a standard upper flange which carries the safety valve and is unaffected by the design of the lower flange; the latter may therefore conform to existing standards. The arrangements shewn at *(c)* and *(d)* are adapters to suit mountings originally provided for Ramsbottom valves. The valve shewn at *(a)* is mounted direct on the boiler pad; in this case the vertical clearances were limited.

The standard range of Ross valves, from 2″ to 4″ diameter, is shewn in Fig. 9 at *(a)*, *(b)*, *(c)*, *(d)* and *(e)* respectively; the overall dimensions, finished weights, and standard flange joints are given in each case. With regard to the latter item, actually the flanges are frequently varied to meet the requirements of individual railways. The valves shewn at *(f)*, *(g)* and *(h)* are designed to observe severe restrictions as regards height. That shewn at *(a)* is for a privately owned shunting engine and is provided with an easing lever to comply with insurance stipulations.

Ramsbottom Safety Valves. Are not much used now as they require more headroom, weigh more, and give a greater fluctuation between blow-off and shut-down pressure than a "pop" valve (5 to 8 lb. per square inch as against 1 to 2 lb. per square inch).

Care must be taken, in order to minimise risk of seizure, that like materials do not work upon one another. The columns in the past have in some instances been made of gunmetal, but cast iron is almost universal in recent examples.

The valves may be either flat or mitre seated. The latter are more difficult to keep steam-tight and, although an easier path is provided for the escaping steam, the effective discharge area is reduced, compared with the flat seating, roughly in the ratio of 7 : 10. The seatings of flat valves are $\frac{1}{16}$″ or $\frac{1}{8}$″ wide; they should be as narrow as possible, but the area of contact must be such that the pressure does not exceed 2,000 lb. per square inch for gunmetal bushes, or 3,000 lb. per square inch for phosphor bronze (Unwin). Provision must be made for the valves to have a free lift of $\frac{1}{8}$″, although the actual lift rarely attains $\frac{1}{16}$″.

The wings of the valves should be bevelled off. Consider-

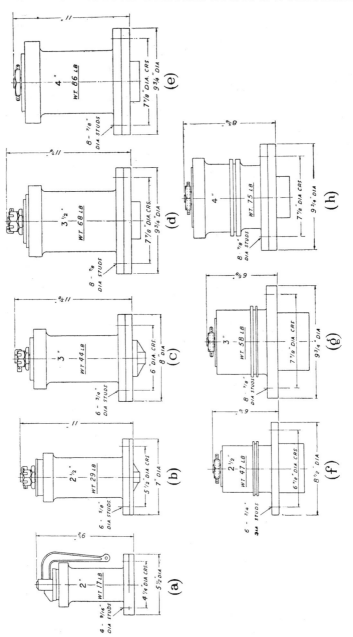

FIG. 9. STANDARD ROSS "POP" SAFETY VALVES.

able variation is exhibited in the amount of clearance allowed between the wing and the face of the bush. On one railway it was found that with a 3″ diameter bush the valve should be (3″ — ·008″) in diameter when cold, in order to provide the ·005″ clearance specified for a warm valve. It is the practice on some railways to provide at least 1/32″ clearance cold. Excessive clearance invalidates the function of the wings; on the other hand, insufficient clearance may cause seizure, with dangerous consequences.

Helical Springs. The total extension of a helical spring of circular section is given by:—

$$E = \frac{8\,W\,N\,D^3}{C\,d^4} \quad \text{..} \quad (107)$$

and for a spring of square section,

$$E = \frac{44\,W\,N\,R^3}{C\,s^4} \quad \text{..} \quad (108)$$

where E = total extension of spring, inches,
$\quad\quad W$ = load applied, lb.,
$\quad\quad D$ = mean diameter of helix, inches,
$\quad\quad R$ = mean radius of helix, inches,
$\quad\quad C$ = modulus of rigidity of material, lb. per square inch (for steel, 13,000,000),
$\quad\quad N$ = number of complete coils in wire,
$\quad\quad d$ = diameter of wire, inches, and
$\quad\quad s$ = side of square section wire, inches.

Safety Valves : General Data. *The appropriate area* to provide for the safety valves may be obtained from:—

$$A = \frac{x\,H}{P} \quad \text{...} \quad (109)$$

where A = total area of safety valves provided, square inches,
$\quad\quad H$ = total evaporative heating surface of boiler, square feet,
$\quad\quad P$ = stipulated blowing off pressure, lb. per square inch absolute, and
$\quad\quad x$ = constant, approximately 1·9 for "pop" valves and 3·0 for Ramsbottom valves.

The value of x given for "pop" valves is in close agreement with formulæ advanced by Mr. MacNicoll in a paper to the Institution of Marine Engineers (October, 1931).

The proportions recommended by the U.S. Association of Master Mechanics are:—

$$DN = \frac{\cdot 036\, H}{L\, P} \qquad \dotfill (110)$$

where D = nominal valve diameter, inches,
N = number of valves provided,
L = vertical lift of valves, inches,
and H and P have the same significance as in the previous formula.

The *discharge* is given in lb. per hour by

$$E = 105\,(L \times P \times D) \qquad \dotfill (111)$$

Usually the value of L is arbitrarily taken as 0.1″ (Proc. I. Loco. E., 1926). In the case of Ramsbottom valves the maximum value of L, for the purposes of calculation, is $\frac{1}{16}$″.

According to Napier's formula,

$$E = 51\cdot43\, Pa \qquad \dotfill (112)$$

where a is the area of the discharge opening in square inches.

Location of Safety Valves.   In British practice the safety valves are usually placed on the firebox, where the greatest ebullition naturally occurs; abroad, a position on the dome is frequently favoured.   In the author's opinion the best location is on the boiler barrel, between the firebox and the dome, preferably nearer the former.   There is then no interference with the firebox stay spacing and less liability to carry over surge water.   With valves of the "pop" type, which have relatively small seatings, the weakening of the barrel would not reach serious proportions.   The only objection which might be raised to this arrangement is that with a long firebox the discharge from the valves, unless violent, would be liable to obscure the enginemen's outlook.

The practice of placing the safety valves on the dome is not to be recommended, as it forms a direct incentive to priming whenever the valves discharge while the regulator is open.

Loss of water will inevitably occur unless the valves are placed as far as possible above the water line.

Pads.   The use of pads for the seating of plugs and mountings is often necessary in order to increase otherwise insufficient area available for thread contact.

Water Gauges.   To ensure true readings, the cross-sectional area of the passages in the columns must be considerably greater than that of the bore of the glass. The lower column must be so placed that, when the water level is at the bottom of the glass, the crown sheet of the firebox is well and completely covered when the engine is:

(a) descending the most severe gradient it can encounter in service, and/or

(b) standing on a curve having maximum superelevation.

Apart from considerations of clearing the regulator handle or other adjacent boiler mountings there is, relatively, a certain amount of freedom for the location of the top column. On American locomotives the upper column is frequently placed above the wrapper plate and, in conjunction with a suitable adapter pipe, enables a great length of glass to be arranged. In this country, however, the distance between the centres of the respective columns rarely exceeds 11″, so that the length of glass effective for reading is limited to 5″ or 6″. Considered solely from the point of view of the functioning of the gauge, a comparatively great length of glass is advantageous, and the somewhat severe limitations observed in British practice have possibly been influenced by the psychological fact that, although a good engineman will not do so, many prefer to " work with a full glass," probably due to lack of self-confidence. Whatever the actual reason therefor this method of working leads, especially in the case of the modern high-pitched boiler with restricted steam space, to an increased tendency to prime and to a reduced degree of superheat, and the only remedy for, or at least mitigation of, the evil is to lower the top column of the water gauge below the highest possible position.

The provision of distant control for the cocks is advisable, as the ball check valves may either be mislaid in the shed or become coated with scale.

Locomotive water gauges, as supplied by Messrs. Dewrance & Co., are usually provided with undrilled flanges of 4″ or 4¼″ diameter, having a 1″ diameter spigot, integral with them, to register in the boiler backplate. The usual dimensions from the centre of the glass tube to the flange joint face are 3″ for " small," 3⅝″ for " standard," and from 4″ to 4½″ for the " massive " pattern gauges.

The approximate length of glass approximates to 1¾″ less than the distance between centres of columns, and the glass diameter usually specified is ⅝″, although the clarity of readings would be improved by increasing this dimension to $\frac{3}{4}''$.   If the columns are so arranged that the centre line of the glass is slightly canted at an angle to the vertical, and the efficient working of the ball check valve will permit of this being done to a maximum extent of about 30°, the breadth of the line denoting the water level in the glass is increased, correspondingly improving the visibility of the reading.   To allow for expansion of the glass, the gland nuts should be drilled $\frac{1}{4}''$ larger than the outside diameter of the glass, and $\frac{1}{8}''$ end play should be allowed on the length of the latter for the same reason.

Various devices utilising the refraction of the water have been introduced, usually in the form of a serrated glass plate, or of a special metallic backplate for the protector, with a view to defining more sharply the water level reading.   It should be noted that, for a given effective reading length, glasses of the prismatic type require a greater distance between column centres than the conventional tube pattern.

If two gauges are fitted per engine, one will act as a check and also as a standby in the event of a glass breaking whilst running; replacement under such conditions is frequently awkward.   For this reason the Dewrance patented glass, in which the movement of a lever attached to the handle of the bottom cock synchronises with the opening of the latter and actuates a finger to hold the top ball off its seat whilst the gauge is being blown through, is very largely used in places abroad where the periodic changing of glasses is irregular or the enginemen cannot be relied upon satisfactorily to deal with a gauge glass bursting on the road.   In this type of gauge, incidentally, the maintenance of steam tightness of the cock plugs is assisted by steam pressure acting on the ends of the inverted cones.

The discharge from the gauge blow-down cock may be led either to the permanent way or to the ashpan.   In the latter event, care must be taken that the end of the pipe is bent transversely across the engine, or preferably finished with a reverse bend, as otherwise, when the water gauge is blown down and the dampers are open, ash is liable to be blown into the motion or big ends, if between the frames.

Special attention must be given to the question of the illumination of the water gauges by night.   This is effected electrically on many colonial and foreign engines, but the oil lamp customarily provided for this purpose in British practice is open to criticism; it is badly located in many cases and gives insufficient light.

Pressure Gauges. Must be so located as to be equally easy to read by day and by night, special attention being accorded the question of illumination. Although the readings chiefly interest the fireman, the gauge should be so placed that it is also convenient for the driver.

Gauges must be provided with either a syphon or field tube to prevent direct access of live steam to the recording mechanism, and a plug cock must also be be fitted to allow of complete isolation from the boiler when desired. The gauge should be mounted on a stout pad, of fibre or wood, to insulate it from the effects of either engine vibration or transmitted heat to which it may be subjected according to its location.

In ordering gauges from the manufacturers the specified recording range should be such that blowing-off pressure is preferably the mean, and certainly not more than two-thirds, of the range of pressures calibrated on the dial. The blowing-off point should be indicated on the dial by a red line or other conspicuous device.

A gauge recording steam chest pressures is useful, as it calls the attention of the driver to any excessive wiredrawing which may occur, thus inducing him to take immediate corrective measures.

The connection between pressure gauges and boiler is usually made with $\frac{3}{8}''$ diameter pipe. The joints should be made with washers, and not with red or white lead, which may choke the orifice more or less completely.

Injectors.

1. *Ordinary Live Steam Injectors.* Table XXI gives particulars of Messrs. Davies and Metcalfe's injectors. The capacities given in this table are average values based on a working steam pressure of 180 lb. per square inch and feed water at an initial temperature of 60°F. Approximate corrections for other operating conditions may be applied as follows:—

   5% reduction in delivery for each 20 lb. per square inch reduction in steam pressure.

   2% reduction in delivery for each increment of 5°F. in the initial temperature of the feed water.

TABLE XXI.
CAPACITIES OF, AND DIMENSIONS OF CONNECTIONS FOR, NON-LIFTING LIVE STEAM INJECTORS (MESSRS. DAVIES & METCALFE LTD.).

Size of Injector	Capacity (gallons per hour)	Internal diameter of pipes (inches)	Flange dimensions (inches)	
			Diameter	Thickness
No 4	390	1	4	$\frac{1}{2}$
No. 5	600	1	4	$\frac{1}{2}$
No. 6	870	$1\frac{1}{4}$	$4\frac{1}{2}$	$\frac{9}{16}$
No. 7	1200	$1\frac{1}{4}$	$4\frac{1}{2}$	$\frac{9}{16}$
No. 8	1550	$1\frac{1}{2}$	5	$\frac{5}{8}$
No. 9	1950	$1\frac{1}{2}$	5	$\frac{5}{8}$
No. 10	2400	$1\frac{3}{4}$	$5\frac{1}{2}$	$\frac{11}{16}$
No. 11	2700	2	6	$\frac{3}{4}$
No. 12	3600	2	6	$\frac{3}{4}$

The minimum delivery of the non-lifting injector is about 60% of the maximum.

Table XXII gives similar particulars for Messrs. Gresham and Craven's combination injectors. Performances are also based on an initial feed temperature of 60°F. with, in these cases, a lift of 3'-0".

The pipe dimensions as given by the manufacturers should be regarded as minima; they may therefore be increased without detriment, provided that the increment be effective throughout the length of the pipes concerned.

By cutting down the supply of feed water to a minimum, the live steam injector may be made to augment the initial temperature of the feed water by 120°F.–130°F. In general, however, the increment is of the order of 90°F.–100°F.

The average steam consumption for this type of injector is 10% of the total boiler evaporation. In extreme cases, i.e., when the quantity of water delivered per lb. steam is minimised, injectors will deliver against a pressure having twice the intensity of that available for feeding.

The efficiency of the injector on a thermal basis, viz.,

$$\eta_t = \frac{\text{(heat returned in feet water)} + \text{(heat returned as work)} - \text{(heat rejected)}}{\text{heat supplied}}$$

TABLE XXII.

DELIVERY OF COMBINATION INJECTORS IN GALLONS PER HOUR (MESSRS. GRESHAM & CRAVEN LTD.).

Size	Delivery at Boiler Pressures in lb. per square inch of													Size of Pipes			
	45	60	75	90	105	120	135	150	165	180	195	210	225	Steam	Water	Overflow	Delivery
No. 5	340	370	430	470	500	540	580	600	590	580	570	550	540	$\frac{3}{4}''$	$1''$	$1''$	$1''$
No. 6	480	550	610	670	730	780	840	870	860	840	810	800	790	$1''$	$1\frac{1}{4}''$	$1\frac{1}{4}''$	$1\frac{1}{4}''$
No. 7	660	750	840	920	1000	1070	1150	1190	1170	1140	1100	1090	1080	$1''$	$1\frac{3}{8}''$	$1\frac{3}{8}''$	$1\frac{3}{8}''$
No. 8	860	980	1100	1200	1300	1400	1500	1550	1530	1490	1440	1420	1410	$1\frac{1}{4}''$	$1\frac{1}{2}''$	$1\frac{1}{2}''$	$1\frac{1}{2}''$
No. 9	1080	1240	1390	1520	1640	1770	1940	1970	1930	1880	1820	1800	1790	$1\frac{1}{4}''$	$1\frac{3}{4}''$	$1\frac{3}{4}''$	$1\frac{3}{4}''$
No. 10	1360	1530	1720	1880	2030	2180	2340	2430	2390	2330	2250	2220	2200	$1\frac{1}{2}''$	$1\frac{3}{4}''$	$1\frac{3}{4}''$	$1\frac{3}{4}''$
No. 11	1590	1850	2090	2270	2460	2650	2840	2940	2890	2820	2720	2700	2670	$1\frac{1}{2}''$	$1\frac{7}{8}''$	$1\frac{7}{8}''$	$1\frac{7}{8}''$
No. 12	1940	2200	2470	2700	2925	3150	3370	3500	3440	3350	3240	3200	3150	$2''$	$2''$	$2\frac{1}{4}''$	$2\frac{1}{4}''$
No. 13	2270	2600	2900	3170	3430	3700	3960	4040	3980	3930	3800	3720	3610	$2''$	$2''$	$2\frac{1}{4}''$	$2\frac{1}{4}''$

very nearly approaches unity (Gresham, Proc. I. Loco. E., 1923), the value actually exceeding 0·985, but the mechanical efficiency,

$$\eta_m = \frac{\text{heat units used in doing work}}{\text{heat supplied}}$$

approximates to only 3% (*ibid.*). The injector is therefore highly efficient as a boiler feeding agent, but is wasteful as a water lifter in those cases when no advantage accrues from the additional temperature obtaining, unless, of course, expediency is the deciding factor.

In American practice the steam supply to the injector is sometimes arranged to pass through a reducing valve in order to obtain constant pressure and, consequently, consistent maintenance of the maximum designed efficiency.

2. *Hot Water Injectors.* The use of hot water injectors is advisable in hot climates. They are capable of dealing with feed at an initial temperature up to 140°F., the delivery temperature, with a boiler pressure of 180 lb. per square inch, approximating to 240°F.–260°F. These injectors work within a wide range of pressures and are capable of high lifts.

Table XXIII compares the range of working pressures and maximum initial feed water temperatures for which various types of Messrs. Gresham and Craven's injectors are designed.

TABLE XXIII.

RANGE OF WORKING PRESSURES AND MAXIMUM INITIAL FEED WATER TEMPERATURES FOR WHICH INJECTORS ARE DESIGNED (MESSRS. GRESHAM & CRAVEN LTD.).

Type of Injector.	Working Pressure (lb. per square inch)		Maximum initial Feed Water Temperature (degrees Fahr.)
	Maximum	Minimum	
Standard ..	180	40	95
High pressure ..	300	50	90
Simplex ..	200	40	120
Special hot water	225	40	140

3. *Exhaust Steam Injectors.* Injectors of this type will be further considered, as feed water heating agents, in Chapter VII. The following particulars refer to the Type " H," (automatic) exhaust steam injectors manufactured by Messrs Davies and Metcalfe.

With feed water at an initial temperature of 60°F., and using exhaust steam only, these injectors are capable of delivering against the following pressures:—

Pressures (lb. per square inch).	
Exhaust	Delivery
1	150
3	165
5	180
10	210
15	240

TABLE XXIV.
PIPE DIMENSIONS FOR, AND CAPACITIES OF, TYPE H (AUTOMATIC) EXHAUST STEAM INJECTORS (MESSRS. DAVIES & METCALFE LTD.).

Size of Injector	Capacity (gallons per hour)		Internal Diameters of Pipes (inches)					
	Max.	Min	Exhaust Steam	Live Steam	Water from Tender	Delivery to Boiler	Over-flow	Connection to Engine Steam Pipe
4	400	210	2	$\frac{3}{4}$	1	1	$1\frac{1}{2}$	$\frac{1}{2}$
5	640	330	$2\frac{1}{4}$	$\frac{3}{4}$	1	1	$1\frac{1}{2}$	$\frac{1}{2}$
6	920	470	$2\frac{1}{2}$	1	$1\frac{1}{4}$	$1\frac{1}{4}$	$1\frac{3}{4}$	$\frac{1}{2}$
7	1250	630	$2\frac{3}{4}$	$1\frac{1}{8}$	$1\frac{1}{4}$	$1\frac{1}{4}$	$1\frac{3}{4}$	$\frac{5}{8}$
8	1600	820	3	$1\frac{1}{4}$	$1\frac{1}{2}$	$1\frac{1}{2}$	2	$\frac{5}{8}$
9	2000	1050	$3\frac{1}{2}$	$1\frac{3}{8}$	$1\frac{3}{4}$	$1\frac{1}{2}$	$2\frac{1}{4}$	$\frac{5}{8}$
10	2500	1300	4	$1\frac{1}{2}$	2	$1\frac{3}{4}$	$2\frac{1}{4}$	$\frac{5}{8}$
11	3000	1600	$4\frac{1}{2}$	$1\frac{3}{4}$	$2\frac{1}{4}$	2	$2\frac{1}{4}$	$\frac{5}{8}$
12	3600	1900	5	$1\frac{7}{8}$	$2\frac{1}{2}$	2	$2\frac{3}{4}$	$\frac{5}{8}$
13	4100	2200	5	2	$2\frac{1}{2}$	$2\frac{1}{4}$	$2\frac{3}{4}$	$\frac{3}{4}$
14	4800	2500	$5\frac{1}{2}$	2	$2\frac{3}{4}$	$2\frac{1}{2}$	3	$\frac{3}{4}$
15	5500	2800	6	$2\frac{1}{8}$	3	$2\frac{3}{4}$	$3\frac{1}{4}$	$\frac{3}{4}$
16	6300	3300	6	$2\frac{1}{2}$	$3\frac{1}{2}$	3	$3\frac{1}{2}$	$\frac{3}{4}$

Table XXIV gives the pipe dimensions and capacities of these injectors. For goods and other slow running engines the internal diameters of the exhaust steam pipes should be $\frac{1}{2}''$ larger than those given in this table.

The grease separator should be located at the lowest level of the exhaust steam branch pipe in order to drain off condensate. The exhaust steam pipe which, if of considerable length, should be lagged, must be so arranged as to be free from bends likely to trap water. Joints should be flanged, and not made with unions; the exhaust steam injector is more sensitive to air leaks than are those operated by live steam. Rubber jointing should not be used in any circumstances.

For all injectors the water inlet should be protected with a sieve. Overflow pipes should be of copper, as otherwise they may rust up and impede the flow. The overflow must be so located as to be easily observed by the enginemen, but at the same time shielded from any grit or foreign matter which may be evident when the fire is being cleaned, etc.

Location of Injectors. The best position for the injector is under the footplate; when thus located the following advantages accrue:—

1. The injector does not have to lift the water in addition to forcing it.
2. The injector can always be flooded, and is therefore not liable to overheat; moreover, it is not exposed either to conducted or radiant heat from the boiler.
3. The injector is not secured to the boiler, where it is in a position peculiarly liable to distortion.
4. Water reaches the injector with a maximum head.
5. Injectors are not so liable to damage by enginemen maltreating them in the event of clack valves sticking.
6. Provided that a master water cock be fitted on the tender, and used, there are no traps in which water may either overheat or freeze.
7. Clack valves are more accessible for grinding in.
8. There are no internal delivery pipes with attendant serious disadvantages.

On the other hand, the combination injector on the backplate, or combination steam and delivery valve used in conjunction with a non-lifting injector, only necessitates the cutting of one hole in one of the weakest parts of the boiler. It is sometimes found that the lifting injector is less liable to make up with scale than the underfeed, but internal delivery pipes, which are essential with these instruments, are to be avoided.

Internal delivery pipes are very prone to excessive corrosion and to blockage owing to the rapid rate at which scale deposits therein. If used, they should be as straight as possible and a plug placed in the smokebox tubeplate, opposite the end of the pipe, to facilitate rodding.

Exhaust steam injectors have in some instances been fitted

in the vicinity of the smokebox. Although the lengths of the exhaust steam induction pipe and feed delivery pipes are thus reduced to a minimum, and the effects of premature condensation correspondingly mitigated, it is extremely difficult to observe the overflow in darkness or fog, and at the same time there is considerable risk of the control rods whipping and jamming. The more usual location under the footplate is therefore to be preferred.

Clack Valves. May have a conical seating and straight wings, or flat seating and curved wings; the latter arrangement gives better results as regards freedom from leakage. On some railways a ball valve is preferred.

The provision of a stop valve is to be recommended, as it permits the clack valve to be ground in or cleaned when the boiler is in steam.

The usual lift allowed is $\frac{3}{16}''$ or $\frac{1}{4}''$; it should not in any case exceed $\frac{3}{8}''$.

When used in conjunction with a feed pump, the clack valve should preferably be spring loaded.

Location of Clack Valves. To secure high circulatory efficiency, the clack valves should be placed as far forward on the boiler as possible, care being taken that the curves in the feed delivery pipes are minimised in number, and of generous radii. In some instances the clack valve is " drowned," *i.e.*, on or near the longitudinal centre line of the boiler, and therefore below the working level of the water in the boiler.

A good case may, however, be made out for **top feed** in which the feed is usually arranged to overflow a series of trays, where a large proportion of the solids held in suspension are thrown down, and then, passing through the steam space either in a thin sheet or in the form of a spray, finally reaches the boiler water level at a high temperature.

With this arrangement the path of contact of the feed with the live steam should be as long as possible; the descent through the steam space should preferably be in spray form, with the final delivery to water level in a thin sheet. The clack valves should be located well forward on the boiler. The success of the system depends entirely on the facility and regularity with which the trays may be removed for cleaning, and the most satisfactory arrangement is undoubtedly a supplementary dome with an accessible and easily broken manhole joint. On the other hand, some engineers consider top feed advantageous, even if trays are not fitted, as the scale deposited in the boiler is largely in the form of a fine powder, and therefore easily washed out.

Although this method uses live steam for feed heating, the heat abstracted being equal to that absorbed by the feed, a small fuel economy, of the order of 2%, is nevertheless achieved, due to increased efficiency of heat transference through the tubes and firebox plates; the transference is accelerated with rise of temperature of the water and consequently improves boiler efficiency.

The slight additional work involved in the shed is further justified on grounds of reduced boiler maintenance costs. The L.B.S.C. section of the S.R. found that top feed increased the life of firebox stays by no less than 300%, whilst the quondam G.E.R. obtained an increase of the order of 20% in the mileages run between boiler clearances. Top feed is standard practice on the G.W.R., where it is located in the safety valve seating; the trays are so disposed that the outfall clears the internal steam pipe by a large margin.

Top feed should in any event be so arranged that delivery does not take place near the regulator or internal steam pipe.

Ejector Connections.   The ejector exhaust pipe should be external. An internal pipe involves the cutting of holes in the boiler, an objectionable practice which should be minimised; further, trouble is likely to arise from leakage at the intermediate joint. The external pipe, which should have an internal diameter of $2\frac{1}{4}''$ or $2\frac{3}{8}''$ and a thickness of about 10 W.G., should be arranged with a constant fall towards the smokebox in order to facilitate the drainage of condensate; bends, if unavoidable, must be to as large a radius as can be arranged.

The steam supply to the ejector should be taken directly from the manifold or dome. In some designs it is bye-passed from the injector supply; this practice is not to be encouraged, as it is liable to effect the introduction of water to the ejector.

Liquid Fuel.   The two chief hindrances to the general application of liquid fuel to the locomotive are the high ultimate cost of the fuel, except in those instances where the railway system serves, or is near an oilfield, and the unsuitability of the orthodox locomotive type boiler for the efficient combustion of this type of fuel. Circumstances occasionally demand a temporary conversion to oil burning, and in this case the best possible compromise must be effected.

Considered generally, liquid fuel offers the following advantages over solid fuels:—

(*a*) Appreciably higher calorific value per lb.

(*b*) If the design of the firebox be modified, more complete combustion can be achieved.

(*c*) The fire may be controlled within fine limits; constancy of pressure, elimination of waste and, if traffic exigencies demand it, quick steam raising, are therefore rendered possible.

(*d*) Reduced liability of tubes to leak by reason of frequent opening of firehole door to feed coal.

(*e*) Improved evaporative capacity of boiler. To give an actual example, an engine which averaged an actual evaporation of 6.7 lb. water per lb. coal increased this figure to 9.0 lb. when converted to liquid fuel.

(*f*) In the event of the fire being allowed to die out whilst the engine is in steam, the ease with which it may be rekindled by throwing a piece of burning waste into the firebox.

(*g*) Danger of spark throwing entirely eliminated.

(*h*) Reduced fuel storage space, both at the depôt and on the tender. Considered from the fundamental aspect of bulk, a ton of bituminous coal occupies 43-48 cubic feet, whilst a similar mass of liquid fuel requires 36·3-39·1 cubic feet according to the specific gravity, which ranges from 0·92 to 0·99 (in round figures, 1 ton of fuel oil is equivalent to 250 gallons). This gives an average reduction of about 17% which, on allowing for the superior calorific value and completeness of combustion of liquid fuel, is substantially enhanced.

(*i*) Eliminated or reduced labour costs of:—

  (1) Unloading and stacking coal and loading on to tender.

  (2) Cleaning and dropping fires.

  (3) Cleaning firegrates, ashpans and smokeboxes.

  (4) Handling of ash and clinker.

(*j*) Reduction in departmental ton-mileage for haulage of fuel.

(*k*)   No deterioration by long periods in storage.

(*l*)   Minimisation of firing labour when running.

On the other hand, the chief disadvantages are:—

(*a*)   As previously mentioned, high prime cost of liquid fuel in countries other than those where it is produced.

(*b*)   Unless the engine is able simultaneously to burn solid fuel, either compressed air or auxiliary steam from an independent source must be provided to enable the burners to function while steam is being raised from cold water.

(*c*)   Increased wear and tear of fireboxes. Few arrangements of firebricking have been devised which will completely nullify the effect on the plates of the intensely hot flames, which are of a distinctly localised nature. In consequence a heavy but unevenly distributed formation of scale may occur on the water side, this leading to an undesirable increase in plate temperature, and therefore leakage. The firebox should in any case be generously lined with refractory material; a further measure sometimes adopted, *viz.*, finishing the fireside heads of firebox rivets flush with the plate, is not to be recommended. The covering of the chimney with a cap, when disposing of engines fitted with liquid fuel apparatus, is beneficial as regards prevention of leakage.

(*d*)   Liability of the burner to stop or to "blow back." May be due to dirt or carbonisation in the oilways, to restricted passages, or to choking of primary air intake by foreign matter.

(*e*)   Deleterious effects of excessive temperature stressing in the boiler components owing to too rapid steam raising ; the ease and rapidity with which pressure may be augmented proves too strong a temptation for enginemen on occasion. There being practically no thermal storage in the firebox when using liquid fuel, the working of stopping trains with this apparatus, with its consequent frequent and wide variations in temperature, entails considerable strain on the tubes and stays, giving rise to leakage. This to a considerable extent counteracts the advantage accruing from keeping the firehole door shut, and is usually aggravated by failure to close the dampers and reduce the atomising steam when the oil supply to the burners is cut down.

(f) Necessity for more frequent cleaning of tubes, tube-plates and crown sheets.

(g) Noise of the burners often subjects the enginemen to considerable personal discomfort.

On the Central Railway of Peru the effects of local heating of the firebox plates and stays are counteracted by coating the plates inside the firebox with asbestos paint.

The flame produced by a liquid fuel burner should be entirely luminous. As complete atomisation of the fuel is essential, the steam used for this purpose should be perfectly dry, and preferably superheated ; the maximum energy per unit of mass is then available and, more important, the quantity of water vapour in the flame is minimised. Atomisation steam may represent from 4% to 6% of the total evaporation : 5% may be taken as a typical figure, although with some burners of improved modern design the consumption of steam may be as low as 2 or 3% of the total evaporation.

The primary air supply, 0·6 to 0·8 lb. per lb. oil fuel, must mingle intimately with the fuel and should therefore be introduced behind and in line with, or concentric with, the burners. To complete combustion, a secondary air supply should be arranged at the sides of the firebox, below the burner centre line. In American practice, a minimum of one square inch of air opening is provided per gallon of oil burnt per hour at the maximum rate of combustion. It should be noted, incidentally, that complete absence of smoke at the chimney denotes excessive air supply. Attention must be given to the arrangement of air intake with regard to the prevention of cold air entering the firebox and encouraging tube leakage and, in this connection, the arrangement of the secondary supply is equally as important as that of the primary intake.

As the flame path exhibits a decided upward tendency on leaving the burner, the burners should not be arranged with an initial upward inclination but horizontally, or even with a slight downward cant, the centre line of the burner, if passing through the water space of the firebox, being not more than 5″ to 6″ above the level of the grate.

The burners must be so located that:—

(a) There is no impedance of the flame by firebrick (or solid fuel, when used conjunctively).

(b) The flame does not strike the side of the firebox, the end of the brick arch or the surface of the grate.

(c) When more than one burner is provided, there is no interference or trespassing of any one flame zone on another.

Where trough type burners are adopted, the oil feed should be above the steam jet. The capacity of "Scarab" type burners, as applied in American practice, is approximately as follows (Proc. I. Loco. E.):—

$$\begin{array}{lll} \text{Up to } 15'' \text{ cylinders,} & 1\tfrac{3}{4}''\text{--}2'' \text{ burners.} \\ \qquad 15''\text{--}20'' & ,, & 2''\text{--}2\tfrac{1}{2}'' & ,, \\ \text{Above } 20'' & ,, & 2\tfrac{1}{2}''\text{--}3\tfrac{1}{4}'' & ,, \end{array}$$

Burners should be attached to the boiler, and not to the engine frames, so that the effects of expansion and of the vibratory movement of the boiler relative to the frames do not disturb their alignment. They may be mounted either at the back of the firebox or in the vicinity of the front damper.

Successful working demands thorough preheating of the fuel, which should be supplied to the burners at a temperature of 140°F.–150°F. Preheating may best be effected by two-fold heating "in series":—

(1) By a steam coil of, say, $\tfrac{3}{8}''$ bore pipe, in the tank. To prevent leakage, intermediate internal joints are best welded, although this necessitates cutting to effect removal. The outlet pipe should in any case be extended vertically into the tank for a short distance, thus forming a "dead" space in which water and any foreign matter present in the liquid fuel may accumulate, and be drained off periodically through a cock or plug provided for this purpose, rather than pass through to the burners.

(2) By a contra-flow steam jacket on the pipe line from the tank to the burners. Should be of piping having a diameter twice that of the enclosed oil pipe which, in turn, should be twice that of the pipes to the individual burners. To be efficient, the minimum length of heater should approximate to 4'-0".

A stop valve should be placed on the oil main, immediately contiguous to the tank and of the plug pattern, to permit of rapid operation in emergency. This cock should be either fully open or shut, and not capable of partial throttling, the adjustment of the oil feed being effected at the burners.

For complete combustion liquid fuel requires a relatively long grate and a firebox of considerable volume, which should be so disposed that the transverse section exhibits a decidedly divergent tendency from the brick arch towards the crown sheet. Air tightness of the ashpan is essential.

Where the firebrick on the grate is formed with a vee-shaped flame trough, it should be of such dimensions that the flame jet impinges on the trough sides, so that the heat in the brickwork accelerates gasification and at the same time prevents the direct ingress of cold air (Proc. I. Loco. E.). The flame channel should be narrow and deep (the depth is about 1'-6" in some instances) at the burner end, gradually widening throughout its length to the flash wall. Wood, incidentally, damages firebrick, and its use should therefore be avoided as far as possible for lighting up, etc.

The last essential in the combustion of liquid fuel is that the heat generated shall be available in its entirety for steam raising, *i.e.*, that the gases of combustion shall not leave the chimney at a higher temperature than is dictated by considerations of superheat. To this end the diameter of the blast orifice should be as large as possible. This contention is the direct antithesis of general experience with converted liquid fuel burning engines in this country, where it has been found that free steaming demands a sharp blast. A possible reason which may be advanced to account for this divergence is that existing fireboxes, specifically designed for coal burning, are not to the best advantage of liquid fuel. In consequence, combustion is often inefficient and, to secure the required quantity of steam, the rate of combustion must be increased considerably beyond the appropriate figure.

Partly to support this contention, the results of some trials conducted by the Santa Fé R.R. have been extracted from the Proceedings of the Institution of Locomotive Engineers and embodied in Table XXV.

Deposits of carbonised fuel in the firebox may be due to insufficient capacity of the burners provided, necessitating an uneconomic rate of combustion, or to incomplete atomisation by reason of a wet steam supply thereto. The more likely causes of this trouble are, however, not usually attributable to faulty design but to operating mismanagement, *e.g.*, excessive

TABLE XXV.

RESULTS OF LIQUID FUEL TRIALS ON MAIN LINE LOCOMO-
TIVES, SANTA FE RAILROAD
(Proc. I. Loco. E.).

Run No.	Diameter of blast pipe orifice, inches.	No. of 2″ air openings per side.	Evaporation, lb. water per lb. liquid fuel.	Lb. liquid fuel per 1,000 ton-miles.
1	$5\frac{1}{2}$	0	11·4	179·7
2	$5\frac{7}{8}$	14	12·6	172·7
3	$6\frac{1}{4}$	14	12·4	162·6
4	$6\frac{1}{4}$	18	12·6	159·9
5	$6\frac{3}{8}$	18	11·9	155·8
6	$6\frac{1}{2}$	20	12·9	160·5
7	$6\frac{1}{2}$	24	12·4	153·3
8	$6\frac{1}{2}$	26	13·8	150·8

proportion of oil supplied to burners, fuel overheated (this does not usually occur in a temperate climate), or burners not correctly aligned or otherwise defective.   Misalignment of burners is a frequent source of trouble.

Right-hand versus Left-hand Drive.   The disposition of the boiler mountings, and brake and valve gear controls, determines whether the engine shall be driven from the right-hand or the left-hand side; which to adopt is a debatable point. Unless the grate is very short or, a somewhat rare occurence, the fireman is naturally left handed, the driver tends to obstruct the fireman and at the same time is himself more liable to injury during the act of firing, when he is located on the left-hand side; against this, he is able to manipulate the regulator handle with the right hand.   Left-hand drive has a further advantage as regards the reading of signals placed on the near side of the line (these remarks apply only to the British "rule of the road"), which are then least likely to be obscured by steam from trains passing in the opposite direction; it must, however, be stated in this connection that signal location, followed to a logical conclusion, should invariably be sub-servient to the requirements of the locomotive department. As regards the rapidity with which " right away " signals are accepted from the traffic staff and translated, the side of drive is immaterial in the case of tank engines which do not turn at the conclusion of each trip.   Where main line engines are concerned, unless island platforms are in the majority,

left-hand drive is again at an advantage, but the frequency
of starts from intermediate stations is so reduced that the relative importance of this point is small.   Shunting engines, and
goods engines when engaged in shunting at wayside stations,
are little affected by the side of drive adopted, as the shunter
naturally accommodates himself as far as possible to whichever side the driver may frequent.   From the purely locomotive point of view, right - hand drive is preferable for the
reasons given above.

(b) STEAM USING AUXILIARIES.

Vacuum Ejector. The small ejector of a Gresham and
Craven " Dreadnought " ejector consumes rather less than
300 lb. steam per hour.   400 lb. per hour may be taken as
a representative allowance for the maintenance of the vacuum
brake on an average main-line passenger train in this country.

TABLE XXVI.

STEAM CONSUMPTION OF VACUUM EJECTORS
(GRESHAM & CRAVEN).

Type of Ejector.	Steam Consumption (lb. per hour).			
	15 mm.	20 mm.	2 × 15 mm.	30 mm.
Super Dreadnought	175	—	350	750
Dreadnought	—	300	—	750
Typ: C.	—	350	—	875

Air Brake Pump.   Consumes approximately one-third of
the quantity of steam required by the vacuum ejector for a
given duty.   Deduced from coal consumptions published in
the *Railway Review* of 24 October, 1924, and assuming an
actual evaporation of 7 lb. water per lb. coal, the following
may be taken as the relative steam consumptions of the two
forms of continuous brake:—
        Vacuum brake, 298·0 lb. steam per hour.
        Air brake, 106·9 lb. steam per hour.
Direct - acting pumps driven from the crosshead or other
reciprocating detail are now much used, and effect an economy
in fuel on engines equipped with automatic vacuum brake
apparatus.

Injectors.   The steam consumption of the ordinary live
steam injector approximates to 10%, and that of the exhaust

steam injector to 2½%, of the total boiler evaporation.   In neither case, of course, does this quantity constitute a direct demand on the boiler since, apart from radiation losses, which are very small, the heat represented is returned to the boiler in the form of feed at an enhanced temperature.

Feed Pump.   Steam consumption is of the order of 2% of the total boiler evaporation.   When used in conjunction with a heater, as is general in modern practice, arrangements are usually made for the return of the heat in the pump exhaust steam to the boiler feed.   The last sentence in the preceding section on injectors therefore applies in this case also.

Train Heating.   Steam consumption cannot be computed with any satisfactory degree of accuracy, owing to the presence of a large number of variable factors, *e.g.*, length of train, speed, difference between atmospheric and internal temperatures, thickness and efficiency of insulation, type of heater employed, and efficiency of drip traps.

From published results of trials conducted on the S.R. with engine No. 453 *King Arthur*, hauling loads of twelve bogie coaches, the average effect of steam heating the latter was to increase the coal consumption by 4·25 lb. per engine mile.   The average evaporation during the trips in question was 6·83 lb. water per lb. coal.   Assuming an average running speed of 55 miles per hour, the consumption of steam for heating a train of twelve coaches is very nearly 1,600 lb. per hour.

The latter figure is supported by allowances of 750–800 lb. per hour made on the L.M.S.R. for trial trains of about one-half the length of the above.

Tube Cleaner.   A steam operated tube cleaner mounted on the locomotive consumes approximately 50 lb. steam per minute.   The "Diamond" soot blower requires a bush through the outer and inner fireboxes having an external diameter of about 4″.

Booster.   Tables XXVII and XXVIII give the steam consumptions of boosters with long and short cut-offs, *i.e.*, 75% and 50% respectively.

The steam consumptions for wheel diameters in inches, pressures in lb. per square inch gauge and Fahrenheit degrees of superheat, other than those given in these tables, may be obtained by deduction.

Tables XXIX and XXX set forth, for long and short cut-offs respectively, coefficients with which the drawbar pulls, exerted at various speeds with varying diameters of wheel, may be obtained.

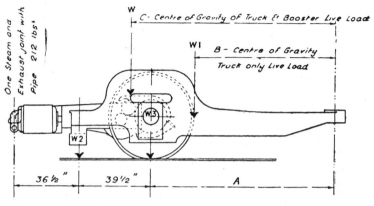

WEIGHT OF BOOSTER EQUIPMENT

Booster Engine ....5990 lbs
    "   Axle gear................... 342 „
    "   Throttle box .... 250 „
    "   Inlet joints ...(3).......... 224 „
    "   Exhaust joints .. (3)...... 272 „
    "   Misc valves.............. 41
                  Total .... 7119 „
    " Pipes and Conn average 1450 lbs

TRAILING WHEEL DEADWEIGHT

9" x 14" axle solid .... 1924 lbs
2 45" wheels ....3200 „
2 Boxes ....1300 „
2 Springs........................ 1000 „
Booster .... 479 „
  "   Axle gear .... 342 „
                Total....8245 „

A	B	C	W	W.I.	W2	W3 Dead wt
93"	78 "	103½	12240	6515	5723	479
100"	82½"	109"	12325	6600	5723	479
110"	89·7"	117 "	12575	6850	5723	479

Weights given in table are for Live Loads of Truck complete including Equalizers Hangers and Pedestal Binders

FIG. 10. WEIGHT DISTRIBUTION DIAGRAM FOR TYPE C2 BOOSTER.

Fig. 10 is a weight distribution diagram for a type C 2 booster.

The author is indebted to Messrs. J. Stone & Co. Ltd. for the foregoing information on boosters. The most recent development in design is the reversible booster which, apart from the interpolation of an additional gear wheel with its control and a drive to a four-wheels coupled bogie, is practically identical mechanically with the original types ; it has been designed chiefly for use on shunting engines and is of especial advantage to those working in hump sidings.

TABLE XXVII.

STEAM CONSUMPTION OF STANDARD LONG (75%) CUT-OFF BOOSTER, 36-INCH WHEEL, LB. PER HOUR.

Pressure, lb. per square inch	..	180	190	200	210	220	230	240	250
Superheat, Fahrenheit	..	100°	100°	100°	100°	100°	100°	100°	100°
Speed, miles per hour — 5		5,350	5,750	6,150	6,450	6,750	7,050	7,300	7,500
7		7,100	7,550	7,930	8,350	8,750	9,150	9,550	10,000
9		8,550	9,050	9,500	9,950	10,400	10,850	11,400	11,900
11		9,750	10,250	10,750	11,300	11,800	12,350	12,900	13,400
13		10,600	11,200	11,800	12,400	13,000	13,500	14,100	14,650
15		11,200	11,950	12,600	13,250	13,800	14,400	15,000	15,700

TABLE XXVIII.

STEAM CONSUMPTION OF STANDARD SHORT (50%) CUT-OFF BOOSTER, 36-INCH WHEEL, LB. PER HOUR.

Pressure, lb. per square inch	..	180	190	200	210	220	230	240	250
Superheat, Fahrenheit	..	100°	100°	100°	100°	100°	100°	100°	100°
Speed, miles per hour — 5		4,300	4,600	4,900	5,150	5,400	5,600	5,800	6,000
7		5,700	6,050	6,350	6,650	7,000	7,350	7,650	8,000
9		6,850	7,200	7,560	7,950	8,300	8,700	9,100	9,500
11		7,800	8,200	8,650	9,000	9,400	9,850	10,300	10,700
13		8,500	8,950	9,400	9,950	10,400	10,800	11,300	11,700
15		8,950	9,600	10,100	10,550	11,000	11,500	12,000	12,500

TABLE XXIX.

STANDARD LONG (75%) CUT-OFF BOOSTER. GEAR RATIO, 2.57:1. DRAWBAR PULL TABLE FOR 100 LB. PER SQUARE INCH BOILER PRESSURE.

M.P.H.	Diameter of Booster Driving Wheel.																		
	36in.	37in.	38in.	39in.	40in.	41in.	42in.	43in.	44in.	45in.	46in.	47in.	48in.	49in.	50in.	51in.	52in.	53in.	54in.
0 ..	6,880	6,690	6,510	6,350	6,190	6,040	5,890	5,760	5,630	5,500	5,380	5,270	5,160	5,050	4,950	4,850	4,760	4,670	4,580
5 ..	5,160	5,060	4,970	4,880	4,790	4,710	4,630	4,550	4,470	4,400	4,330	4,260	4,190	4,120	4,060	3,990	3,930	3,870	3,810
7 ..	4,480	4,410	4,350	4,290	4,230	4,170	4,110	4,050	4,000	3,950	3,900	3,850	3,800	3,750	3,700	3,650	3,600	3,560	3,520
9 ..	3,970	3,920	3,870	3,820	3,770	3,720	3,670	3,620	3,570	3,530	3,490	3,450	3,410	3,370	3,330	3,290	3,260	3,230	3,200
11 ..	3,560	3,520	3,480	3,440	3,400	3,360	3,320	3,280	3,240	3,200	3,160	3,130	3,100	3,070	3,040	3,010	2,980	2,950	2,920
13 ..	3,160	3,140	3,120	3,100	3,080	3,060	3,030	3,000	2,970	2,940	2,910	2,880	2,850	2,820	2,790	2,770	2,750	2,730	2,710
15 ..	2,770	2,770	2,770	2,770	2,760	2,750	2,740	2,720	2,700	2,680	2,660	2,640	2,620	2,600	2,580	2,560	2,540	2,520	2,500
17 ..	2,410	2,410	2,420	2,430	2,440	2,440	2,440	2,440	2,430	2,420	2,410	2,400	2,390	2,380	2,370	2,360	2,350	2,340	2,330
19 ..						2,150	2,160	2,170	2,180	2,180	2,180	2,180	2,180	2,180	2,180	2,180	2,170	2,160	2,150
21 ..											1,940	1,960	1,960	1,970	1,980	1,980	1,980	1,980	1,980
23 ..															1,780	1,790	1,790	1,790	1,790
25 ..																			1,630

Remarks. Booster drawbar pull at start $= \dfrac{2475 \times \text{boiler pressure (lb. per square inch)}}{\text{diameter of wheel (inches)}}$

Example. Required to find booster drawbar pull at 5 miles per hour for a 43-in. wheel and 200 lb. per square inch boiler pressure.

Solution:—D.B.P. $= 4550 \times 2 = 9,100$ lb.

TABLE XXX.

STANDARD SHORT (50%) CUT-OFF BOOSTER. GEAR RATIO, 2.57:1. DRAWBAR PULL TABLE FOR 100 LB. PER SQUARE INCH BOILER PRESSURE.

M.P.H.	Diameter of Booster Driving Wheel.																		
	36in.	37in.	38in.	39in.	40in.	41in.	42in.	43in.	44in.	45in.	46in.	47in.	48in.	49in.	50in.	51in.	52in.	53in.	54in.
0 ..	6,250	6,080	5,920	5,770	5,630	5,490	5,360	5,230	5,110	5,000	4,890	4,790	4,690	4,690	4,500	4,410	4,330	4,250	4,170
5 ..	4,690	4,600	4,520	4,440	4,360	4,280	4,210	4,140	4,070	4,000	3,940	3,880	3,820	3,760	3,700	3,640	3,550	3,520	3,470
7 ..	4,080	4,020	3,960	3,910	3,850	3,790	3,740	3,690	3,640	3,590	3,550	3,500	3,460	3,410	3,370	3,320	3,280	3,240	3,200
9 ..	3,610	3,570	3,520	3,480	3,330	3,390	3,340	3,290	3,250	3,210	3,170	3,140	3,100	3,070	3,030	3,000	2,970	2,940	2,910
11 ..	3,260	3,220	3,180	3,140	3,100	3,070	3,030	2,990	2,050	2,920	2,880	2,850	2,820	2,790	2,760	2,740	2,720	2,690	2,560
13 ..	2,920	2,900	2,850	2,860	2,840	2,810	2,780	2,750	2,720	2,690	2,660	2,630	2,600	2,570	2,550	2,530	2,610	2,490	2,470
15 ..	2,580	2,580	2,570	2,570	2,560	2,540	2,520	2,500	2,480	2,460	2,440	2,420	2,400	2,380	2,360	2,340	2,320	2,300	2,280
17 ..	2,260	2,260	2,270	2,270	2,280	2,280	2,270	2,270	2,260	2,250	2,240	2,220	2,200	2,190	2,180	2,170	2,160	2,160	2,140
19 ..						2,020	2,030	2,040	2,040	2,030	2,030	2,030	2,030	2,020	2,020	2,020	2,010	2,000	1,990
21 ..											1,830	1,830	1,840	1,840	1,840	1,840	1,840	1,840	1,840
23 ..															1,670	1,670	1,670	1,670	1,670
25 ..																			1,530

Remarks. Booster drawbar pull at start = $\dfrac{2250 \times \text{boiler pressure (lb. per square inch)}}{\text{diameter of wheel (inches)}}$

Example. Required to find booster drawbar pull at **5** miles per hour for a **43**-in. wheel and **200** lb. per square inch boiler pressure.

Solution:—D.B.P. = 4,140 × 2 = 8,280 lb.

Turbo Generator for Electric Light. The turbo generators manufactured by Messrs. J. Stone and Company, Limited, Deptford, for locomotive purposes are made in two sizes, of 350 and 500 watts capacity respectively, wound either for 24 or 32 volts.

They are designed to work within the pressure range of 100 and 250 lb. per square inch and, although it is preferable that the turbine should be supplied with saturated steam where possible, it can be operated satisfactorily with superheated steam, provided that a total temperature of 550°F. be not exceeded.

The leading particulars of the 500 watt turbo generator are as follows:—

Approximate length	$1'-9\frac{1}{2}''$
Width	$1'-1\frac{5}{16}''$
Height	$10\frac{5}{8}''$
Weight	149 lb.
Capacity	500 watts.
Voltage	24 or 32
Diameter of steam pipe	$\frac{1}{2}''$
Diameter of exhaust pipe	$1\frac{1}{2}''$

The unit, which is secured by three bolts, can be mounted in any convenient position on the locomotive, the two customary positions being transversely over the boiler, either behind the chimney or ahead of the firebox. Where possible, the exhaust pipe should be so arranged that the turbine exhausts into the smokebox, but in cases where this cannot be done and where the turbine is mounted in front of the firebox, the exhaust pipe should be of sufficient length to ensure that the exhaust steam discharges over the cab roof.

A drain pipe, having a diameter of $\frac{3}{8}''$ and arranged to discharge at a suitable point, should be connected to the drain hole provided in the turbine casing; this drain must always be open to atmosphere.

Table XXXI gives the approximate steam consumption at various loads.

These figures relate to the most recent type of TGF generator and, naturally, steam consumptions are materially improved at working pressures higher than that quoted in the table.

Mechanical Stoker. The steam consumption is from 0·8% to 1% of the total evaporation, varying according to the rate of firing. The engine speed of the stoker may be varied to fire from 100 to 20,000 lb. per hour. The stoker is capable

Output, watts.	Approximate Steam Consumption, lb. per hour, at working pressure of 120 lb. per square inch.
	TABLE XXXI. APPROXIMATE STEAM CONSUMPTION OF STONE'S TURBO GENERATORS.
100	61
200	72
300	83
400	94
500	105

of handling inferior fuel such as lignite, having a calorific value of only 7,500 B.Th.U. per lb. and a moisture content of from 29% to 36%; the maximum size of a lump of coal which the du Pont-Simplex Type B stoker can handle is a 20 inch cube.

This latter type of stoker distributes the fuel from a point below the level of the firehole door (which is kept closed whilst the engine is running), and thus eliminates the use of vertical conveyors. The two-cylinder driving engine, which requires a clearance space approximately 3'-5" long, 1'-11" wide, and 1'-1" high, weighs 4,121 lb. This engine is usually placed on the locomotive, but in those instances where, owing to the use of a booster or for other reasons, the load on the trailing axle closely approaches the permissible limit, the stoker engine may be located with equal facility in the tender. By so doing, the weight of the stoker apparatus on the locomotive is reduced to approximately 2,000 lb. and, further, there is no undesirable concentration of weight on the leading tender wheels, since the weight of the stoker engine nearly equals that of the water it displaces. By leading the stoker engine exhaust to the tender, it has been found that there is an increase in feed temperature of the order of 13°F. which, besides being advantageous, is insufficient to affect the working of a live steam injector.

The BK type stoker, also manufactured by the Standard Stoker Company of New York, has been designed especially for application to existing manually-fired locomotives, and has a working range of from 1,000 to 25,000 lb. fuel per hour. The total weight of the apparatus in this case is 5,334 lb. Since the stoker engine is identical with that used for the type

B equipment, its removal to the tender reduces the weight of the apparatus on the engine to 1,213 lb.

The principal factor influencing the fitting of a mechanical stoker is not, despite the popular conception, the limiting grate area which can be fired manually, but the extent of the horse power which must be sustained at the drawbar; since, for any engine, the grate area and heating surfaces are quantities fixed by design, it follows that the ultimate criterion is the rate of firing necessary, with a given quality of fuel, to secure the required power output.   Consideration must naturally be given to the physical capacity of the fireman, and it should be noted that the limit is reached comparatively rapidly with high speeds in conjunction with heavy loadings, notably in tropical climates and, also, with inferior grades of fuel.

As the feed of coal to the grate with a mechanical stoker is at all times under the control of the fireman, who is relieved of all heavy manual labour, the rate of firing may be varied as desired.   On the other hand, the normally uniform feed of coal by mechanical means and the accompanying habitual shallowness of the fuel bed on the grate encourage high efficiency as regards firebox conditions.

The stokers previously described are of American origin. A representative type, especially designed to meet colonial conditions, is now manufactured in Great Britain by the North British Locomotive Co. Ltd. in collaboration with Messrs. Whitelegg & Rogers.

Chapter VII.

SUPERHEATERS AND FEED WATER HEATERS.

(a) SUPERHEATING.

Advantages of Superheating.

1. When steam is superheated to a final temperature of 650°-700°F., economies of 15 to 25% in fuel and 25 to 35% in water are attainable. With 300°F. superheat, the water and coal consumptions may be as low as 16 lb. and 1·8 lb. per I.H.P.-hour respectively. In general, the steam economy is roughly proportional to the relative specific volumes of saturated and superheated steam at the pressure of generation (Grime, Proc. I. Loco. E.).

2. As a corollary to 1, the operating range of any given engine is increased ; this is of especial benefit to tank engines and to all engines working in areas where fuel is expensive or water scarce. The proportion of time spent in taking water and fuel, or alternatively, the frequency with which these operations are necessary, is therefore reduced.

3. Although the maintenance of the superheater itself is an additional charge, boiler repairs are reduced in cost, especially as regards the firebox, owing to the smaller steam demand and lower rate of combustion for given work.

4. Engines which are under-boilered may have their lives and availability extended by the addition of a superheater.

5. For a given tractive effort, the cylinders may be increased in diameter and the boiler pressure correspondingly reduced. This procedure is, however, open to objection in that the installation of a superheater, as mentioned in Chapter II, slightly increases the pressure drop between boiler and cylinders, and is therefore not usually followed in modern practice.

6. Where the final temperature of the superheated steam does not exceed about 550°F., or alternatively, with a degree of superheat of 200°F., existing flat valves and packings may be retained, provided that the valves are of bronze, efficiently lubricated and, preferably, balanced. The substitution of cast iron or, as is more general, steel, for copper piping is, however, essential. When the final steam temperature exceeds 550°F., cast iron or special alloy packings, in conjunction with poppet or piston valves are then necessary; special attention must also be given to lubrication.

7. Thermal losses by condensation are reduced or entirely eliminated, according to the degree of superheat provided.

Definitions of Degree of Superheat.

There is an unfortunate lack of uniformity in the practical application of the descriptions given to steam in its various states. The acceptance of the following is, however, fairly general:—

Any apparatus giving a superheat of 10–20°F. is termed *a steam drier*.

A *low degree superheater* is one giving a superheat of 50°–100°F.; 100°–200°F. constitutes *moderate superheat*, and *high degree superheat* is that in excess of 200°F.

Form of Superheating Apparatus.

All observations on superheating made herein apply only to the fire- or smoke-tube type of apparatus, the application of which to locomotive boilers of orthodox design is now universal. Smokebox superheaters have been tried, but have not proved successful; the degree of superheat obtained was extremely low, and the apparatus was subject to practical difficulties in addition to the objections usually associated with smokebox fittings. Superheaters incorporated with the boiler itself have been installed in the past, but proved to be both costly and inaccessible. The remaining disposition is in the firebox, where the gas temperatures certainly attain their maximum value; no attempt, however, has been made so to locate the superheater, and it is certain that protection of the apparatus from burning would give rise to an almost insuperable difficulty in this case.

Characteristics of Superheated Steam.

Compared with saturated steam, superheated steam:—

1. Possesses a larger volume and greater total heat value per unit of mass.
2. More nearly approaches the condition of a perfect gas. It is therefore more fluid; hence, frictional resistance to flow is reduced and, consequently, a higher flow velocity attained under given conditions.
3. Of itself possesses no lubricating properties whatsoever, and is intensely cutting in action. This explains the necessity for the adoption of cast iron or, preferably, steel for piping, together with the other measures previously mentioned.
4. Does not increase the load starting capacity of any given locomotive, but provides a considerable increase in the power output when running.
5. Gives a more rapidly falling expansion curve on the indicator diagram, but coincidentally the back pressure is reduced, and the compression curve improved, to such an extent that the mean effective pressure is not impaired, and is in fact higher at piston speeds of 1,000 feet per minute and over.
6. Has a lower heat conductivity.
7. Must lose all superheat before condensation can commence.
8. Enables the water to be carried at a lower level in the boiler, as the evaporation is not so rapid and high rates of combustion are unnecessary. Incidentally, this procedure also conduces to a higher dryness fraction, and therefore tends to raise the degree of superheat.

The degree of superheat attained rises as the engine is more heavily worked, and also as the rate of evaporation is increased. The greater economy effected when a superheater engine is working with late cut-offs is due to the fact that there is then less cylinder condensation to be eliminated. Although on the other hand, with early cut-offs, a greater quantity of superheat is extracted from the steam before it is released to exhaust, it must be remembered that there is actually no great thermal loss, if any, should the steam be partially superheated at exhaust, because the increases in specific volume, due to superheating, augment at a far more rapid rate than the corresponding additions to the total heat of the steam (see Table

XXXVI), and cylinder condensation is reduced by the decrease in fluctuation of temperature.

The maximum rate of heat transference for the purpose of superheating occurs when the respective paths of the steam and flue gases are in contra-flow.

A high initial dryness fraction is relatively more important for superheated than for saturated steam, as the additional heat represented by superheat, the extent of which is affected by the value of the dryness fraction, is more efficient and valuable than that added for evaporation.   Further, the presence of excessive moisture in the steam leads, in practice, to internal erosion of the superheater elements, and also, should it be characteristic of the feed, to corrosion.

Proportioning of Superheater Surface.

The chief factors governing the extent of the superheater surface are:—

Available length between tubeplates: determines the length of the elements.

Diameter of the barrel: limits the number of elements which can be fitted.

Diameter of tubing adopted for elements (varies only within narrow limits).

Whether the steam path is two- or four-fold, and whether short return loops are fitted.

It will therefore be seen that the proportioning for any given locomotive is largely determined by purely practical considerations.   In general, to obtain a given degree of superheat, more superheater surface must be provided for engines which normally run with an early cut-off, employ compound expansion, or in which the draught is light by reason of the provision of a relatively large grate area.

In any case, the cross-sectional area available for steam flow through the superheater elements must be larger than that of the main steam pipe, not only by an amount to allow for the volumetric increase, but also by an additional increment to allow for the effects of flow friction.   Where a represents the cross-sectional area of the main steam pipe, that through the superheater elements is usually $1 \cdot 1 \, a$, and may be equivalent to $1 \cdot 5 \, a$ for high degree superheat.

Allowance must also be made for the fitting of exhaust steam injectors and other feed-water heaters which reclaim heat from the exhaust; such apparatus lowers the degree of superheat by at least 30°F., owing to the reduced draught on the fire and to the lower rate of firing required for given work.

On the average, the provision of a superheater reduces the evaporative heating surface of the boiler by some 25-30%, the flues forming about 30-35% of the total tube heating surface.

For examples of proportions adopted in practice, reference may be made to Tables XIII to XVI (ante) inclusive.

Modern practice favours the general adoption of augmented superheater surface for the following reasons:—

(a) The larger firebox volumes now provided conspire with long lap valves to reduce the initial temperature of the gases entering the flues, owing to the relatively light draught created when running.

(b) Reduced steam spaces in the boiler, and, more particularly, water areas, result in a lower dryness fraction of the steam. There may be 5% or more moisture present in the steam prior to superheating; from 12° to 17°F. superheat are lost for each 1% moisture initially present in the steam.

(c) The greater the area available for steam flow through the superheater, the lower will be the pressure drop between boiler and cylinders.

(d) The higher the degree of superheat (in conjunction with a high working pressure), the higher will be the m.e.p., power and thermal efficiency of the engine.

Properties and Theory of Superheated Steam.

The total heat of superheated steam is given by

$$H_s = H + s\,(t_s - t_f) \quad \dotfill \quad (113)$$

where H_s = total heat of superheated steam, B.Th.U. per lb.

H = total heat of saturated steam at given generation pressure, B.Th.U. per lb.,

s = specific heat of superheated steam,

t_s = final steam temperature, subsequent to superheating, °F.,

and t_f = temperature of saturated steam at given generation pressure, °F.,

According to Rowlands (Proc. I Loco. E.) the mean specific heat of superheated steam at a pressure of 180 lb. per square inch gauge, between temperature of saturation and any absolute temperature t, is given by

$$s = \left\{ 0.44 + \frac{48}{t - 650} \right\} \quad \text{.......................... (114)}$$

Mr. Rowlands suggests that a representative value of s for average high superheats is 0·54.

An approximate determination of the volume of superheated steam, due to Goudie, is given by

$$V = v (1 + 0.0016 t_s) \quad \text{.............................. (115)}$$

where v = volume of dry saturated steam at pressure of generation, cubic feet per lb.,

      t_s = Fahrenheit degrees of superheat, and

      V = volume of steam subsequent to superheating, cubic feet per lb.

TABLE XXXII.

MEAN SPECIFIC HEAT OF SUPERHEATED STEAM FROM SATURATION TEMPERATURE (KEMPE).

Pressure, lb. per square inch absolute.	Superheat, degrees Fahrenheit.						
	50	100	150	200	250	300	350
20	·503	·500	·497	·495	·494	·492	·491
30	·51	·507	·503	·501	·499	·497	·495
40	·519	·514	·509	·506	·503	·501	·499
50	·525	·519	·515	·511	·508	·505	·502
60	·532	·525	·519	·515	·511	·508	·505
70	·537	·529	·524	·519	·515	·512	·509
80	·542	·534	·528	·523	·519	·515	·512
90	·547	·538	·532	·527	·522	·518	·515
100	·549	·542	·535	·530	·525	·521	·517
120	·560	·551	·543	·536	·531	·526	·522
140	·568	·558	·549	·542	·537	·531	·527
160	·575	·565	·555	·548	·542	·536	·531
180	·580	·570	·561	·553	·546	·540	·535
200	·587	·577	·566	·558	·551	·545	540
250	·604	·591	·579	·570	·562	·555	·550
300	·618	·603	·591	·581	·572	·563	·556

Another formula, in metric and Centigrade units, is that of Zeuner, as corrected by le Beau:—

$$V = C_m (v + 100) \left(\frac{t_1 - t_2}{P} \right) \quad \text{...................... (116)}$$

where V = specific volume of superheated steam,

      v = specific volume of saturated steam,

     C_m = mean specific heat of superheated steam,

P = absolute pressure, kilogrammes per square centimetre,

t_1 = temperature of superheated steam, degrees Centigrade,

and t_2 = temperature of saturated steam, degrees Centigrade.

Table XXXIII shews the extent of initial condensation present at various cut-offs, together with the degree of superheat necessary to eliminate it, and has been prepared from curves accompanying a paper read before the Institution of Locomotive Engineers by Mr. Geer (see Proceedings, 1927).

TABLE XXXIII.

SUPERHEAT NECESSARY TO ELIMINATE INITIAL CONDENSATION IN CYLINDERS.

Cut-off, percentage of stroke.	Initial Condensation, %	Superheat required to eliminate initial condensation, degrees Fahrenheit.
10	42·7	254·3
20	28·66	189·5
30	21·33	147·2
40	16·0	114·3
50	12·93	85·2

It will be observed that a minimum of 200°F. superheat is required to overcome condensation under normal working conditions. This table demonstrates the necessity for high degree superheat with engines intended to run with early cut-offs.

The effects of superheat present in the exhaust are shewn by Table XXXIV (Geer, Proc. I. Loco. E., 1927), which is based on the assumptions that an engine is working at a boiler pressure of 200 lb. per square inch and running with 35% cut-off at a piston speed of 900 ft. per minute. According to this tabulated example, although the extent of superheat in the exhaust increases with that provided initially, the ultimate heat loss is less as the exhaust temperatures rise; the reasons for this apparent paradox were given earlier in this chapter. It must, however, be realised that the fundamental laws governing the efficiency of any heat engine cannot be disregarded and, beyond a certain defined limit, any further rise in the temperature at which the steam is exhausted is not conducive to increased thermal efficiency.

TABLE XXXIV.

EFFECTS OF SUPERHEAT PRESENT IN EXHAUST STEAM.

Superheat, degrees F.		Steam Consumption, lb. per I.H.P.-hour.	Total heat in steam, B.Th.U.				Reduction of total heat in steam, %	Total heat used during stroke, %	Total heat exhausted, %
In Steam chest	In Exhaust		Steam chest.		Exhaust.				
			Per lb.	Per I.H.P.-hr.	Per lb.	Per I.H.P.-hr.			
175	Nil	19·6	1,297	25,421	1,156	22,658	Datum	10·87	89·13
200	10	18·5	1,310	24,235	1,161	21,478	4·67	11·37	88·63
225	21	17·65	1,322	23,333	1,166	20,580	8·21	11·80	88·20
250	34	16·95	1,334	22,611	1,172	19,865	11·05	12·14	87·86
275	50	16·4	1,347	22,091	1,180	19,352	13·10	12·40	87·60
300	68	16·0	1,359	21,744	1,188	19,008	14·46	12·58	87·42

TABLE XXXV.

REDUCTION IN SUPERHEAT DUE TO PRESENCE OF INITIAL
MOISTURE IN STEAM.

(Geer, Proc. I. Loco. E., 1927).

Initial Moisture in Steam, %	Superheat, degrees F.	Steam, lb per I.H.P.-hour.	Total B Th.U. in steam per I.H.P.-hour.	Increase in Total Heat used per I.H.P.-hour, %
1	300	16·0	21,744	Datum
2	288	16·2	21,902	0·73
3	275	16·4	22,091	1·60
4	261	16·7	22,294	2·53
5	246	17·05	22,793	4·83
6	231	17·4	23,038	5·95
7	215	17·95	23,640	8·72
8	199	18·5	24,235	11·45
9	183	19·2	24,979	14·88
10	166	20·0	25,860	18·93

Table XXXV shews the decrease in superheat occurring on account of the presence of initial moisture in the steam. It will be seen that an average of 13·4°F. superheat are lost for each 1% initial moisture present in the steam. Having regard to the fact that the dryness fraction in loco-motive practice may be as low as 0·93, the advisability of taking measures to ensure a supply of dry steam to the super-heater is emphasised.

Table XXXVI shews the comparative volumetric and

TABLE XXXVI

COMPARATIVE INCREASES IN VOLUME AND TOTAL HEAT OF
STEAM DUE TO SUPERHEATING.

Condition of Steam.	Volume, cubic feet per lb.	Total Heat, B.Th.U. per lb.	Increase over saturated steam, %	
			Volume.	Total Heat.
Dry saturated at 250 lb per square inch absolute ‥	1·839	1204·2	—	—
Superheated 100 F. ‥ ‥	2·133	1263·3	15·99	4·91
Superheated 200° F. ‥ ‥	2·427	1318·2	32·00	9·47
Superheated 300° F. ‥ ‥	2·722	1370·7	48·05	13·82

thermal increments respectively attributable to the superheating of steam generated at a pressure of 250 lb. per square inch absolute.

Headers.   Were originally cast in steel, but this material has proved to be somewhat unreliable; cast iron (cylinder mixture) may be used, but increases the weight.   The material used by the Superheater Company is a special close grained cast iron mixture having a high steel content; the ultimate tensile stress is specified to be not less than 28,000 lb. per square inch.

Usually, one header only is fitted and is located transversely across the upper part of the smokebox.   When two are provided, the second casting (for the collection of superheated steam) is placed at a lower level than, and parallel to, the first. Irrespective of the arrangement adopted, the following desiderata apply:—

(1)   The flue tubes should be located in the upper portion of the tube zone, so that the maximum flue gas temperature is available for superheating.

(2)   The saturated steam portion of the header should be isolated, if possible, from that devoted to the collection of the superheated steam.   The construction of the casting is thereby simplified, and the undesirable heat transfer occurring when the saturated and superheated steam compartments adjoin is at the same time eliminated.

Temperature stresses in the material of the header are also reduced.   The outer surfaces of the header, for example, are exposed to gases at a temperature varying from approximately 550°F. to 850°F., according to the vacuum obtaining in the smokebox.   Where alternate compartments are provided in the same header for saturated and superheated steam at temperatures of, say, 380°F. and 750°F. respectively, the corresponding temperature difference across adjacent walls, to which the header material is subjected, has a maximum value under these conditions of 470°F.

Lastly, the provision of an insulating space between common compartments for saturated and superheated steam respectively is also of advantage in that it facilitates the accommodation of the retaining bolts for the element joints, should the superheater be equipped with this type of joint.

(3) The passages and contours of the header casting must be so designed as to ensure an easy, unobstructed flow of steam; sharp corners and pockets cause eddying.

The internal walls of the header, if of ordinary cast iron, should be about $\frac{5}{8}''$ thick, and external walls $\frac{7}{8}''$ thick; the thickness of stiffening webs may be $\frac{3}{4}''$.   Where special mixtures are employed, the usual practice is to adopt a uniform thickness of $\frac{3}{4}''$ for all walls with the exception of that forming the face to which the elements are actually attached; in this case the thickness is generally $1''$.

The headers are usually supported centrally at the boiler main steampipe end and also bracketed at the ends to the smokebox wrapper.   Covered apertures may with advantage be provided in the latter to facilitate access to the header joints.

Elements. Are usually of cold drawn weldless steel tube; the normal internal diameter is either $1\frac{3}{8}''$ or $1\frac{1}{2}''$, with a thickness of 9 W.G.

The material used by the Superheater Company conforms to the following analysis:—

Carbon	...	From	0·08 to 0·15%
Manganese	...	,,	0·30 ,, 0·60%
Silicon	...		Not over 0·03%
Phosphorus	...		,, ,, 0·03%
Sulphur	...		,, ,, 0·03%

The specified ultimate tensile strength is 20–26 tons per square inch with a minimum elongation of 28% in $8''$.

The element usually terminates at a distance of about $1'-8''$ from the fireside of the tubeplate; this dimension may be reduced to a minimum of $12''$ in favourable circumstances, but should be at least $2'-0''$ in the case of engines burning liquid fuel.   With boilers of average dimensions the element return bend at the smokebox end extends into the smokebox itself, as the minimum prevailing gas temperature is sufficiently high to benefit the superheat.   When, however, the length between tubeplates exceeds approximately $18'-0''$, the final temperature of the superheated steam in the element may exceed that of the surrounding gases.   To prevent this condition arising the length of the return loop is considerably reduced, in some cases by 50%, without sacrifice of superheat transfer efficiency; reductions in cost and weight are also thereby effected.

Element Return Bends must:—

(1) Be capable of withstanding the high temperature and velocity of the furnace gases.

(2) Be so formed that they obstruct the flow of gas over their exterior surface, and of steam by the interior surface, to the minimum extent. They must therefore be free from sharp corners and pockets where the steam flow may be disturbed or become sluggish.

(3) Be so proportioned that the area available for steam flow is greater than that of the element, in order to minimise eddying with consequent reductions in velocity and pressure.

(4) Be of sufficient thickness to prevent deformation or collapse when heated to a dull red and then subjected to boiler pressure, with a further allowance for the erosive and corrosive action of the furnace gases to which they are subjected externally.

The various methods of forming and attaching the return bends to the elements are:—

Malleable or cast steel return bends screwed on to the element tubing. Difficulty is experienced in keeping the screwed joints steam-tight, leakage being aggravated by vibration, expansion and contraction, and corrosion. The gas flow area is also restricted to an undesirable extent; two return bends of this type occupy 57% of the cross sectional area of the flue. This compares with 42% occupied by the equivalent integral machine forged end; the four element sections themselves occupy 31% of the flue area.

In some cases the joint is effected by welding, either alone or in addition to the screwed joint. Unless carefully carried out, however, welding may affect the structure of the material locally, with the result that rapid corrosion occurs; the welding metal itself is liable rapidly to oxidise. Any weld for the firebox end return bend joints should be at least 12″ from the extremity of the element; even so, trouble has been experienced, and it has been suggested (Falconer, Proc. I. Loco. E.) that this dimension should be increased to 3′-6″.

By bending and welding element ends together, and building up tip with deposited metal. Care and experience are necessary for this procedure to be successful. In addition to the possible local affection of the material by welding, previously mentioned, this method suffers from the following disadvantages:—

(1) It is impossible to guarantee correctness of external section or of internal area of the end.

(2) Inner surfaces may be left uneven, owing to the percolation of welding metal.

(3) The reinforcing metal is rapidly attacked by heat and corrosion, especially if its external surface is left rough or it is not properly integrated with the surface of the elements.

By butt welding a forged cap to the element ends. Here again the possibility of the formation of an internal fin arises.

The "M.L.S" machine forged return bend, in which the end is forged integrally with the elements (this is a patented process carried out by the Superheater Company Ltd.) is designed to overcome the above disadvantages and at the same time to fulfil the stipulations postulated at the commencement of this section.

The return bend of itself exerts a beneficial influence on the efficiency of the superheater as a whole, in that the sudden change in direction which the steam is forced to take tends to break up the central core of steam; this core entrains a moisture content which is otherwise difficult to eliminate.

Element Joints. The superheater element is virtually a cantilever supported at the header; its own weight and that of the contained steam form the relatively small static loading, to which must be added the dynamic load, considerably greater in extent but indeterminate, due to the vibration and springing of the element when the engine is running. The joint of the element with the header must therefore be sufficiently flexible to satisfy these latter conditions, and at the same time possess the rigidity dictated by the maintenance of steam-tightness.

Element joints may be broadly divided into two categories, *viz.:*—

(*a*) The simple expanded joint of the Robinson type.

(*b*) The various forms of flanged joints retained by bolts.

The effectiveness of the latter type of joint depends entirely upon the capability of the bolts as regards resistance to stretching ; the Superheater Company therefore specify for their bolt steel a minimum ultimate tensile strength of 50 tons

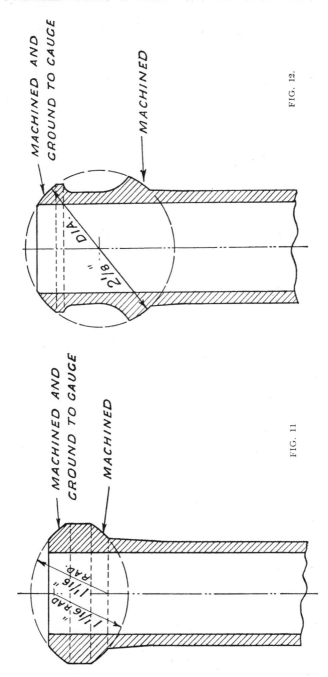

FIG. 12.

MACHINED AND GROUND TO GAUGE

MACHINED

2'⅛" DIA.

FIG. 11

MACHINED AND GROUND TO GAUGE

MACHINED

1 1/16" RAD.

1 1/16" RAD.

per square inch, with a yield point at not less than 35 tons per square inch and a minimum elongation of 16% in 2". The bolts are usually 1" in diameter, and each supports one element.

The steel for the nuts must be of the same strength as that for the bolts, up to its yield point. The nuts, incidentally, should preferably be located above the header; they are then more accessible and, at the same time, more protected from the direct action of hot gases. Two nuts should be used per bolt; the second nut not only serves as a lock but also pro-

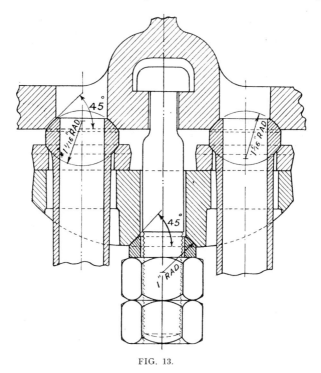

FIG. 13.

tects the threads on the bolt, the length of which should be such that the end does not protrude beyond the face of the second nut, but terminates a short distance within it.

The "M.L.S." ball joint, manufactured by the Superheater Company Ltd., affords a metal-to-metal connection without the interposition of any jointing material. The element ends are jumped up in a forging machine, machined, and the spherical

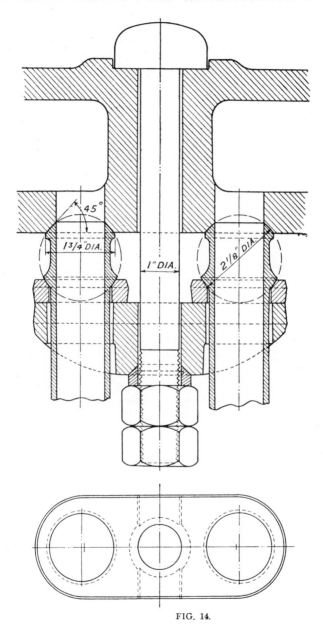

FIG. 14.

surfaces at the extreme ends, which form the steam-tight joints, are finally ground to a radius of 1⅛". The two types of end manufactured on this principle, and known as the "short" and "long" ball respectively, are shewn by Figs. 11 and 12. Figs. 13 and 14 shew them in position on headers. The clamps and also the washers on which the ball ends seat are drop forgings; the bevel-seated washers for the nuts are of mild steel.

A plain copper ring joint is used on the G.W.R. in conjunction with the "Swindon" superheater, and has given satisfactory results in service.

Maintenance of Element Location relative to the Flue.

Measures must be taken to maintain the elements centrally in the flue, in order that heat transference may occur in the central core of the gases and therefore be at a maximum, to obviate distortion of the elements in service and bending in handling, to prevent actual contact with the flue surface (this causes heat loss), and also as far as possible to relieve the element joints of the effects of vibration. *Supports* and *bands* are used to preserve the desired position of the elements in the flues.

Care must be taken that the bearing surfaces of the supports are sufficient in area, and free from sharp corners, in order to prevent pitting and grooving of the flues, and that the material comprising the bands is sufficiently substantial to withstand working conditions and the action of the gases.

The supports standardised by the Superheater Company Ltd. have each two bearing feet, of strip steel 2" in length and ⅞" wide, riveted thereto; the material for the support itself, as for the bands, has a thickness of 14 W.G.

The usual allocation of supports and bands is as follows:—

Length of element, up to 11'-6": one support about 2'-6" from the firebox end, and one band about 1'-10" from smokebox end.

Length of element, up to 18'-0"; two supports and one band.

Length of element, over 18'-0": three supports and one band.

Apart from their purely mechanical functions, the supports and bands assist the transference of heat to the steam under superheat by retarding locally the flow of the flue gases.

Protective Measures to prevent Burning of Elements.

The most effective procedure is undoubtedly to place the

regulator between the superheater and the cylinders (as discussed at some length in Chapter VI), so that the elements are continuously filled with steam.   Alternatively, draught retarders, which operate automatically when the blower is applied, or circulating steam, which is controlled in a similar manner by the movement of the regulator, may be provided; the latter system is at a disadvantage in that steam may accumulate in sufficient quantities to start the engine unless a header discharge valve is provided.

The damper system originally installed has been discarded for three reasons.   When the regulator was shut:—

1. The heating surface of the flues was not available for evaporation.

2. The elements were not maintained at a temperature favourable to the rapid attainment of a high superheat on reopening the regulator, and

3. The ensuing deposit of ash caused pitting and corrosion of the elements.

With the regulator in the conventional position, *i.e.*, on the boiler side of the superheater, anti-vacuum valves on the saturated steam side of the header exercise a very beneficial influence as regards prevention of element burning.

Weight of Superheating Apparatus.

As a typical example, an engine having a 24-element superheater and a length between tubeplates of 13′-0″ is taken:—

Weight of header casting	0·3 ton
,, elements	1·0 ,,
Total	1·3 ,,
Less weight of water displaced by the apparatus, as compared with a saturated steam engine	0·5 ,,
Nett total	0·8 ton

It may therefore be taken that the addition of a superheater to an engine of average dimensions increases the weight by approximately 1 ton, which is fairly evenly distributed.

Superheat Temperature Recording Instruments.

The fitting of pyrometers and kindred instruments is, in general, not to be recommended. They are inherently too delicate for ordinary locomotive service; the enginemen are apt to rely on them and, when low readings are recorded, are prone to book examinations and repairs to the boiler when, actually, the defect lies in the recording apparatus.

Economic Considerations.

The cost of installing superheating apparatus is less than 5% of the total cost of the locomotive. Upkeep of the superheater itself is equivalent to roughly 10% of the boiler maintenance charges for the equivalent saturated steam engine. These additional charges are more than balanced by the greater loads hauled, economies effected in fuel and water consumptions and reductions in the cost of the maintenance of the boiler itself.

(b) FEED WATER HEATING.

Although, as mentioned in the previous chapter, the live steam injector augments considerably the temperature of the feed, no direct thermal advantage thereby accrues, since the heat taken up by the feed is directly abstracted from the boiler and therefore involves a definite expenditure of fuel.

The universal interpretation of the term "feed water heating" tacitly implies the use of otherwise waste heat for the attainment of increased feed water delivery temperature; in the case of the locomotive there are in practice two possible sources of supply, *viz.*, the exhaust steam and the smokebox gases. In a heat balance drawn up by him some years ago, Professor Dalby estimated that of the total heat, as represented by the coal fired, no less than 59% was lost in the exhaust steam, whilst 36% was discharged in gases of combustion ejected at the chimney. Modern development in design has reduced considerably the actual numerical value of these percentages; nevertheless they will serve as a rough indication of the extent to which the thermal efficiency of the locomotive is capable of improvement by reclamation.

As regards the heat in the smokebox gases, it is not practicable to secure a high fuel economy by its utilisation. Although these gases are at a high temperature, the rate of heat transference from them to the feed water is not rapid ; a large extent of heating surface is therefore required, but is rendered impossible by loading gauge and other restrictions. The apparatus is also disproportionately heavy, since the thickness of the tubes and other details is dictated by the ability continu-

ously to withstand abrasive and corrosive action rather than
the pressure to which they are subjected. Further, any apparatus installed in the smokebox, apart from that which is
essential, is objectionable in that charges for its maintenance
are high and the availability of the engine for traffic is
adversely effected.

Due to the limitations mentioned above, heaters of the
smokebox gas type are, in general, only capable of raising
the feed temperature by approximately 70°-80°F., the corresponding fuel economy ranging approximately from 4%
to 6%.

From the foregoing it will be appreciated that the most
profitable source of heat is that in the exhaust steam. Heaters
of this type may follow the principle of either the surface or
the jet condenser. In the former case, the efficiency
falls rapidly with the formation of scale; the deposit of scale,
unless means are provided for its easy removal, is neglected
and eventually causes tube leakage, which in some instances
is further aggravated by mechanical imperfections of the
measures taken for the neutralisation or absorption of movement due to expansion. For this reason, and also due to the
facts that they deliver the feed at higher temperatures, that
these temperatures are not affected by the formation of scale
and that a minimum surface of the apparatus is under pressure, most modern exhaust steam heaters are of the " direct
contact " type, *i.e.*, they conform to the principle of the jet
condenser.

From the point of view of thermal efficiency, the ideal temperature at which the feed is delivered is equal to that of the
exhaust steam.

Advantages of Feed Water Heating, with especial Reference to Apparatus utilising Exhaust Steam.

1. Fuel economy due to higher feed temperature, and to
   greater boiler efficiency resulting from lower rate of combustion and the reduction in unburnt fuel loss by reason
   of lower exhaust pressures.
2. Water economy due to utilisation of condensate from
   exhaust steam. This represents roughly from 12 to
   15% of the total feed and is equivalent in quality
   to distilled water; the mileage run between wash-outs
   may therefore be increased.

3. Reduced boiler maintenance charges due to the deposit of impurities, held in solution in the feed water, in the heater prior to delivery, to the reduced demand on the boiler for given work, and to the reduction in temperature variation. In most designs provision is also made for the liberation, prior to delivery, of the gases contained in the feed, with the result that internal pitting and corrosion of the boiler are diminished in extent.

4. Reduction in weight and first cost of boiler for given duty.

5. Range of operation of tender increased, or conversely, a smaller and less costly tender may be used.

6. Indicated horse power increased on account of reduction in back pressure.

It will be noted that the advantages enumerated above cannot be claimed *in toto* for the feed water heater as some of the items are corollaries and others alternatives. Briefly, the fitting of a feed water heater to an engine leads to the more economical performance of given work, to increased power output for a given fuel consumption, or to a compromise, *i.e.*, a combination of both these characteristics.

A general formula for the determination of the fuel economy due to feed heating (*Locomotive Superheating and Feed Water Heating Supplement*) is given by

$$S = \frac{100\ (t - t_1)}{H + 32 - t_1} \quad \dots\dots\dots\dots\dots\dots\dots\dots\dots \quad (117)$$

where S = percentage fuel saving,

t = final temperature of feed water, degrees F.,

t_1 = initial temperature of feed water, degrees F.,

H = total heat of steam at boiler pressure, B.Th.U. per lb.

According to an old empirical rule, 1% fuel economy is obtained for each increment of 11°F. in the feed water temperature arising from the utilisation of exhaust steam. Actually, a well-designed open heater in good condition will give maximum fuel and water economies of about 15% and 12% respectively when compared with a live steam injector. The fuel economy maintained over a protracted period in normal rostered service, when allowance is made for progressive decline in the condition of both the engine generally and the feet heating apparatus itself, would range from 6% to 12%.

Economies due to Feed Water Heating.   These are amenable to theoretical treatment and, assuming the availability of certain operating data, may easily be calculated.   The method is best demonstrated by concrete examples, as given below. The standard of comparison is the live steam injector.

(a) *Comparison of quantity of heat necessary to generate steam with live steam injector and exhaust steam feed water heater respectively.*

Required to generate 1 lb. steam at a pressure of 180 lb. per square inch, and superheated 250°F., from feed water at initial temperature of 60°F.

Total heat in steam, as specified, above 32°F.	=	1333 B.Th.U.
Deduct heat value of 1 lb. feed water at 60°F.	=	28 B.Th.U.
Then heat required to generate 1 lb. steam	=	1305 B.Th.U.

		Heater.	*Injector.*
Deduction due to delivery at 225°F. (heater)	=	165 B.Th.U.	
Deduction due to delivery at 160°F. (injector)	=		100 B.Th.U.
Hence, nett heat required	=	1140 B.Th.U.	1205 B.Th.U.
Increase by 2% (live steam for pump)	=	23	
Increase by 10% (live steam for injector)	=	——	121
Total heat required	=	1163 B.Th.U.	1326 B.Th.U.
Therefore economy due to heater	=	12.3%	
When pump exhaust steam is returned to feed, deduct 20 B.Th.U. from total heat required	=	1143 B.Th.U.	
Then, economy in heat units to be generated, due to heater	=	13.8%	

The fuel economy actually attained should be more than is indicated here, on account of the improvement occurring in boiler efficiency as the rate of combustion is reduced. Assuming that the mean boiler efficiency is increased from 65% to 68% by the provision of a feed water heater on the engine, and taking as a basis the lower of the calculated economies, *viz.*, 12·3%, then,

The relative consumpton with the heater is

$$\frac{65}{68}\left(\frac{100 - 12\cdot3}{100}\right) = \cdot8382$$

Whence, the corresponding fuel economy is

$$100 - 83\cdot82 = 16\cdot18\%.$$

(*b*) *Quantity of exhaust steam necessary for feed heating.*

With the feed water at an initial temperature of 60°F., and delivery at 225°F., the quantity of heat to be taken up, per lb., = 165 B.Th.U.

Assuming exhaust to occur at a pressure of 20 lb. per square inch absolute, heat value of steam per lb. = 1151 B.Th.U.

Since the quantity of heat in 1 lb. water condensed from exhaust steam at 225°F. = 193 B.Th.U.

Then the heat given up during condensation of the steam = 1151—193 = 958 B.Th.U.

Hence, the proportion of exhaust steam necessary to raise feed temperature from

$$60°F. \text{ to } 225°F. = \left(\frac{165}{958} \times 100\right) = 17\cdot2\%$$

Deduct heat available in feed pump exhaust = 2·0%

Whence, exhaust steam abstracted from locomotive cylinders = 15·2%

But, allowing for return of condensate in feed, the nett quantity of exhaust steam abstracted from the locomotive cylinders

$$= \frac{15\cdot2 (100 - 17\cdot2)}{100} = 12\cdot6\%$$

Theoretically, the demand for exhaust steam from the main cylinders should be somewhat less than the calculated result, because the heat value of the exhaust steam contributed by the feed pump is greater than that from the main cylinders, and not identical, as assumed above.   Actually, up to 15% of the main engine exhaust may be utilised by the heater.

(c) *Water economy due to use of feed water heater.*

Let steam demand for main cylinders	=	100%
Add live steam consumption of feed pump	=	2%

Then gross steam demand	=	102%
Deduct exhaust steam condensed and returned with feed = ($\cdot$172 × 102)	=	17$\cdot$54%

Whence, quantity of feed actually used by locomotive, as compared with live steam injector	=	84$\cdot$46%
Corresponding reduction in water consumption	=	15$\cdot$54%

Since of the 15$\cdot$54% of the feed which may be recovered, 15$\cdot$54% may be saved, it follows that the necessary water capacity of the tank may be reduced by

$$\{ \cdot1554 + (\cdot1554 \times \cdot1554) \} \ i.e., \text{ very nearly } 18\%.$$

Some claims advanced by an American manufacturing firm in their treatise on locomotive feed water heating are interesting, but must be accepted with reserve, as they are based on conditions of operation which are ideal from the point of view of the feed water heating apparatus.   The numerical values given must therefore be substantially reduced to render them applicable to normal service conditions over lengthy periods, and therefore to fundamental considerations of design. Briefly summarised, the advantages claimed are as follows:—

1. Total boiler evaporation increased by 17%.
2. Decrease of 13$\cdot$5% in loaded weight of boiler for given output.
3. First cost less for boiler with feed water heater than for boiler without one, each having the same steam producing capacity.   Further, the smaller boiler with feed water heater burns 15$\cdot$9% less fuel.
4. Overall boiler efficiency increased by from 14% to 24%, varying directly with amount of work done by the engine.

5. Indicated horse power increased 6·4%, due to reduction in back pressure.
6. Tender capacity increased 15% to 22%.
7. Total saving in weight of engine and tender of modern freight locomotive = 40,400 lb. with boilers of equal capacity.
8. Fuel saving of from 15% to 22%.

With reference to claim 1, the *average* equivalent increase in steam production due to the installation of a feed heater of the exhaust steam type approximates to 9% (Sauvage, Proc. I. Mech. E., 1922).

Design Desiderata (All Types of Heater).

1. Increase in feed temperature prior to delivery to be attained by the utilisation of otherwise waste heat.
2. The construction of the heater to be as simple as possible.
3. The space occupied by, and weight of, the apparatus to be as small as possible.
4. The number of moving parts, which are of course the most liable to wear and to failure, to be minimised.
5. The apparatus to be able to deliver a continuous hot feed, which must be capable of fine adjustment. The feed temperature to rise with the pressure of the exhaust steam or temperature of smokebox gases, as the case may be.
6. Means to be provided for the evacuation of gases held in solution in the feed, in order to reduce pitting and grooving of the boiler.
7. The components of the heater to be capable of easy removal, replacement and cleaning (*e.g.*, removal of scale).
8. When exhaust steam is utilised for feed heating, effective measures to be taken for the extraction of lubricating oil.
9. In the case of smokebox gas heaters, interference with the normal flow of the gases to be minimised. The number of joints in the smokebox, liable to be broken, also to be minimised.
10. The feed preferably to be heated subsequent to pumping in order to eliminate scoring of the pump barrel, valve seatings, etc., by scale.

Comparison of Various Forms of Exhaust Steam Heater.

The simplest form of feed water heater is the exhaust steam

injector. The following information applies to the Type H (automatic) injector manufactured by Messrs Davies & Metcalfe Ltd.:—

Maximum feed temperature, 230°F.

Normal feed temperature, 190°F. to 200°F.

Fuel economy, 8% to 12%.

Water economy, due to return of condensate to feed, 10% to 12%.

Utilisation of exhaust steam causes a reduction of approximately 5% in the smokebox vacuum; the effect is, however, negligible in comparison with the increased steam production, and therefore does not involve any alteration in the draught arrangements.

The absolute back pressure is reduced by about 10%.

Live steam consumption, when delivering against pressures above 150 lb. per square inch, $2\frac{1}{2}\%$ of boiler evaporation.

Lower limit of working range, 50% to 60% of maximum capacity.

Exhaust steam injectors in general offer the following advantages over pump-operated heaters:—

1. Lower cost of installation. Assuming the cost of an injector, in position on the locomotive, to be £130, this represents less than 50% of the cost, on a comparable basis, of a pump-driven heater of equivalent capacity.
2. Less complicated and fewer moving parts.
3. Lower weight.
4. Less space occupied.
5. No danger of relatively cold feed being delivered when the regulator is closed.
6. Exhaust steam is utilised for forcing, in addition to heating, the feed.

Further claims advanced for the injector with regard to reductions in maintenance and replacement costs, and facilities with which repairs can be executed when the engine is in steam, are not always realised in practice when the injector is compared with a pump - driven heater which has been carefully designed.

Pump-driven heaters, on the other hand, are superior to exhaust steam injectors as regards:—

1. Higher average feed delivery temperatures attained.
2. Greater fuel economies realised in consequence.

3. Lower consumption of live steam. A pump consumes from 1·5% to 2% of the total boiler evaporation.

4. Greater flexibility and finer adjustment of rate of delivery.

Comparison of Weights of Feed Water Heating Apparatus.

For a boiler having a seating surface of about 1,900 square feet, the approximate weights of feed heaters would be:—

Exhaust steam injector, slightly over ...	0·1 ton
Weir heater (surface type)	0·95 ton
ACFI heater (direct contact type) ...	1·18 tons
Worthington - Simpson heater (direct contact type)	1·5 tons

Feed Pumps.

In order to prevent hammering action by the feed water, and also to increase the life of the valves, the provision of multiple valves having a small lift is preferable to one valve

TABLE XXXVII.

HOURLY DELIVERY OF ACFI FEED WATER PUMPS AND NETT WEIGHT OF APPARATUS.

Pump No.		1	2	3
Diameter of steam cylinder .. inches.		6·29	8·26	10·0
Diameter of water cylinders .. inches.		4·92	6·53	7·99
Piston stroke .. .. .. inches.		9·05	9·05	10·23
Delivery in gallons per hour, for pump speeds (single strokes per minute) of	5 ..	156	277	477
	10 ..	313	555	955
	15 ..	469	832	1,432
	20 ..	626	1,109	1,909
	25 ..	782	1,386	2,386
	30 ..	939	1,663	2,864
	35 ..	1,095	1,941	3,340
	40 ..	1,251	2,219	3,819
	45 ..	1,407	2,496	4,296
Weight of Pump .. .. .. lb.		771	1,091	1,543
Weight of Heater Apparatus .. lb.		812	859	882
Total Weight* .. .. .. lb.		1,583	1 950	2,425

*The weights as given are strictly nett, and exclude that of the piping and of the water contained in the apparatus. Allowances were made for these and included with the weight of 1.18 tons previously quoted for the No. 2 size apparatus.

of large diameter with a comparatively high lift. For the same reason, compound pumps are at an advantage in that they give a very gentle impulse to the water pumped, apart from any consideration of reduced consumption of live steam.

In the case of the ACFI feed pump (simple expansion), which is designed to give a feed flow velocity of about 4·9 feet per second, arrangements are made for a sensible deceleration of the pump at each end of its stroke, the lift of the valves being at the same time severely restricted. Table XXXVII gives the capacities of the various sizes of pump manufactured by this firm.

These heaters give maximum feed temperatures of about 230°F. with simple expansion engines and 280°F. with compounds; in the latter case, the steam used for feed heating is taken from the receiver.

Worthington-Simpson heaters are made in five sizes, having capacities of 2,000, 3,200, 4,425, 6,000, and 8,300 gallons per hour respectively.

In some instances air brake pumps have been modified to serve as feed pumps. A Westinghouse pump with a steam cylinder 8″ in diameter, water cylinder 5½″ in diameter and a common stroke of 10″, will deliver 2,600 gallons of water per hour when making twenty double strokes per minute. The weight of such a pump is about 0.26 ton.

The effect of utilising the exhaust steam from feed pumps for feed heating purposes is to increase the feed temperature by about 20°F.

When the feed pump is driven mechanically, the attachment is preferably made to the engine crosshead or to a return crank specially provided. The use of motion components for this purpose is to be deprecated as additional stresses, the actual magnitude of which is not definitely known, are thereby imposed upon details which, in many instances, are already sufficiently loaded. With the Dabeg apparatus, which is mechanically operated, a three-way regulating cock is so controlled by the reversing rod that, when the engine is working with early cut-offs, excess feed water is returned to the tank or tender.

Chapter VIII.

THE SMOKEBOX, BLAST PIPE AND CHIMNEY.

THAT design of the draught apparatus in the first instance is still largely empirical, and satisfactory results are obtained only by conducting continued experiments of the "trial and error" variety, must be attributed to the large number of variables present in any given design of locomotive.

The strength of blast necessary to ensure free steaming depends on such factors as:—

Grate area, nature of fuel, and normal thickness of firebed on grate.

Total cross sectional (*i.e.*, gas) area and length of tubes: the greater the ratio of tube length to diameter, the greater is the draught necessary to induce gas flow through them.

Cubic capacity of smokebox.

The resistance due to the blast pipe is, of course, zero when the engine is starting, and at a piston speed of 1,300 feet per minute is equivalent to the absorption of 70 horse power (Weatherburn, Pro. I. Loco. E.), the average loss due to this cause being 40 horse power (J. W. Smith, *ibid.*). These latter quotations are not necessarily suitable for general application, and are repeated only as an indication of the quantities involved.

Draught Apparatus : General Stipulations and Data.

(1) The back pressure must be as low as possible for the generation of the given quantity of steam.

(2) There must be no abrupt change either of form or in direction of the exhaust steam passages, which must be as direct and free from bends as possible. The reduction in area between the exhaust openings or ports in the cylinders and the blast orifice must therefore be gradual and easy throughout.

(3) The combining point of the exhausts from the individual cylinders must be as low as possible, consistent with (2), and the angle of convergence as small as possible.

(4) The combining point must be vertically below the centre

of the blast orifice in order to provide a guiding effect. The latter is essential to ensure the coincidence of the centre line of the jet with that of the chimney. It has been advocated that the combining point in the case of a bifurcated blast pipe should be 18″ below the orifice in order to prevent eccentric discharge of the jet through the chimney. Having regard to the limitations imposed by the loading gauge in this country, in conjunction with consideration of item (6) following, this dimension must be regarded as a counsel of perfection. The usual distance from combining point to orifice is one-quarter the height of the blast pipe.

(5) The entry to the exhaust nozzle must be easy and free from shoulders or sudden changes of section.

(6) The area of entrainment, *i.e.*, surface presented by the exhaust steam to the smokebox gases for the purpose of eduction, should be large. The maximum extent in any given instance may be obtained:

(*a*) By increasing the perimeter of the blast orifice with some such artifice as the provision of nibs, *viz.*, inward radial projections; and

(*b*) By increasing the distance of the blast orifice below the centre line of the smokebox (see dimension *F*, Fig. 15). The effect of lowering the orifice is to increase the mean draught obtainable from a given diameter of nozzle, to reduce the range of fluctuation of the draught, and also to equalise its effect over the tubeplate as a whole. Nevertheless, there is a practical limit; the orifice must not be lowered to such an extent that the possibility of ashes normally accumulating in the smokebox to a higher level than that of the nozzle may arise. With bituminous coal of good quality, and assuming that no ash ejector is fitted, the deposit of ash in the smokebox may be taken, in favourable circumstances, as about 1% by weight of the total coal burnt; this quantity may amount to 5% in extreme cases. The actual extent of ash accumulation in the smokebox is directly affected by the relative intensity of the blast and by characteristics of the fuel consumed. Smokebox ash weighs from about 27.5 to 28 lb. per cubic foot.

(7) By increasing dimension *K* (see Fig. 15), a more even draught is secured over the whole of the grate area, and the danger of spark throwing which, incidentally, increases

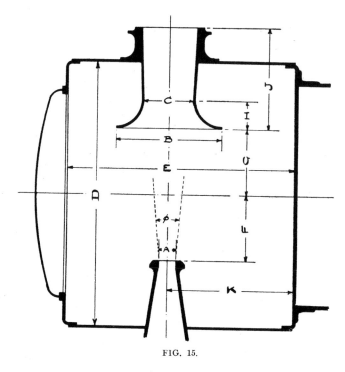

FIG. 15.

as dimension F augments, is at the same time lessened. K is in part governed by considerations of clearance for the super-heater header.

(8) The natural diametral taper of the blast jet, subsequent to leaving the nozzle, does not exceed 1 in 6 (subtended angle, 9° 18′), and is frequently found to be 1 in 8, for which the corresponding value of ϕ (Fig. 15) is 7° 8′. In many cases ϕ is taken as 8°.

(9) The frictional resistance of the exhaust jet increases with the length of the chimney (dimension J, *ibid*). The chimney should in any case be so designed that the jet fills it only at the top. The chimney diameters for some locomotives are, in fact, such that an annulus for the accommodation of the gases, having a width of from 1″ to 2″, surrounds the column of steam between the choke and the top of the chimney.

As the effect of air currents set up by the motion of the engine is to deflect the upper portion of the column of exhaust steam from its intended position, coincident with the chimney axis, the blast pipe has been set forward by about ¼" in some cases of engines running principally in fore gear, with a view to correcting this tendency.

Proportions of Draught Apparatus. Fig. 15 shews diagrammatically the sectional elevation of a smokebox. The various dimensions are:—

A = diameter of blast pipe orifice.
B = diameter of bell mouth.
C = diameter of choke.
D = diameter of smokebox.
E = length of smokebox.
F = distance of blast pipe orifice below smokebox centre line.
G = distance from smokebox centre line to bell mouth.
H = distance from bell mouth to choke.
J = total length of chimney.
K = distance from tubeplate to centre line of blast pipe.

These dimensions are interdependent; alteration to any one of them is therefore likely immediately to affect the intensity and/or distribution of draught, and in any case must not be given effect without due consideration of the necessary modifications of the remainder. For instance, inability of any given class of engine to steam is usually corrected in the shed by reducing A only. A minimum of alteration is thereby involved, and this course is consequently the best to pursue from a purely practical aspect; the treatment is, however, illogical, and may easily become so drastic that the desired result 's obtained at the cost of excessive back pressure. In such cases it will generally be found more satisfactory to increase F, but in doing so, dimension C, and frequently B, may need to be increased, and others possibly modified, to suit.

The first dimension to consider is the diameter of the blast orifice, A. For superheated engines this, in British practice, is usually given approximately by:—

$$A = 0.25 \delta \quad \dotfill \quad (118)$$

A proportion to be preferred is:—

$$A = 0.267 \delta \quad \dotfill \quad (119)$$

The values given by (118) and (119) should be increased by ⅛" for saturated steam, to allow for the greater weight of steam discharged in a given time. In the above formulæ, A and δ are both in inches, δ being the cylinder diameter.

A formula on a more logical basis is

$$A = \sqrt{4\cdot7\ (x \times y)} \quad \dots\dots\dots\dots\dots\dots\dots (120)$$

where x = total working cylinder volume, cubic feet, and
          y = weight of steam at boiler pressure, lb. per cubic foot.

This formula allows for the abstraction of exhaust steam for feed water heating purposes and is applicable to superheated engines with three and four cylinders.

In modern German practice, A may be determined from:—

Area of blast nozzle (square centimetres) = from 0.8 to 0.85 (heating surface of boiler, square metres) .... (121)

According to von Borries and Tröske,

$$A = 0\cdot156 \sqrt{\frac{g \times t}{g + 0.3t}} \quad \dots\dots\dots\dots\dots\dots\dots (122)$$

where g = grate area, square inches, and
          t = cross sectional area through tubes, square inches.

It has been pointed out (Proc. I. Loco. E., 1917) that this formula gives low results, and the substitution of 0·168 for the coefficient given was suggested.

A formula which agrees with American practice is that due to Meyer:—

$$\text{Area of blast nozzle (square inches)} = \frac{g}{200} \quad \dots\dots\dots\dots (123)$$

where g is as stated previously.

It will be noted that the three preceding formulæ are based purely on boiler proportions and do not differentiate between the number of cylinders employed.   The favourable effect on the draught of six or eight light exhaust impulses per revolution, as compared with four relatively heavy beats, is of course considerable, and enables the multi-cylindered engine to run with a blast orifice of larger diameter than that suitable for an equivalent two-cylinder engine.

The recommendations of the American Railway Master Mechanics' Association for the determination of proportions of the draught apparatus are as follows:—

Having made $(J - H)$ and F as great as possible,

$$C = 0\cdot21\ D + 0\cdot16\ F$$
$$H = 0\cdot22\ D$$
$$B = 2\ C \text{ or } 0\cdot5\ D$$

Level of bell mouth = $0\cdot32\ D$ below smokebox top,
          and E = $0\cdot6\ D$ or $0\cdot9$ D, but not intermediate values.

At the time these recommendations were published (1906), the relation E was not well established.

The following proportions, the actual origin of which is unknown to the author, are quoted as typical of British practice:

$$C \text{ (inches)} = 0.42\ \theta + 8.15'' \quad \dots\dots\dots\dots\dots \quad (124)$$

$$\text{or } C \text{ (inches)} = 2.6 + 7.28'' \quad \dots\dots\dots\dots\dots \quad (125)$$

where

$$\theta = \frac{\text{evaporative heating surface (square feet)} \times \text{volume of one cylinder (cubic inches)}}{1,000,000}$$

$$= \frac{\theta}{A}$$

Also, for superheater engines,

$$(F + G + H) = \frac{11.4\ C}{A} \quad \dots\dots\dots\dots\dots \quad (126)$$

and, for saturated steam engines,

$$(F + G + H) = \left(\frac{11.4\ C}{A}\right) - 2'' \quad \dots\dots\dots\dots \quad (127)$$

Empirically,

$$C = 0.25\ D \quad \dots\dots\dots\dots\dots\dots\dots\dots\dots\dots \quad (128)$$

$$H = C \quad \dots\dots\dots\dots\dots\dots\dots\dots\dots\dots\dots\dots \quad (129)$$

$$\text{and } B = 2\ C \quad \dots\dots\dots\dots\dots\dots\dots\dots\dots\dots \quad (130)$$

Also, B is not less than $4A$.

In German practice the length $(F + G)$ is usually arranged to exceed one metre (this agrees with British applications to chimneys of parallel bore), the chimney diameter is made equal to $4A$ and the blast orifice is located $8''$ to $10''$ above the smokebox floor level.

With regard to the form of chimney adopted, modern British practice favours a taper section with the maximum diameter at the top; the taper is not so great as that natural to the blast jet, and ranges from $\frac{1}{2}''$ to $1''$ per foot. In order to increase the area of entrainment, however, some engineers prefer either to reverse the direction of the taper or to adopt a parallel bore; in both cases C must then be taken as the diameter at the top of the chimney.

According to Goss:—

With the blast orifice on the smokebox centre line,

$$C = 0.246 + (0.00123 \ J) \ D \quad \dots\dots\dots\dots \ (131)$$

With the blast orifice above the smokebox centre line,
For parallel chimneys,

$$C = 0.246 + (0.00123 \ J) \ D - 0.19 \ F \quad \dots\dots\dots \ (132)$$

For taper chimneys,

$$C = 0.25 \ D - 0.16 \ F \quad \dots\dots\dots\dots\dots \ (133)$$

With the blast orifice below the smokebox centre line,
For parallel chimneys,

$$C = 0.246 + (0.00123 \ J) \ D + 0.19 \ F \quad \dots\dots\dots \ (134)$$

For taper chimneys,

$$C = 0.25 \ D + 0.16 \ F \quad \dots\dots\dots\dots\dots \ (135)$$

It has been suggested that J should be from 3 to 4 times greater than C, and that the area of a parallel chimney should be 12 times that of the blast orifice, with an increase of 12% at the base in the case of taper chimneys. Such recommendations are of a purely empirical nature and too misleading for indiscriminate application to any specific case; rigid adherence to rule of thumb in the design of draught arrangements is fatal.

Having determined A, F and G, chimney dimensions, in the author's opinion, should be found with the production of angle ϕ for the blast jet to the top of the chimney as a basis. Incidentally, any increase in existing dimensional values of A, F or G calls for an increase in C and other chimney dimensions, and may also involve H.

Smokebox.

The smokebox acts as a reservoir for the gases of combustion prior to ejection. At low rates of revolution the action of the blast may be compared with that of a plunger; at high rotational speeds the blast acts as a jet. The greater the cubic capacity of the smokebox, the greater is its ability to maintain the vacuum between individual exhaust beats and to modify the more or less intermittent character of the blast; in short, the range of draught fluctuations above and below the mean is decreased and unburnt fuel losses are reduced in consequence. The practical advantages of the extended smokebox are that greater accommodation is provided for the deposited ash, and that spark emission and scoring of the tubes by the abrasive action of fuel particles are both reduced. Further, there is greater clearance available for the details housed therein, with a corresponding improvement as regards accessibility.

The smokebox gases are of a corrosive nature, as also is ash; nuts used in the smokebox should therefore be of non-ferrous material and capped, or other means adopted to protect the threads of bolts. For the same reason, all internal details should be as simple as possible and free from moving parts and from pockets or traps capable of harbouring ash; the number of such details must be minimised. The lower portion of the tube plate is frequently provided with a protector plate, of low grade cast iron, having a thickness of approximately $\frac{1}{2}''$. Owing to the high ruling temperatures, oil pipes should be excluded from the smokebox, as otherwise carbonisation is bound to occur.

The chief mechanical function of the smokebox is to resist the tendency of the boiler to move laterally in the frames when the engine is running, and it must possess sufficient structural rigidity to do this. The thickness of the steel wrapper plates varies from $\frac{7}{16}''$ to $\frac{3}{4}''$, the latter dimension being applied to drumhead type smokeboxes of the largest diameter. Rivets are pitched at about $2''$ centres, and vary from $\frac{7}{16}''$ to $\frac{5}{8}''$ in diameter. The use of rivets with the outside heads counter-sunk assists in the maintenance of cleanliness and improves appearance; snap heads are, however, preferable, having regard to the relative thinness of the plate and to the effects of vibration, in that they form a stronger joint.

The front plate may be of $\frac{3}{8}''$ or $\frac{1}{2}''$ plate, either flanged to an outside radius of $\frac{3}{4}''$ or $1''$, or stiffened by angle of about $3'' \times 2\frac{1}{2}'' \times \frac{1}{2}''$ section. The door may be of $\frac{3}{8}''$ plate and, to provide the flexibility necessary to counteract possible distortion, must be generously dished; the dishing should be at least $4''$ with a door diameter of the order of $4'$-$6''$. The radius of the door adjacent to its periphery should be small (not more than $1\frac{1}{2}''$).

As the effects of expansion are more uniformly distributed in the case of the drumhead type smokebox, it is easier to maintain airtight than the horse-shoe form. It is also easier to clean, but requires a relatively greater extension to accommodate the deposited ash. On the other hand, trouble may be experienced at the root of the tubeplate flange, in which case the substitution of an angle section is advantageous. Difficulty may also be experienced in fitting the smokebox to the saddle with the high degree of accuracy demanded, and also in the making of steam and exhaust pipe joints with the saddle.

A saddle in conjunction with a drumhead smokebox provides a more rigid but heavier construction than the horse - shoe pattern box. Weight may be minimised by using cast steel in place of cast iron, although the former material is not so satisfactory when the possible existence of blowholes is considered. Another method of reducing weight is to use only two small steel end castings and build up the saddle sides with plate. The heaviest and most expensive construction, which gives, however, the greatest rigidity and reliability as regards air-tightness, is to cast either half the saddle with one outside cylinder or the saddle *en bloc* with the cylinders, as in American practice. The disadvantages of this method are that there is an undesirable concentration of weight at the leading end of the engine, the casting itself is difficult to make, heavy expense is incurred in the event of a defective cast being made or of replacement, *e.g.*, should breakage occur in service, and it is difficult to effect more than one machining operation at any given time during manufacture. The use of bar framing explains the prevalence of this form of construction in the U.S.A.

Facilities must be provided for the removal of ash. When this operation is performed manually, the layer of brick and/or fireclay at the bottom of the smokebox should slope downwards towards, and below, the door, and any recesses or pockets which are inaccessible or too small to be cleared with the shovel must be strictly avoided. The quantity of ash accumulating may be minimised by using an ejector. In some cases the smokebox is cleared by discharging, with the assistance of a steam jet or hot water ejector (as regards prevention of corrosion, the former is better) through a hopper ; although this practice forms a great advance theoretically, difficulty is sometimes experienced in keeping the hopper doors tight. The latter are particularly liable to distortion and corrosion.

The use of ash ejectors and hoppers, and of self-contained tube cleaning apparatus on the engine, together with the greater reliability of modern superheater apparatus, have reduced the necessary minimum diameter of the smokebox door. Small doors are now usual in American, and frequently encountered in colonial, practice. The lower edge of the door is consequently at a relatively high level, the door is less liable to make direct contact with ash, and cases of burning and warping are therefore less numerous. In the U.S.A., smokebox-fronts are either of cast steel or cast iron (the door being of cast iron) and are bolted; this permits of easy removal for repairs.

Also, for the reasons given above, and when the tubes are cleaned by air or steam from the firebox end, the smokebox door does not need to be opened so frequently as in the past. Dogs may therefore be used in such cases to maintain a uniform pressure on the door when closed. Their use is, however, not to be recommended when the door requires to be opened at rather frequent intervals, owing to the comparatively lengthy time necessary for adjustment; in this case the dart is preferable. The most satisfactory type of smokebox door joint, in the author's experience, is that in which graphited asbestos packing of rectangular section, of which one side forms the seating for the edge of the door, is inserted in a recessed ring fitted to the smokebox front.

According to Goss, the smokebox draught may be calculated from:—

Vacuum (inches of water) = 0·037 × lb. coal per square foot of grate area per hour ... (136)

This formula applies to bituminous coals.

The following smokebox vacua (in inches of water) were published by Mr. Gresley (Proc. I. Mech .E., 1925):—

Speed.	2-cylinder 2-8-0.		3-cylinder 2-8-0.		Remarks.
	Max.	Min.	Max.	Min.	
3 m.p.h.	10″	Pressure, during plenum, 1″	7″	Pressure, during plenum, ½″	
15 ,,	10½″	Vacuum, 1″			Cut-off, 47%, Pressure, 145 lb. per square inch.
16 ,,			7″	Vacuum, 0″	
30 ,,	8½″	,, 3″	6″	,, 1½″	Cut-off, 47% Pressure, 110 lb. per square inch.

These vacua were recorded with 1″ bore piping located on the centre line of the smokebox, 1″ below and 15″ behind the blast pipe orifice. Mr. Gresley reported that the effect of closing the dampers was to increase the vacuum by 2″.

The weight of the gases displaced from the smokebox may be computed from

$$G = W \sqrt{\dfrac{2\left(\dfrac{T}{S}\right)^2 \left(1 - \dfrac{a}{S}\right)}{\dfrac{a}{S}\left\{L + 2\left(\dfrac{T}{S}\right)^2\right\}}} \quad\quad\quad (137)$$

where G = weight of gases displaced, lb. per minute,
  W = weight of steam discharged from orifice, lb. per minute,
  a = area of blast orifice, square inches,
  S = cross-sectional area of chimney, square inches,
  T = cross-sectional area through tubes, square inches,
and L = constant = 4.

Steam Pipes in Smokebox. Are usually of steel, although cast iron is sometimes used, especially in the U.S.A. Copper has been utilised in the past but, owing to the intense scouring action of the steam, cannot be employed when superheaters are fitted. It is claimed that the non-ferrous metal is less susceptible to the corrosive action of the smokebox gases; on the other hand, it is not so well able to withstand attrition set up by particles of unburnt fuel and ash.

The radii of bends must be as large as can be accommodated, in order to minimise frictional resistance to steam flow. Reversal of direction must be avoided for the same reason. The radii must in any case be such that the pipes are clear of the tubes.

As with blast pipes and all other smokebox fittings, the nuts for the flange bolts must be capped in order to protect the threads from corrosion, and care must be exercised that the location of the bolts renders them as accessible as possible. Repairs in the smokebox are, even in the most favourable circumstances, dirty and unpleasant ; there is therefore considerable risk of the work being scamped unless progress is as far as possible facilitated.

To this end special attention is now given to smokebox pipe joints. It is claimed for the American loose ring type joint that the only attention necessary is re-grinding when the engine is shopped. Both faces of the joint ring, which is of cast iron, are ground initially, one with a flat surface and the other to a convex radius which is usually rather less than the internal diameter of the pipe for which the joint is intended; thus, the joint ring for a 6″ diameter pipe may be ground to a radius of about 5″.   This type of joint is applicable to all the major steam pipes; where the joint is made with the cylinder casting or tee piece, as the case may be, the curved face of the joint ring abuts on the latter, and not on the pipe flange.

The lens ring, similarly employed to prevent flange contact and consequently to eliminate bedding down, is ground on both faces to a concave radius.

Where sheet copper joints are still employed, the pipe flanges should be recessed for them in order to prevent corrosion; the latter action is further retarded by liberal smearing with graphite paste in the shops.

Blast Pipe.

Is usually of cast iron, the ruling wall thickness being from $\frac{1}{2}$″ to $\frac{3}{4}$″, according to size; the thickness of the flange at the base and lugs for retaining studs is usually about $1\frac{3}{8}$″. The studs are $\frac{7}{8}$″ or 1″ in diameter, and, for engines with inside cylinders, four are usually provided, viz., two at each side of the pipe.   Care must be taken that none of these studs is located at the back of the blast pipe, i.e., adjacent to the tubeplate, owing to the inaccessibility of this position.

The provision of a detachable nozzle for the blast pipe not only facilitates cleaning in service, but also permits of easily made minor adjustments in the diameter and height of the orifice.

The most satisfactory method for the disposal of the exhausts from air brake compressors or vacuum ejectors is undoubtedly by means of a ring, integral with the petticoat, and having drilled exhaust ports.   These exhausts should not be led into the petticoat by means of an open ended pipe, as frequently happens.   By so doing, interference with the main exhaust jet is caused ; the latter may also impinge on the auxiliary exhaust pipe elbows or joints.   A better arrangement would be to provide discharges for these and kindred auxiliaries, and also for the blower, by arranging concentric exhausts within the blast pipe itself and coincident with the centre line of the main exhaust jet.   The central jet would of course be solid, and the remainder annular in form.   It may be noticed that the weakness of many existing arrangements of blowers is that they are liable, sooner or later, to discharge eccentrically in service.

The provision of **spark arresters** is compulsory in certain countries. A diaphragm plate frequently forms part of the apparatus and tends to give a more even draught over the tube-plate as a whole, *i.e.*, the draught through the lower rows of tubes is strengthened at the expense of those at the top. The general effect of providing spark arresting apparatus is that a more intense blast is required for the provision of a given quantity of steam.

The **chimney damper** almost invariably found in Continental practice is very useful for the exclusion of cold air while the engine is in process of cooling down, and is especially valuable on engines using liquid fuel, with which the effects of cold air currents may otherwise be extreme.

Chapter IX.

THE ENGINE.

FOR present purposes the term "engine" is understood to comprise the cylinders with piston heads and rods, crossheads and slidebars, connecting and coupling rods, crank and straight axles, coupled wheels and axleboxes. Lubrication of the various details will be considered separately. Ports, valves and valve gears are for the present excluded and will be considered in the following chapter.

In designing the details enumerated above the most rigorous conditions of operation, *i.e.*, piston loads computed at full working pressure, with allowances for possible excesses due to over-compression or priming and to the effect of re-boring, and rates of revolution taken to correspond with peak running speeds, must be adopted as the basis of calculation. Before the various details can receive individual consideration certain information, which is of a general character and affects each to a varying extent, must be obtained; such data will be set forth in the first instance. Much of this work is not indigenous to the locomotive and comes under the category of general steam engine dynamics; as this subject is fully treated in the standard text books, to which readers are referred for the development and proof of the various formulæ tabulated hereafter, it will be merely briefly outlined here in the sequence of application.

It will be noticed that treatment in many instances is elementary and that the selected formulæ are not always those giving the most correct solution when subjected to rigid mathematical analysis. The author would defend this apparently slipshod method of working by stating that, in addition to those which are amenable to calculation, stresses of unknown extent arise in service, affecting practically every detail of the locomotive engine, for which allowances, in the form of a factor of safety based purely on practical experience, must be made. It is obviously a waste of time to calculate individual stresses to several places of decimals when they form but a fraction of the total to which the detail concerned is subjected, or are computed from formulæ having as a basis assumptions of an academic nature which may or may not be admissible in practice.

Throughout the ensuing arguments, unless otherwise stated, the significance of the symbols used is as follows:—

v_p = velocity of piston head and rod and cross-head, feet per second,

v_c = linear velocity of crankpin, feet per second,

l = length of connecting rod, feet,

r = length of crank (*i.e.*, ½ piston stroke), feet,

ω = angular velocity of crank, radians per second

$$= \frac{v_c}{r}$$

$$n = \frac{l}{r}$$

θ = crank axle measured from the inner dead centre, degrees,

and ϕ = angle between connecting rod and crank, degrees.

Velocity and Acceleration of the Piston Head and Rod and Crosshead.

By calculation,

$$v_p = \omega r \left(sin\,\theta + \frac{sin\,2\,\theta}{2n} \right) \quad\dots\dots\dots\dots\dots (138)$$

v_p may be conveniently determined graphically by the instantaneous centre method (Fig. 16). Set out connecting rod AB and crank BC for various values of θ, producing, when necessary, AB to cut EF in D. Then, assuming the crankpin to be rotating at uniform velocity, v_c will have a constant value and, for any given position of the crank,

$$v_p = \frac{CD}{BC}\,v_c \quad\dots\dots\dots\dots\dots\dots\dots\dots\dots\dots\dots (139)$$

v_p is obviously zero at the dead centres. The maximum value occurs when $\phi = 90°$; assuming the length of the connecting rod to be infinite, v_p is then equal to v_c. For a connecting rod

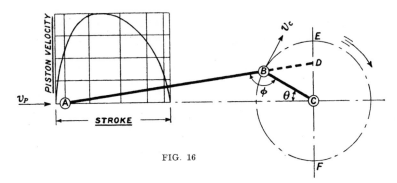

FIG. 16

of finite length the maximum value of v_p exceeds the constant v_c by a proportion which decreases as the value of n increases.

The acceleration of the piston head and rod and crosshead, denoted by a_p feet per second per second, may be calculated, with reference to the values at the dead centre, from:—
At the inner dead centre, *i.e.*, when the piston is remote from the crank axle,

$$a_p = \omega^2 r \left(1 + \frac{1}{n} \right) \quad \dots\dots\dots\dots\dots\dots\dots\dots (140)$$

At the outer dead centre,

$$a_p = \omega^2 r \left(1 - \frac{1}{n} \right) \quad \dots\dots\dots\dots\dots\dots\dots\dots (141)$$

Then mark off the point of zero acceleration, in accordance with (143) or (144), and obtain accelerations, at sufficient intermediate points to enable a curve to be drawn, by Klein's construction (Fig. 17).

For this construction connecting rod $A B$ and crank $B C$ must be drawn out in selected positions, $A B$ being produced, when necessary, to cut the perpendicular through C in D. With B as centre and radius $B D$ describe a circle; also describe a circle on $A B$ with $A B$ as diameter. Draw the common chord to these two circles, and produce it if necessary to cut $A C$ in E. Then CE represents the acceleration of the piston head and rod and crosshead to the same scale that the central acceleration of B, *viz.*, $\dfrac{v_c^2}{r}$, is represented by BC.

Since the inertia forces are directly proportional to the

acceleration and are equal to $\dfrac{W\,a_p}{g}$ lb., where W is the mass of the reciprocating parts in pounds, it is obvious that the acceleration curve may also be utilised, merely by re-adjustment of the vertical scale, as an inertia force curve.

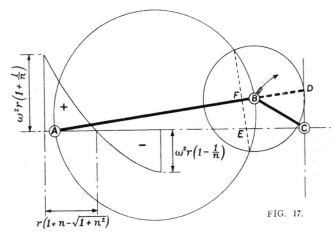

FIG. 17.

With further reference to Fig. 17, the angular acceleration of the connecting rod is equal to $\omega^2 \dfrac{E\,F}{A\,B}$.

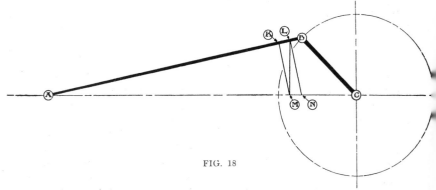

FIG. 18

An alternative construction is that due to Bennett (Fig. 18). Having again drawn out connecting rod AB and crank BC in a selected position, a point K must be located in AB such that

$$BK \times AB = BC^2$$

Then draw KM at right-angles to AB, ML at right-angles to the line of stroke AC, and finally LN at right-angles to connecting rod AB. The distance CN represents the acceleration of A to the scale on which BC represents that of the crankpin B.

This construction is less complicated than Klein's, but tends to become somewhat cramped for the values of n usually associated with locomotive practice.

The general expression for the determination of the piston acceleration is:—

$$a_\mathrm{p} = \omega^2 r \left(\cos \theta + \frac{1}{n} \cos 2\theta \right) \dots\dots\dots\dots\dots (142)$$

The displacement of the piston from commencement of stroke to the point of zero acceleration may be found (Inchley) from

$$x = r (1 + n - \sqrt{1 + n^2}) \dots\dots\dots\dots\dots (143)$$

or, more generally,

$$x = r \cos \theta - \frac{r^2}{2l} \sin^2\theta \dots\dots\dots\dots\dots (144)$$

where x is the required displacement in feet.

Rubbing Speeds of Bearings.

1. *Axle Journal in Axlebox.*

Rubbing speed in feet per minute $= 2 \pi r_j N$ ...... (145)

where r_j = radius of journal, feet, and

N = number of revolutions per minute.

2. *Crankpin in Big End.*

Maximum value of rubbing speed in feet per minute

$$= r_c \omega \left(1 + \frac{1}{n} \right) \dots\dots\dots\dots\dots (146)$$

where r_c = radius of crankpin, feet.

3. *Gudgeon Pin in Small End.*

Rubbing speed in feet per minute $= \dfrac{\omega \, r_g}{n}$ ...... (147)

where r_g = radius of gudgeon pin, feet.

Crank Shaft Torque.

Fundamentally, the torque exerted at any instant is given (Fig. 19) by

$$T = Q \times CD \quad \dots\dots\dots\dots\dots\dots\dots\dots \quad (148)$$

where Q = thrust, or pull, in connecting rod, lb.,
 $\quad CD$ = perpendicular distance from line of connecting
 $\qquad\qquad$ rod to C , feet, and
 $\quad T$ = turning moment in pound-feet.

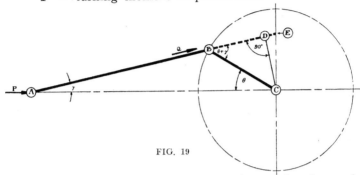

FIG. 19

Or, more conveniently for calculation, it may be shewn that
$$T = P \times CE \quad \dots\dots\dots\dots\dots\dots\dots\dots \quad (149)$$
where P is the effective force acting on the piston, pounds, and
the distance CE is of course scaled in feet. Also,

$$T = Pr \times \frac{\sin (\theta + \gamma)}{\cos \gamma} \quad \dots\dots\dots\dots\dots\dots\dots \quad (150)$$

For the purposes of equations (149) and (150), P must be
evaluated. Referring to Fig. 20, diagram (i) shews an indicator diagram, the ordinates of which have been disproportionately increased for the sake of clearness.

Let Δ = effective diameter of piston head, inches,
 $\quad \delta_1$ = effective diameter of tail rod (if fitted), inches,
and δ_2 = effective diameter of piston rod, inches.

Then, at any given position b , when the crank is rotating
towards the outer dead centre, the apparent value of P is given
in lb. by

$$P = \frac{\pi}{4} \left[\left\{ \left(\Delta^2 - \delta_1^2 \right) ab \right\} - \left\{ \left(\Delta^2 - \delta_2^2 \right) bc \right\} \right] \quad \dots\dots\dots\dots (151)$$

Were δ_1 and δ_2 either ignored (as is usually the case in
practice) or equal in value, P would be zero at d and have a
minus value thence to the end of the stroke. The effects of
their inclusion are to delay the actual zero point until later in
the out-stroke and to accelerate its incidence during the return
or in-stroke.

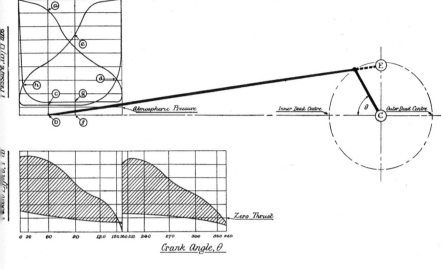

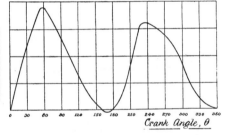

Crank Angle, θ

FIG. 20

Conversely, when the crank is rotating towards the inner dead centre, the apparent value of P, at any given point f, is obtained from

$$P = \frac{\pi}{4}\left[\left\{\left(\Delta^2 - \delta_2^2\right)ef\right\} - \left\{\left(\Delta^2 - \delta_1^2\right)fg\right\}\right]\text{lb.} \quad\quad (152)$$

Similarly, the apparent zero point is h.

A curve of P for one revolution is plotted in diagram (ii). Inertia curves, as previously described, are also here incorporated. The weight taken comprises that of the piston head with rings and nut, piston and tail rods, crosshead with cotters, and a certain proportion of the total weight of the connecting rod. The latter item is conventionally determined by resolving the connecting rod into two separate masses, one of which is assumed to be revolving at the crankpin and the other reciprocating at the crosshead. The numerical values of these two masses are inversely as the mass centre of the connecting rod divides a line joining the centre of the crankpin with the centre of the gudgeon pin, and their sum is of course equal to the mass of the rod. This convention, incidentally, may also be observed when solving balancing problems.

Reverting to diagram (ii), the inertia curves must be subtracted algebraically from the piston effort curve, *i.e.*, the effective value of P at any point is given by the length of ordinate within the shaded area.

The final diagram, (iii), shews the P curve resolved to a straight line base (on which, it should be observed, the angular positions of the crank have been equalised), and multiplied by the appropriate value of CE, *vide* (149), to give the torque in lb.-ft. The incidence of a local negative sense of the torque, due to the effects of compression and pre-admission, will be noted.

Considering the question of torque generally, for any given pressure and cylinder dimensions, T, especially for two-cylinder engines, is not appreciably affected by varying the value of n *(viz., l/r)* within the usual limits of locomotive practice, *i.e.*, approximately from 6 to 10. The turning moment available for starting as the regulator is opened is, however, sensibly diminished when the maximum cut-off is restricted, as there are then an increasing number of crank positions in which one or more cylinders are either closed to admission steam or unable to exert leverage.

Formulæ for the determination of the maximum torque developed by locomotives having various cylinder arrangements will be found in a later section of this chapter dealing with coupling rods.

When starting a train, slipping is most likely to occur when T is at a maximum value; the minimum, on the other hand, tends to inability to start a heavy load from rest. It therefore follows, quite apart from any consideration of uniformity of stress in the various components, that the engine having the minimum range of torque fluctuation per revolution will be least liable to suffer from either of these disadvantages. On this point three- and four-cylinder engines have a decided advantage over the two-cylinder; readers are referred to a paper by Mr. Gresley (Proc. I. Mech. E., 1925) for some very

interesting diagrams shewing comparative fluctuations above
and below mean torque. It may be noted that Mr. Gresley
advocated 8 as the most suitable value of n for three-cylinder
engines.

CYLINDERS.

The minimum thickness of the cylinder wall, when of cast
iron, is given (Pettigrew) in inches by

$$t = \frac{p \times D}{5,000} + 0.6 \quad\dots\dots\dots\dots\dots\dots\dots\dots\dots\dots\dots\dots\dots\dots (153)$$

where p = maximum steam pressure, lb. per square inch,
and D = cylinder diameter, inches.

The above is inclusive of an allowance for re-boring.

According to Kempe,

$$t = 0.02\,D + 0.75 \quad\dots\dots\dots\dots\dots\dots\dots\dots\dots\dots\dots\dots\dots (154)$$

It will be noted that pressure is disregarded in this latter
formula, from which the value of t obtained is low; the application of (154) should therefore be confined to those cases
where weight limitation is more important than cylinder life.

The "thin cylinder" formula cannot be applied to locomotive cylinders when designing in the first instance on account
of possible lack of uniformity in the mixture, practical considerations as regards casting, and allowance for wear. It
may, however, be used as a guide to the determination of the
scrapping limit. Superheater engines working at a pressure
of 180 lb. per square inch should not in general be allowed
to run with a wall thickness of less than about $\frac{3}{8}''$.

Suitable initial allowances for wear are:—

		On the diameter
For cylinders having a diameter of 19" or over	...	$\frac{3}{4}''$
,, ,, ,, ,, of 18" to 19"	...	$\frac{5}{8}''$
,, ,, ,, ,, of less than 18"...		$\frac{1}{2}''$

Ordinary cast-iron mixtures for superheated engine cylinders
may be improved by the inclusion of about 12% steel scrap,
thus increasing the percentage of combined carbon.

The radial depth of intermediate strengthening webs for the
barrel may be made equal to about 0.9 t, when t is determined
from (153), or 1.3 t if (154) is used; the width should also be
about 0.9 t.   One web is sufficient for strokes of 18" or under,
two from 18" to 24", and three for strokes in excess of 24".

The thickness of end flanges should not be less than 1.25 t, on the assumption that sufficient length into which the studs may be screwed is then secured, with a width of three times the stud diameter.

The **studs** should not be arranged to provide an excessively strong joint, in order to minimise the effects of possible connecting or piston rod failures, or of priming, on the cylinder casting. The tensile stress set up in the studs by the working steam pressure should not exceed approximately 3 tons per square inch of effective area. The nominal diameter should not be less than $\frac{3}{4}''$ for small cylinders and may be $\frac{7}{8}''$ or $1''$ for larger cylinders.

The diameter of the studs at the bottom of the thread, d_s inches, is obtained from

$$d_s = D \sqrt{\frac{p}{nf_t}} \qquad\qquad \dots\dots\dots\dots\dots\dots (155)$$

where n = number of studs provided, and
f_t = working tensile stress in studs, lb. per square inch,
p and D having the same significance as in (153).

The pitch of the studs (Pettigrew) should not exceed

$$\sqrt{\frac{t_f \times 100}{p}} \qquad\qquad \dots\dots\dots\dots\dots\dots\dots\dots (156)$$

where t_f = thickness of cover flange in sixteenths of an inch.

The **thickness of metal for steam passage and piston valve chamber walls** may be from $0.7\,t$ to $0.75\,t$. With a view to minimising heat transference, the exhaust cavity should be as far removed as possible from the cylinder walls. Where slide valves are still used, an initial allowance of from $\frac{1}{2}''$ to $\frac{3}{4}''$ should be made for wear of the cylinder casting at the port face.

The cylinder bore should be slightly tapered at the front end (taper about 1 in 3.5 on diameter over a length not exceeding $2''$), and the bore increased in diameter over a similar length at the back end. This procedure facilitates the insertion and withdrawal of the piston head with rings, prevents the formation of ridges in service, as the total length of parallel bore is made slightly less than (stroke + width over piston rings), and minimises damage due to the possible presence of foreign bodies.

The **piston clearance** should be at least $\frac{3}{16}''$ at each end of the stroke. Disregarding the smallest engines, this dimension is advisable only in conjunction with big ends of the solid type and hornblocks without wedge adjustment. Generally speaking, unless the standard of maintenance is high, a clearance of $\frac{5}{16}''$ or $\frac{3}{8}''$ is preferable. The latter amount leaves only a small margin for contingencies in the case of an engine which is in bad condition mechanically.

Cylinder bolts may have a nominal diameter of from $1''$ to $1\frac{1}{4}''$, according to the size of the cylinders, and must be turned a driving fit. The requisite number is governed jointly by the maximum piston shock load, the desirable shear stress in the bolts and the bearing pressure on them. On some railways heat treated steel with a 3% nickel content is now used for these bolts.

Cylinder covers are frequently made considerably thicker than is necessary; when dished and ribbed a ruling thickness of $\frac{5}{8}''$ or $\frac{3}{4}''$ is sufficient. A suitable number of ribs is one for every $3''$ or $4''$ of cylinder diameter, and their thickness, according to Unwin, $(t-\frac{1}{8})''$. The flange thickness should not be less than five-eighths that of the cylinder. The covers should register in the cylinder barrel for a length of $\frac{1}{4}''$ or $\frac{3}{8}''$. Where cast steel is employed for the cylinder cover in place of cast iron, the ruling thickness may be reduced by about 20%.

Cylinder liners of cast iron are used in those cases where the main casting is of steel, which may include alloys in its composition in order to reduce weight, or of inferior iron, to reduce cost. In such instances the thickness of the liner may be made equal to t, *vide* (153) and (154). The wall thickness of the outer or main casting may then be reduced, if of cast iron, to about 0.9 t, and of course further reduced if cast in steel. Although the practice is very rarely followed now, it may nevertheless be mentioned that inside cylinders should not be cast separately. The joint itself invariably gives trouble, accuracy of erection is jeopardised, and it has been reported (Mr. Hookham, Proc. I. Loco. E.) that uneven wear of slide valves is thereby engendered. When weight restrictions are severe the inside cylinders, or junction casting in the case of outside cylinders, may be utilised as a support for the bogie centre.

Inclination of Cylinders.

Where coupled wheels of small diameter are employed or inside drive to other than the leading coupled axle is arranged, the cylinders must be inclined in order to increase the clearance, above rail level in the one case and between the connecting rod and the leading coupled axle in the other, and also to provide more effective protection of the motion from grit, etc. With express engines, however, it is preferable for the longitudinal centre line of the cylinders to be horizontal if it can be arranged. The fact that the lines of the forces acting on the pistons are parallel with the line of the effort exerted at the wheel tread is conducive to smooth riding. In such cases it is usual to place the cylinder centre line about $\frac{3}{8}''$ or $\frac{1}{2}''$ (approximately $2''$ in the case of American engines with compensating gear) above that of the coupled axles to allow for the engine settling down on the springs, and for tyre wear, etc. This procedure necessitates the provision of rather greater clearance at the back than at the front end of the cylinder.

The necessary extent of clearance is also affected by the form of **cylinder cover joint** adopted. This, in British practice, is usually a face to face joint made with red lead or boiled oil, no insertion being used. American engineers, on the other hand, usually adopt the copper ring joint, for which it is claimed that fitting work is minimised and that the ring is capable of continued use, provided that it be annealed each time the joint is broken. At the same time the clearance volume is appreciably increased and any attempt to tighten joints of this type must be made with the greatest care, as otherwise the risk of cracking the casting is entailed.

Drain cocks should be of $\frac{3}{8}''$ or $\frac{1}{2}''$ bore. The usual plug type was superseded on the quondam S.E.C.R. by mushroom valves actuated by steam pistons, the latter being controlled from the cab by one valve.

Cylinder relief valves are essential to release water which would otherwise be trapped in cylinders having piston or poppet valves. The chief troubles to be countered when designing are carbonisation, leakage and inability to act spontaneously, this latter fault being due partly to the carbonisation previously mentioned and in part to the inertia of the moving parts. The spring should be readily accessible for cleaning and set to blow off at about 20 lb. per square inch above the working pressure, and may conveniently be made from $\frac{1}{4}''$ diameter steel wire. The valve may with advantage incorporate a protruding stem or spindle of about $\frac{5}{8}''$ diameter, enabling the

valve to be rotated on its seat when in position; the smallest
diameter of the valve for standard gauge express engines
should be about $1\frac{1}{2}''$, the steam passage leading thereto having
a diameter of $1''$. Ten or twelve holes, $\frac{1}{16}''$ or $\frac{1}{8}''$ diameter,
should be drilled through the valve body to enable any water
or steam released to pass to atmosphere. One relief valve must
be provided at each end of the cylinder.

ANTI-VACUUM (SNIFTING) VALVES.

As these valves, if of large diameter, are inclined to chatter
should the engine be coasting in full gear at high speeds, it is
advisable to provide two small valves rather than one of large
size. The permissible lift should in any case be severely restricted; $\frac{1}{4}''$ should be taken as the maximum. The external
diameter of the valve should not exceed $4''$.

When the regulator is in the conventional position, *i.e.*, between boiler and superheater, the best location for the anti-
vacuum valves is undoubtedly on the superheater header. A
supply of cool air is then admitted, when the engine is coasting, to the elements, which are otherwise liable to burn. Moreover, the incoming air is suitably warmed during its passage
through the superheater, so that the liability of the film of
lubricant in the valves and cylinders to carbonise is also reduced, and undue cooling of the cylinder castings, possibly
to the extent of the formation of incipient fissures, is at the
same time prevented. Further, in the position mentioned, the
quantity of dust and grit drawn in is considerably less than
that obtaining when these valves are mounted on the steam
chests.

The application of anti-vacuum valves need not necessarily
be restricted to superheater engines, and engines using
saturated steam may also with advantage be so equipped. The
steam supply to any auxiliaries requiring steam only when the
regulator is open may conveniently be taken from the body
of a snifting valve, thereby eliminating superfluous steam
cocks by reason of the automatic control of the steam supply
thus secured.

Anti-vacuum valves, used in conjunction with cylinder relief
valves, may well replace the somewhat elaborate bye-pass valve
arrangements fitted to some piston valve cylinders.

SPECIAL MATERIALS FOR RECIPROCATING AND OTHER PARTS.

The magnitude of bending stresses due to centrifugal action

on connecting and coupling rods are relatively very high in comparison with the static loading and are proportional to the masses of the rods. The total weight of all reciprocating and rotating parts immediately affects the balancing and, due to the former, the extent of hammer blow. For these reasons every effort is made to secure adequate strength for these details in conjunction with minimum weight, and recourse is had to special materials; particulars of three of these are given here.

"Vibrac" is a molybdenum steel manufactured by the English Steel Corporation Limited, and is preferably produced in an acid open hearth furnace. The heat treatment to which the forgings are subjected consists of oil or air hardening, followed in either case by a tempering heat treatment. The only difference between the mechanical test figures obtained as a result of these two heat treatments is that, with air hardening, the Izod impact figure is generally somewhat lower than that resulting from the oil hardening and tempering operation.

The customary specification is:—

Ultimate tensile strength, 55-65 tons per square inch, at which the elongation on 2″ usually exceeds 20% with a reduction in area of over 55%, the Izod impact value being over 50 ft.-lb. (oil hardened) or 35 ft.-lb. when air hardened.

Typical test results are:—

Yield, tons per sq. inch.	Break, tons per sq. inch.	Elonga- tion, %	Reduc- tion, %	Bend.	Impacts, ft.-lb.
49·0	58·5	21·0	60·0		58 x 57 x 46
53·0	63·0	19·5	57·0		53 x 54 x 49
51·0	60·0	20·0	59·0	180°	58 x 57 x 59
52·0	59·8	22·0	60·0		55 x 69 x 67
50·0	59·2	22·0	62.0		54 x 64 x 60

The first locomotives on which this steel was used were the S.R. "Lord Nelson" class. In addition to the reciprocating parts, "Vibrac" is also applicable to other highly stressed details, such as axles and screw couplings.

The other alloys to be mentioned, nickel and vanadium, are alike in that they are used not only for steel castings and forgings, but also in cast iron. When included with the latter material, chiefly for cylinders, the tensile strength of the iron is increased, greater uniformity of the mixture achieved and

machining facilitated; further, a longer life is obtained by
reason of additional resistance to wear.

As regards nickel, for small castings in iron the silicon
content is decreased and up to about 1.5% nickel incorporated, the percentage for cylinders being from 0.5 to 1.0.
It is claimed that castings in nickel and nickel-chromium iron
are ultimately cheaper than ordinary cast iron, especially for
intricate work, owing to the sensible reduction in the proportion
of rejected castings; the usual proportion of chromium is
0.5% below that of the nickel.

The following shews comparatively the physical properties
of nickel and carbon steels:—

	FORGINGS.		CASTINGS.	
	Chromium -nickel Steel.	Carbon Steel Specifi- cations.	Nickel or Chrome- nickel Steel.	Carbon Steel.
Yield Point, tons per square inch..	35	22	22-29	11-15·5
Tensile Strength, tons per square inch..	51	35	38-45	24
% Elongation on 2″ ..	21	20	18-28	20-25
% Reduction of area..	55	40	28-38	30-35

Another comparison is made with reference to some alloy
steel frame castings for Canadian Pacific Railway locomotives:

	High Carbon Vanadium Steel.	Low Carbon Nickel Steel.
Average tensile strength, lb. per square inch	87,590	79,472
Average yield point, lb. per square inch ..	49,442	48,495
Average yield point expressed as % tensile strength.	56·5	61·0
Average elongation, %	28·5	30·4
Average reduction of area, %	53·6	55·8
Brinell hardness.	150 to 165	140 to 150
Analyses:	%	%
Carbon	0·36	0·17
Manganese	0·94	0·80
Phosphorus	0·015	0·014
Sulphur	0·028	0·028
Silicon	0·35	0·34
Nickel	—	2·70
Vanadium	0·19	—

Mr. Gresley quoted the following analysis (Proc. I. Loco.E., 1921), for steel forgings:—

Carbon	0.33%
Silicon	0.21%
Manganese	0.6%
Sulphur	0.032%
Phosphorus	0.039%
Nickel	3.42%
Chromium	0.60%

The physical properties of this steel are:—

Tensile strength, 58 tons per square inch. Yield stress, 48.4 tons per square inch. Elongation on 2″, 20%.

Nickel to the extent of 3% is now frequently included in the steel for boiler plates in Canadian and American practice. The analysis and physical properties compare with those of carbon steel as follows:—

	3% Nickel Steel Boiler Plate.	Carbon Steel Boiler Plate.
No. of tests on which averages are based. ..	523	385
Carbon Average percentage	0·163	0·193
Manganese ,, ,,	0·557	0·041
Phosphorus ,, ,,	0·021	0·022
Sulphur ,, :,	0·029	0·033
Silicon ,, ,,	0·203	—
Nickel ,, ,,	2·960	—
Ultimate tensile strength, lb. per square inch	77,880	59,200
Yield Point, lb. per square inch	47,550	36,200
Elongation, % on 8″	26·33	28·64
Reduction of area, %	54·15	Not determined.
Impact Value, Izod.	63·4 ft.-lb.	Not determined.

The following results of tensile tests are important in that they shew the effects of temperature rise on 3% nickel steel.

Temperature.	68°F.	480°F.	660°F.
Ultimate tensile strength, lb. per square inch	62,200	64,000	54,100
Elastic limit, lb. per square inch	42,700	28,500	25,600
Elongation, %	27·5	21·9	33·1
Reduction of area, %	71·0	63·0	73·1
Impact, ft.-lb.	30·6	29·8	28·4

Steel with a carbon content of from 0.10% to 0.20% and about 20% nickel has been used in America for boiler tubes.

It is stated that their life is from 7 to 15 times as great as that of carbon steel tubes, and that scale does not readily adhere to them. For stay bolts a 2% nickel steel has been satisfactorily adopted.

The author is indebted to the Bureau of Information on Nickel for the foregoing data.

Forged vanadium steel, as largely used in Canada and the United States for reciprocating parts, axles, crankpins, etc., has the following physical properties:—

	Up to 9" diameter or thickness.	9" to 13" diameter or thickness.
Yield Point, lb. per square inch	60,000	58,000
Tensile strength, lb. per square inch ..	90,000	90,000
Elongation on 2"	20°/o	20°/o
Reduction of area.	40°/o	40°/o

The physical properties of castings in vanadium steel for frames, crossheads and other details are as follows:—

	Vanadium Cast Steel.	Vanadium High Test Cast Steel.
Yield Point, lb. per square inch	40,000	50,000
Tensile Strength, lb. per square inch ..	70,000	80,000
Elongation on 2"	20°/o	20°/o
Reduction of area.	40°/o	40°/o

The following average of test results on twelve cast vanadium steel frames, made by the Union Steel Casting Company, has been published (Proc. I. Mech.E., 1929):—

Elastic limit, 47,000 lb. per square inch.
Tensile strength, 78,500 lb. per square inch.
Elongation on 2", 26%.
Reduction of area, 49%.
Average composition:—

Carbon 0.235%
Manganese 0.61%
Silicon 0.281%
Vanadium 0.186%

Carbon vanadium steel which, apart from annealing after forging, is not heat treated, is not affected by local heating. The maximum vanadium content is approximately 0.25%.

The chief disadvantages of alloy steels in general are the cost, roughly 30% greater than that of carbon steels, and the difficulty experienced in finish machining subsequent to heat treatment; rods are machined to within $\frac{1}{4}''$ of final dimensions, heat treated (which causes buckling), and then milled to finished size. On the other hand, the presence of any flaw is made obvious by the heat treatment, while the greater strength and higher yield point, with the consequent reduction in weight effected, far outweigh the disadvantages. This latter point may be emphasised by comparing the weights of reciprocating parts per lb. piston load for carbon and alloy steels respectively.

PISTON HEADS.

The provision of sufficient metal, in the boss for the reception of the piston rod and at the rim to accommodate the grooves for the rings, usually necessitates, irrespective of whether the head is forged or cast, a considerably heavier intervening section for the head than is dictated by the load due to the steam pressure acting thereon, even when allowance is included for over-compression. For this reason design of the head is largely empirical, and therefore open to criticism; in many cases piston heads could be considerably reduced in weight with safety.

For dished (conical) piston heads of pressed steel, Unwin suggested that the thickness, in inches, near the central boss be:—

$$t_b = (D + 15)(0.0012 \sqrt{p} + 0.012) \dots\dots\dots (157)$$

and near the rim,

$$t_r = (0.68 - 0.002D)t_b \dots\dots\dots\dots (158)$$

where D = piston diameter, inches, and
p = greatest difference of the pressures on either side of the head, lb. per square inch.

The diameter of the boss = (1.9 × diameter of piston rod screw).

Professor Unwin stated that the above formulæ were based on marine practice; they are, however, applicable to dished pistons of forged steel for locomotives.

Two dished piston heads of recent locomotive design may be compared. In both instances they are for cylinders 20″ in diameter and working at a pressure of 180 lb. per square inch; in one case the head is of nickel-chrome steel and the other is of 27 tons per square inch carbon steel. In both examples t_b is $1''$; for the alloy steel t_r is $\frac{1}{2}''$, and for the carbon steel, $\frac{5}{8}''$. When the location of the cylinders is unavoidably near the driving axle, the piston heads may be dished in order to increase the connecting rod length.

The dishing of piston heads is not justifiable for small cylinders; some engineers still prefer either the plain (*i.e.*, not dished) or box piston for large cylinders on the grounds that the surface presented to condensation is substantially reduced, in some cases by as much as 30%, and that with box pistons a reduction in clearance volume may be effected. For plain heads the values of t_b and t_r should be approximately 25% greater than those given by (157) and (158) respectively. The minimum thickness of each side, for a box piston, may be made equal to $\frac{5}{8}$ t_r.

There is no uniformity of practice with regard to the allowance for clearance of the piston head in the cylinder; the diameter of the head is the bore of the cylinder less an amount which varies actually between the wide limits of $1/64''$ and $\frac{1}{8}''$, approximately proportional to the cylinder diameter, scrapping occurring when these amounts are increased to $\frac{1}{8}''$ or, in some cases of steel heads, $\frac{3}{16}''$. In the majority of cases the original total clearance provided is $1/32''$ or $\frac{1}{16}''$, and is less for cast iron than for other materials ; clearances of from $0.04''$ to $0.06''$ are common with cast iron piston heads.

Cast iron is widely used, as wear of the head, and also laterally in the grooves, is small with this material. The use of cast steel is emphatically not to be recommended as it leads to excessive scoring of the barrel when contact with the latter commences. Mild forging steel is quite satisfactory; drop forgings of an aluminium-silicon alloy, of tensile strength equal to that of mild steel and not liable to corrosion, have been employed on the Continent in order to reduce weight. Special steels, as previously mentioned, are sometimes used in this country. In those cases where the head is forged integrally with the rod, thereby eliminating a troublesome joint, a detachable rim should be provided as, owing to wear of the barrel, the normal scrapping limit of the head is attained considerably earlier than that of the rod. These rims may be attached by rivets, screws, or bolts which, in view of the alternating stresses involved, should be attached alternately from opposite sides of the head. In order to avoid the effects of discrepancies in the coefficients of expansion, the rim should be of ferrous material; cast iron is suitable. Some American engineers, however, have adopted bronze; a typical example of the latter contains 86-89% copper and 4-6% each of phosphor-tin and tin.

PISTON RINGS.

Although a ring may be designed to exert a uniform spring pressure, the latter is so small by comparison with that exerted on the cylinder wall by the steam underneath the ring that the consequent additional expense of manufacture is not justifiable. The radial thickness in locomotive practice is therefore generally made uniform throughout and is determined purely by practical considerations, the maximum bending stress usually occurring when the ring is sprung over the head into position; the thickness may either be a fixed dimension, *e.g.*, $\frac{9}{16}''$, or varies approximately from 0.025 D to 0.038 D.

Frictional resistance, and therefore wear, increases with the width of the ring. On the other hand, the width must be such that with the piston head at the extreme end of its stroke, and making allowance for the reduction in clearance occurring in service as wear is taken up on the big ends, etc., the end ring does not over-run into the port, but bears for part of its width (a minimum of one-half may be recommended) on the parallel portion of the cylinder barrel. It follows from this that the necessary width of the ring, which is usually about $\frac{5}{16}''$ in modern practice, is partly determined by the position of its groove relative to the rim face of the piston head.

The cut in the ring must be made diagonally in order to obviate grooving of the barrel, and also to minimise leakage, the width of gap being initially π (difference between the turned outside diameter of ring and bore of cylinder).

The clearance between the inner face of the ring and the bottom of the groove in the piston head may be from $\frac{1}{16}''$ to $\frac{1}{8}''$, and the total clearance between ring and groove, about 0.002″.

As one is insufficient to ensure steam tightness, two rings should be fitted to each head. They should be placed as near the end faces of the rim as possible in order to minimise the area on which the steam, subsequent to the dropping of the head in service, can act, and so accelerate the wear of the cylinder barrel. Three rings are not always considered necessary, even for cylinder diameters of 20″ or more; when fitted, the central ring, in order to minimise frictional losses, should not be so wide as those at the ends, since it is not subjected to the limiting conditions mentioned above.   In connection with this matter it should be mentioned that three narrow rings are preferable to two wide rings.

The usual material for the rings is cast iron (cylinder mixture), and this is probably the most suitable for superheated steam.   Bronze is, however, sometimes used, the composition of that adopted by the Union Pacific R.R. being:—

Copper	...	...	...	82.96%
Tin ...	...	...	...	14.66%
Phosphorus	...	...	...	0.188%
Lead	...	...	...	Nil
Impurities	...	...	...	2.262%

Rings of special form have been introduced at various times with the object of preventing the " packing " of the steam underneath the rings.   One of these is the Allen segmental ring, so designed that the only frictional resistance set up by the rings is that due to a predetermined spring pressure. Consider for the purpose of comparison an $18\frac{1}{2}''$ diameter piston running at a speed of 1,000 feet per minute, the m.e.p. being 80 lb. per square inch; the theoretical work done is then equivalent to 650 H.P.   The calculated frictional losses under these conditions are with Ramsbottom rings, 31.3 H.P., and with Allen patent rings, 1.125 H.P.

PISTON RODS.

The strength must be determined for the centre portion, at the crosshead cotter, and at the bottom of the threads where screwed to receive the nut.

In determining the diameter of the centre portion, the rod, when under compression, is frequently treated as a column. Great care must be exercised in so doing that the assumed type of end fixings approximates closely to actual conditions. In many cases the rod is considered as a column fixed at one end and guided at the other ($\lambda = 0.7\ L$), but having regard to the clearances provided, limitations of workmanship and the fact that the packing, especially if of the floating pattern, provides no intermediate support, it is more reasonable to treat it as a column with rounded ends ($\lambda = L$).

Then, adopting Rankine's formula and equating, we have

$$\frac{\pi}{4} D^2 p = \frac{W}{S} = \frac{f_c A}{1 + \left(\dfrac{f_c}{\pi^2 E} \times \dfrac{L^2}{\kappa^2} \right)} \quad \text{.................} \quad (159)$$

where D = cylinder diameter, inches,

p = greatest difference in pressures on either side of piston, inclusive of allowance for over-compression (which may be taken as pressure at which relief valves lift), lb. per square inch,

W = crushing load on rod, lb.,

S = factor of safety,

f_c = ultimate compressive strength of material, lb. per square inch,

A = cross sectional area of rod, square inches,

E = Young's Modulus for material, lb. per square inch,

L = overall length of rod, inches, and

κ = radius of gyration of rod, inches.

The working value of the compressive stress in the material, in view of the alternating loads, should be based on the elastic limit, and not on the ultimate strength, and should not exceed one-third of the former. A more scientific treatment, however, is to take as a basis the range of stress and then apply a formula of the Launhardt-Weyrauch type.

The value of κ^2 for a solid rod is $\dfrac{d^2}{16}$, where d is the diameter in inches, and for a hollow rod, $\dfrac{d_1{}^2 + d_2{}^2}{16}$, where d_1 represents the external and d_2 the internal diameter respectively. It is, however, frequently convenient to use the solid rod as the basis for comparison. Considering two rods, one solid of radius R and the other hollow of external radius R and internal radius xR (the value of x being less than unity), the ratio of the buckling loads of the solid to the hollow rod is $\dfrac{I \text{ solid}}{I \text{ hollow}} = \dfrac{1}{1 - x^4}$, the ratio of their weights for a given length being $\dfrac{1}{1 - x^2}$ (Johnson, Proc. I. Mech. E., 1929). This is an application of Euler's well-known theory, which states that the buckling load is proportional to the moment of inertia of the section.

An empirical rule, applicable to solid piston rods of steel having an ultimate tensile strength of 40-45 tons per square inch, is to make $d = 0.165\ D$, where d is the diameter of the centre portion of the rod and D the bore of the cylinder. It will be observed that this rule does not take into account the value of the L/d ratio.

With regard to the threaded portion of the rod, this is subjected purely to tensile stress, the working value of which, based on the area at the root of the thread, should give a factor of safety of at least 5; practical considerations may raise the value of the factor to approximately 8. The outside diameter, *i.e.*, over the crests of the threads, ranges in actual practice from about $\frac{3}{8}''$ or $\frac{1}{2}''$ less than that of the body of the rod, when the diameter of the latter is from 3″ to $3\frac{1}{2}''$, to $\frac{1}{8}''$ less in the case of 2″ diameter rods. A suitable pitch for the larger rods is six threads per inch, a finer thread being employed as the diameter of the rod becomes smaller.

Collars for the seating of the piston head are a potential source of failure and should be avoided; a plain tapered seating is infinitely preferable. The taper provided on the diameter may be from 1 in 4 to 1 in 6, and at the other extremity of the rod, that for the cottered joint with the crosshead may be from 1 in 14 to 1 in 16.

When the piston rod, cotter and crosshead are all of steel, as is usual in locomotive practice, the following working stresses are frequently accepted:—

For the material of the piston rod on either side of the cotter: 5 tons per square inch.

For the area of cotter resisting shear: 4 tons per square inch.

For the bearing pressure of the cotter: 8 tons per square inch.

The general consideration of cottered joints will receive more detailed consideration subsequently.

Reverting to the body, or central portion, of the rod, as an empirical rule, applicable to 40-45 tons per square inch forging steel, the initial diameter of the rod may be such that the tensile stress due to the piston load does not exceed 3 tons per square inch. With average dimensions this will be found to permit of approximately $\frac{1}{8}''$ wear on the diameter ; some engineers, however, arrange for $\frac{3}{8}''$ diametral wear to occur before the scrapping limit is reached.

When alloy steels are used, the piston rod is sometimes made hollow in order to reduce weight and also to secure greater uniformity of heat treatment. The greater strength of these materials usually obviates the necessity for the outside diameter of such rods to be larger than that of an equivalent solid rod in carbon steel.

The piston rod should, if possible, be made of sufficient length to enable the head to be withdrawn, for periodical examination and for renewal of the rings, without breaking the crosshead joint. Bending stresses and reciprocating weights are both thereby increased, the effective length of the connecting rod for given cylinder-axle centres is reduced, and difficulty may be experienced in placing the head and rod in the cylinder; nevertheless, the practical advantage accruing from this procedure entitles it to consideration. The length of rod in such cases should be such that the piston head can clear the surface of the cylinder front joint by approximately 1″.

Cast-iron packing is now largely used in place of white metal and has a considerably longer life, increases of about 200% being reported in some instances. Each ring is in two parts and the surfaces on which the smaller slides into the larger, horseshoe-shaped portion must be made steamtight. The end faces, however, should not make actual contact, but should be provided with initial clearance to allow for wear, a clip spring maintaining the two pieces in position on the rod. The adjacent side faces of the individual rings must also make steamtight contact one with another, and the main spring must be so designed as to exert a uniformly distributed pressure on the end ring. Generous clearance should be provided between the rings and the housing, as otherwise any play present in the crosshead slippers will set up hammering on the rings, increasing the pressure on, and therefore the wear of, the piston rod. Care must also be taken with the boring in order that the packing may fit closely to the rod.

A hard, close grained iron must be used for the rings. The old North Staffordshire Railway used No. 4 quality with 30% Barrow hæmatite; pearlitic iron is now used for this purpose on the Indian State Railways.

Packings of any description will blow if the slidebars are out of alignment, the crosshead slippers worn, or the piston rod not true. Trouble of this nature therefore does not necessarily indicate that revision of the design of the packing is required.

Tail Rods.

Although seldom used in modern British practice, the adoption of tail rods is, in general, a fairly open question. Their employment is certainly advisable should the piston head be of cast steel, and may in any case be considered when the cylinder diameter exceeds 20″. It is essential that the bush be capable of rotation as wear occurs and that the lubrication be applied to the under surface of the rod. The chief weakness of tail rods is the difficulty experienced in providing sufficient bearing area; 25 square inches has been suggested as the desirable minimum surface. American engineers generally provide slideblocks and bars to assist the tail rod in preventing the piston head from bearing on the cylinder barrel; this adds to the frictional resistance.

The disadvantages of tail rods are the frequent adjustments necessary and the increases involved in reciprocating weight, clearance volume, leakage, and frictional losses. Tail rods do not function successfully in conjunction with floating packings, and the pumping effect of the steam entering and leaving the casing disturbs lubrication.

As many valve gears, notably Stephenson's, give an earlier cut-off at the front end of the cylinder than at the back, no advantage is gained by providing tail rods with a view to equalising the effective piston area, and consequently the work done per stroke. Further, due to the angularity of the connecting rod, for equal cut-offs, the steam acts for a slightly longer period of time on the back of the piston than on the front face.

Cottered Joints.

Although the following remarks are primarily intended for the joint between the piston rod and crosshead, they are of course applicable to cottered joints generally. The symbols

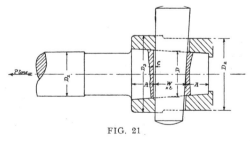

FIG. 21

utilised for the purpose of argument are shewn in Fig. 21; all dimensions are in inches, loads in tons, and f_t, f_c, and f_s represent the working stresses in tons per square inch of tension, compression and shear respectively.

(i) *Strength of Cotter.*

Assume the cotter to be of thickness t and mean width W. Disregarding for the moment the diminution due to the rounding of the edges, its average cross sectional area is therefore Wt. The maximum applied load is P; as the load is alternating, the value of (1.25 × piston load) should be taken. Then, equating the resistance in shear to that in compression, we have

$$2\,W\,t\,f_s = D\,t\,f_c = P$$

whence,

$$W = \frac{D\,f_c}{2\,f_s} \quad\dotfill (160)$$

When the cotter is of steel, as is customary, it may be deduced from this that $W = 1.25\,D$.

The cotter must be sufficiently strong to resist possible bending action. Based on Professor Unwin's premises,

$$M\,max = \frac{P}{2}\left(\frac{D}{4} + \frac{D_3 - D}{6}\right) = f\,Z \quad\dotfill (161)$$

where f is the maximum fibre stress in tons per square inch, either tensile or compressive, due to bending.

The usual taper for crosshead cotters is of the order of 1 in 30.

(ii) *Strength of Rod.*

Usually,

$$\frac{\pi}{4}\,D^2 - D\,t = \frac{\pi}{4}\,D_1^2 \quad\dotfill (162)$$

Next, the tensile resistance of the rod at the cotter hole is given by

$$\left(\frac{\pi}{4}\,D^2 - D\,t\right)f_t$$

Then, for equal strength:—

$$2\,W\,t\,f_s = D\,t\,f_c = \left(\frac{\pi}{4}\,D^2 - D\,t\right)f_t \quad\dotfill (163)$$

whence, with the values of f_c and f_t appropriate to steel, $t = .26\,D$.

The proportion of dimensions A varies within the limits of $0.5\,D$ and D, the usual value being $0.75\,D$.

The amount of draw, C, should not exceed $\tfrac{1}{16}''$.

(iii) *Strength of Socket.*

Equating the resistances to tension, shear and compression respectively, we have

$$\left\{ \frac{\pi}{4}(D_3{}^2 - D^2) - (D_3 - D)t \right\} f_t = 2(D_3 - D)A f_s = (D_3 - D)t f_c \quad (164)$$

Further, equating the shear in the socket to that in the rod end,

$$2(D_3 - D) A f_s = 2D A f_s \quad \dots\dots\dots\dots\dots\dots (165)$$

It follows from this that where the values of f_s for both socket and rod are identical, $D_3 = 2D$.

D_2 should not be less than $1.5 D$.

It is essential that the rod end should bed positively in the socket body as otherwise, when the socket is in compression, *i.e.*, with the sense of P reversed, the thrust sets up excessively high circumferential stresses.

It will be noticed in Fig. 21 that a hole is shewn drilled through the end of the socket; this facilitates the removal of the rod.

CROSSHEADS AND SLIDEBARS.

With the crosshead in side elevation the gudgeon pin should be so located that its centre is in the same transverse plane as that of the piston rod and that its vertical centre line bisects the length of the slipper blocks. The dimensions of the gudgeon pin are determined by the provision of adequate bearing surface rather than by considerations of strength; pressures due to piston load vary in practice approximately within the limits of 4,000 and 6,000 lb. per square inch of projected area. As the use of forked connecting rod ends is not favoured in locomotive practice, on account of the very dubious distribution of stress, the pin is almost invariably supported at either end. Assuming the effective length between supports to be l inches and the diameter d inches, l and d are usually made approximately equal. Having proportioned these dimensions to give the desired bearing pressure, the strength of the pin may then be checked from

$$M\ max = \frac{P\ l}{8} = .0982\ d^3\ f \quad \dots\dots\dots\dots\dots\dots (166)$$

where P is the maximum piston load in units to agree with those adopted for the maximum working stress, f, due to bending; a representative value of f is 6,500 lb. per square inch.

Pettigrew gives an empirical rule which states that d may be made equal to (diameter of piston rod — $\frac{1}{8}$) inches.

The taper for the gudgeon pin head, where bearing in the crosshead wall, and also for that portion of the pin fitting into the opposite wall, may be 1 in 5 on the diameter. The pin may be either of forging steel, with an ultimate tensile strength of 40-50 tons per square inch, or of alloy steel. A suitable allowance for wear of that portion of the pin on which the small end bears is 0.03″ on the diameter.

When the engine is running in fore gear with the regulator open, the thrust normally exerted by the crosshead on the slidebars, neglecting the effects of friction, is vertically upwards in sense throughout the revolution, and of course downwards when in back gear. In some instances, *e.g.*, on main line engines performing the bulk of their work in fore gear, it will be noticed that the bearing surface of the apparently redundant slipper has been reduced, but having regard to the zero values of the crosshead thrust at the dead centres and to the reversal of its direction occurring when the engine is coasting, this practice is not to be encouraged.

The magnitude of the crosshead thrust at any instant may be determined by construction (Fig. 22). As in previous diagrams, $A\ B$ and $B\ C$ represent the connecting rod and

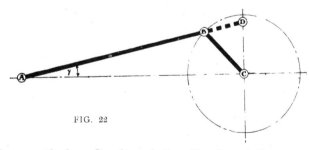

FIG. 22

crank respectively. Produce $A\ B$ to D. Let $A\ C$ represent the piston load, P, to scale. Then, for any given value of angle γ, $C\ D$ represents the crosshead thrust to the same scale that $A\ C$ represents P, and is equal to $A\ C\ tan\ \gamma$.

It is sufficiently accurate for all practical purposes to assume that the

$$\text{Maximum crosshead thrust} = \frac{P}{n}\ \text{lb.} \quad\ldots\ldots\ldots\ldots\ldots\ldots\ (167)$$

where P = piston load (maximum value, with allowance for contingencies) lb., and, as before,

n = ratio of connecting rod length to crank radius, and occurs at half stroke.

The slipper blocks should be so designed that the maximum bearing pressure does not exceed 120 lb. per square inch, and this pressure should only be tolerated in exceptional circumstances, *e.g.*, with inside cylinder engines having very limited clearances. In order to keep wear within reasonable limits a working pressure of 60-80 lb. per square inch should, in view of exposure to grit, especially with outside cylinders, be regarded as desirable. In some designs the bearing pressure is as low as 40 lb. per square inch.

It is not possible, for instance, with single bar crossheads, but where the design permits, the slipper blocks should be distinct from the body of the crosshead proper and pivoted thereon in order uniformly to distribute the thrust over the whole area of the bearing surface. If not thus provided, a certain amount of flexibility should be arranged in the horizontal plane to assist the engine in accommodating itself to curves, a corresponding amount of play also being allowed in the slidebars.

With four bar crossheads, if of cast iron, a minimum thickness of $\frac{1}{2}''$ will generally be found ample for the slide blocks, although other considerations usually dictate a greater thickness than that required purely for strength. There should be over 1" thickness of metal round the gudgeon pin; the flanges may have a thickness of $\frac{3}{4}''$.

The body of the crosshead should be renewed when the wear in the hole for the gudgeon pin exceeds 0.01".

A clearance of about 0.005" should be allowed between the slipper block and each face of the slide bar; on some railways the stipulated tolerance is 0.003". When the slipper block is lined with white metal the thickness of the latter may be $\frac{1}{8}''$.

Although involving a heavier crosshead, the single slidebar design offers several advantages. The wearing surfaces are relatively high above rail level and therefore more protected from grit and dust; this point has considerable weight with industrial locomotives and many of those for foreign railways. There is only one slidebar per cylinder to machine, set and keep aligned in service, with a consequent minimisation of both first and maintenance costs. The single slidebar also gives, in most instances, the minimum deflection under load, and this property of stiffness is fundamentally important in the design of these details; clearances usually limit the possible depth of multi-bar arrangements, with the result that the deflection is considerable in these cases. The cap portions of single bar crossheads are secured with from six to ten bolts having a diameter of $\frac{3}{4}''$ or $\frac{7}{8}''$.

For the determination of the maximum bending stress in the slidebar (167) may be used as a basis, the effective length of beam being the distance between centres of the retaining bolts and the nature of the load considered as concentrated. In order to prevent grooved wear the total length of the wearing surface should be slightly less than (length of slipper block + piston stroke). Steel with an elastic limit of about 25 tons per square inch is usually employed for the slidebars, and in such cases a maximum working stress due to bending of 4 tons per square inch may be allowed although, under exceptional conditions, when using steel of 40-45 tons per square inch ultimate tensile strength, stresses up to 8 tons per square inch are safe. In general, however, the slidebar dimensions necessary to keep the slideblock pressure within the low limits previously mentioned also engender a very moderate value for the fibre stresses in the bar. In order to obtain the desired stiffness the bars should, if practicable, be supported as near the mid-stroke position of the crosshead as possible.

The desirability of allowing a measure of freedom, to provide for the flexibility in the transverse plane of the engine as a whole, has already been mentioned. To this end the seatings for the slidebars should be devoid of ledges or lugs registering with, and therefore preventing horizontal movement of, the slidebar. At the same time the shear stress in the retaining studs or bolts, due to this permitted movement, should be kept within reasonable limits by slotting (*i.e.*, elongating) the holes for their reception at the end of the bar remote from the cylinders.

Gun metal liners about $\frac{1}{4}''$ thick should be provided between the slidebar and its seatings to permit of vertical adjustment.

Slidebars are liable to overheat should the piston packings blow and displace the lubricant. Provision should therefore be made, where possible, for this contingency.

CONNECTING RODS.

The greatest stresses to which the connecting rod is subjected are those due to its inertia; by comparison, the direct stresses due to the pull and thrust of the piston load are unimportant. The effect of the inertia loading on the rod is to cause a deflection, with the result that the actual application of the direct piston load is slightly excentric. Although not of frequent occurrence, the connecting rod may further be subjected to torsion in the event of the driving axleboxes not being at the same height in the hornblocks; the effects of this latter condition, which are not amenable to definite computation, are most marked in the case of narrow gauge engines, especially when outside framing is adopted.

The preliminary calculation is to determine the stresses due to inertia.

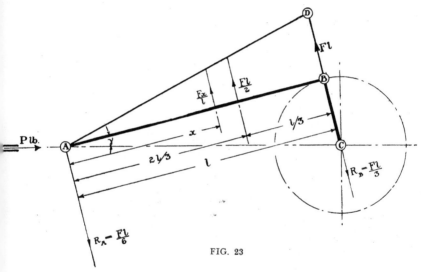

FIG. 23

Let $A B$ (Fig. 23) represent a connecting rod l inches in length, and let its average weight per inch run be m lb.; in this connection, one cubic inch of steel weighs 0.284 lb. Assume the big end to be rotating at its peak speed (this, for a main line engine, may be taken for the purpose of design as 6 or 7 revolutions per second), such that the corresponding mean crankpin velocity is v feet per second. The maximum radial acceleration of crankpin B occurs when $\angle ABC = 90°$ and, if the length of crank BC be R feet, is equal to $\dfrac{v^2}{R}$ feet per second.

At the same time the acceleration of gudgeon pin A is zero. Hence, $\triangle ADB$ represents the variation in acceleration, and therefore the distribution of inertia loading, throughout the length of the connecting rod. The resultant load on the rod is $\dfrac{F\,l}{2}$ lb.,

$$\text{where } F = \frac{m\,v^2}{g\,R} \text{ lb.,} \quad\text{.................................. (168)}$$

and acts at distance $\dfrac{l}{3}$ from B.

Then, taking moments about B to determine the reaction R_A,

$$R_A\,l = \frac{F\,l}{2} \times \frac{l}{3}$$

$$\text{whence } R_A = \frac{F\,l}{6} \quad\text{..................................... (169)}$$

Similarly, it follows that $R_B = \dfrac{F\,l}{3}$

Now, let the point of maximum bending be at some point distant x inches from A. The inertia load at this point will be equal to $\dfrac{F\,x}{l}$ lb., and the extent of the shear force will be

$$\frac{F\,l}{6} - \frac{F\,x}{l} \times \frac{x}{2} \text{ lb.}$$

Then, since the point of maximum bending coincides with that of zero shear,

$$\frac{F\,l}{6} = \frac{F\,x^2}{2\,l}$$

$$\text{whence } x = \frac{l}{\sqrt{3}} = 0.577\ l \quad\text{....................... (170)}$$

The bending moment at x is therefore expressed by

$$M\ max = \frac{F\ l}{6}\ x - \frac{F\ x}{l} \times \frac{x}{2} \times \frac{x}{3}$$

$$= \frac{F\ lx}{6} - \frac{F\ x^3}{6l}$$

$$= \frac{F}{6}\left(lx - \frac{x^3}{l}\right) \quad\dots\dots\dots\dots\dots\dots (171)$$

Substituting in (171) the values obtained by (168) and (170), we have

$$M\ max = \frac{m\ v^2\ l^2}{15.59\ g\ R}\ \text{lb.-inches} \quad\dots\dots\dots\dots\ (172)$$

The maximum fibre stress due to inertia, which may be either tensile or compressive according to the quadrant in which the crankpin is rotating, is therefore given by

$$f_i = \frac{m\ v^2\ l^2}{15.59\ g\ R\ Z} = \frac{m\ v^2\ l^2\ y}{15.59\ g\ R\ A\ \kappa^2} =$$

$$\frac{m\ v^2\ l^2\ y}{15.59\ g\ R\ I}\ \text{lb. per square inch} \quad\dots\dots\ (173)$$

where Z = modulus of section at x, inch units,

A = cross sectional area of section at x, square inches,

κ = radius of gyration at x, inches,

y = distance from neutral axis to surface of section at x, inches,

and I = moment of inertia of section at x, inch units.

Fig. 24 recapitulates the properties, with respect to both axes, of the sections customarily employed for connecting rods, and also for coupling rods. With regard to the I section which, giving the most favourable distribution of material from the point of view of strength, is now applied to all but the smaller connecting rods, it will be noted that the effects of fillets are here disregarded.

As advocated in the very able series of articles on locomotive design which appeared in the *Railway Engineer* over a con-

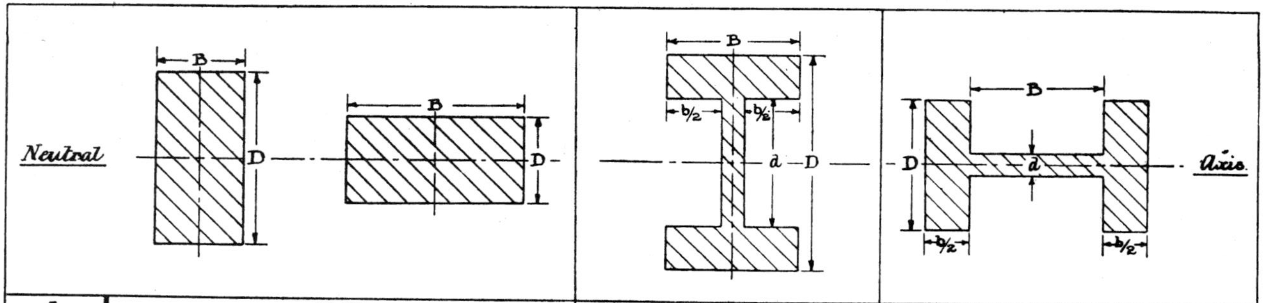

	Rectangle	H-section	I-section
A	BD	$BD - bd$	$bD + Bd$
y	$\dfrac{D}{2}$	$\dfrac{D}{2}$	$\dfrac{D}{2}$
I_{NA}	$\dfrac{BD^3}{12}$	$\dfrac{BD^3 - bd^3}{12}$	$\dfrac{bD^3 + Bd^3}{12}$
Z_{NA}	$\dfrac{BD^2}{6}$	$\dfrac{BD^3 - bd^3}{6D}$	$\dfrac{bD^3 + Bd^3}{6D}$
κ^2_{NA}	$\dfrac{D^2}{12}$	$\dfrac{BD^3 - bd^3}{12(BD - bd)}$	$\dfrac{bD^3 + Bd^3}{12(bD + Bd)}$

FIG. 24

PROPERTIES OF SECTIONS COMMONLY EMPLOYED FOR CONNECTING AND COUPLING RODS.

siderable period (1915-1924), it will be found very useful to determine the value of F, equation (168), when m equals unity.

The resultant load, $\dfrac{F\,l}{2}$ lb., then becomes the dynamic augment, or quantity by which each pound mass of connecting rod is increased when rotating at the given crank radius and velocity. This procedure, which is of course equally applicable to coupling rods, is especially beneficial should any adjustment or alteration subsequently be found necessary in the design of the rod section.

When the connecting rod is rotating in the upper quadrants the value of the maximum fibre stress actually obtaining is somewhat lower than that given by (172), as the bending stresses due to the dead weight of the rod may be deducted. In the lower quadrants, however, the weight acts in the same direction as the inertia force and should then be added to the latter, but the effect on the stresses in the rod is relatively small and is therefore usually disregarded; the static bending stresses due to the weight of the connecting rod in normal locomotive practice represent approximately 1/40 to 1/50 of those due to its inertia.

Should it be desired to recognise the effect of the dead weight, the following argument may be employed.

Let the total mass of the connecting rod be W lb., and assume it to be concentrated at the centre of gravity of the rod, distant y inches from A (see Fig. 25), its line of action being inclined at $a°$ to the longitudinal centre line of the rod.

Resolving W into components, the maximum pure bending moment due to the vertical component will be given in lb.-inches by

$$M\ max = \frac{W\ sin\ a \times (l-y) \times y}{l}$$

whence $$f = \frac{W\ sin\ a \times (l-y) \times y}{l \times Z_y}$$

in which Z_y is the modulus of the section at the centre of gravity of the rod. Further, due to the horizontal component, there will be a direct tensile stress of maximum value $\dfrac{W\ cos\ a}{A\ _{min}}$, where A_{min} is the cross sectional area in square inches of the smallest rod section.

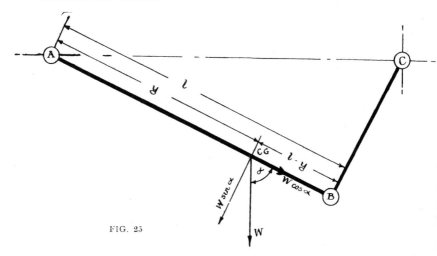

FIG. 25

The total stress at any given cross section of the rod, y, due to the dead weight of the connecting rod, is therefore

$$f_{dw} = \frac{W \sin \alpha \times (l-y) \times y}{l \times Z_y} \pm \frac{W \cos \alpha}{A_y} \quad \ldots\ldots\ldots\ldots (174)$$

It is obvious that the maximum stress (tensile) is given by

$$f_{dw} \; max = \frac{W \sin \alpha \times (l-y) \times y}{l \times Z_y} + \frac{W \cos \alpha}{A_y} \quad \ldots\ldots\ldots (175)$$

From the foregoing it will be seen that the maximum instantaneous fibre stresses, due to the bending of the rod under dynamic and static loads acting in the vertical plane, comprise

$$\Sigma f_v = f_i + f_{dw} \quad \ldots\ldots\ldots\ldots\ldots\ldots\ldots\ldots\ldots\ldots\ldots\ldots\ldots\ldots\ldots\ldots (176)$$

Care must be exercised in using (176) that the worst possible combination of f_i and f_{dw} is taken, *i.e.*, their respective maximum values do not necessarily coincide at a given angular position of the rod.   The variation throughout the revolution, under various conditions of working, of Σf_v should in any case be plotted, as the information will be required in connection with the design of other details.

The connecting rod has hitherto been considered as a beam, and by limiting the working value of Σf_v to about 8,000 lb. per square inch (this value applies to ordinary mild steel, and may be increased where alloy steels are employed), it will generally be found that the rod has sufficient strength when subsequently treated as a long strut. In general, f_v for high speeds should represent about $\frac{1}{8}$, and certainly not more than $\frac{1}{6}$, of the ultimate strength of the material. It is essential that the strength of the rod as a column be checked, preferably by Euler's formula.

Where bending in the vertical plane is concerned, the connecting rod may be considered as a strut with both ends rounded ($\lambda = l$). The stresses due to the piston load, which are next to be reviewed, tend to cause buckling. This would be more liable to occur where the rod is weakest as a column, viz., in the horizontal plane; in this case the connecting rod must be considered as a column with both ends flat ($\lambda = \dfrac{l}{2}$).

The maximum direct stress due to the piston load at any instant is given by

$$f_{pl} = \frac{P \sec \gamma}{A_{min}} \quad\dotfill\quad (177)$$

where P = piston load, inclusive of allowances for over-compression, reboring, etc., as previously enumerated, lb.,

γ = angle between axis of connecting rod and cylinder respectively (see Fig. 23 *ante*) and

A_{min} = minimum cross sectional area of connecting rod, square inches.

P should in any event be calculated on full boiler pressure.

Although, as previously mentioned, the application of the piston thrust is somewhat excentric, due to the deflection of the rod under the inertia loading, the bending stresses thereby set up are so small that they may be safely ignored. The rod must, however, be considered as a strut, and its ability to resist buckling in the horizontal plane verified.

Care must also be taken, with especial reference to the small end, that A_{min} is sufficient in extent to keep the stress within reasonable limits. In this case the actual elastic limit of the forging may be assumed to be 50% of the ultimate strength, and for mild steel with an ultimate strength of 30 tons per square inch, f_{pl} should be from 3 to $3\frac{1}{4}$ tons per square inch, and for wrought iron from 2 to $2\frac{1}{2}$ tons per square inch (*The Railway Engineer*).

In general, the inertia loading determines the depth, and the piston load the width, of a connecting rod of rectangular section. Provided the rod is sufficient in depth to resist the dynamic forces in the vertical plane, it will usually be found capable of resisting bending stresses in the same plane due to the piston load if not stressed beyond the limits mentioned in the preceding paragraph.

It may be noted that the web thickness of the nickel-chrome steel connecting rods for the L.N.E.R. "Pacific" type engines is only $\frac{3}{8}''$.

Small End. Should not be forked. The dimensions of gudgeon pins have already been considered; taking as a unit the diameter of this pin, d, the overall diameter of the small end of the connecting rod is generally made from ($2\ d - \frac{1}{8}$) to ($2\ d + \frac{1}{2}$) inches. The thickness of the bush, which, it is strongly recommended, should be keyed, varies from $\frac{3}{8}''$ to $\frac{5}{8}''$; of this, in some instances, up to $\frac{3}{16}''$ may comprise a white metal liner. It is neither customary nor desirable to provide means for taking up wear, which is not great, in the small end.

Big End. Big end pins, which will be discussed in greater detail, according to whether inside or outside cylinders are concerned, when crank axles and outside crankpins respectively are considered, are usually designed for bearing pressures of from 1,000 to 2,000 lb. per square inch of projected area, an average figure being in the region of 1,350-1,400 lb. per square inch for inside big ends, and 1,600 upwards for outside, the more rapid radiation of heat in this case permitting of higher pressures. Pressures indicative of U.S.A. practice are 1,600 lb. per square inch of projected area for superheated, and 1,700 for saturated steam engines; these latter pressures refer to outside big ends.

The use of solid big ends, preferably with floating bushes, is to be recommended for outside cylinders. Although, when adjusting for wear, to take down the connecting rod and re-bush is admittedly a bigger job than to adjust a cotter and wedge, the wear is more even and reduced, the big end lighter and more compact, there are fewer parts liable to fail, and the taking up of wear does not call for such a high standard of workmanship. Taking as a unit the journal diameter, d, the outside diameter of the floating bronze bush may be made 1.3d, and that of the fixed steel bush, 1.4 d.   A suitable diametral tolerance for both internal and external diameters of the floating bush is 0.016″.   When a fixed bush only is employed, its external diameter may approximate to 1.2d; such bushes should be definitely located with either a key or a set-bolt.   The overall diameter of the big end of the connecting rod should not be less than 1.83d.

Up to ⅛″ sideplay may be allowed between the brass and the journal.   In some instances the diameter of the brass, as measured on the vertical centre line, is made about 1/32″ larger than that at the longitudinal centre line of the big end.   This corrects the tendency of the brass to close in as it warms up, and also facilitates the entry of oil to the bearing, assuming it to be introduced at the vertical centre line of the latter.

Mr. Clayton has stated (Proc. I. Loco. E.) that S.R. experience proves a continuous white metal liner to be essential for big ends, and also for coupling rod bushes, when working on crankpins of alloy steel; the latter material causes heating, or at least scoring, if in contact with brass or bronze bushes. The composition of white metal specified for solid big ends on the Central Argentine Ry. (also abstracted from the Proc. I. Loco. E.) is:—

Tin	83 %
Copper	11.5%
Antimony	5.5%

Crushing load:—10,820 lb. per square inch.

The Engineer (13th January 1933) mentions a bearing metal which is reported to have given good results, as regards wear and consumption of lubricant, with nitralloy steel crankpins. This is made up of:—

Copper	80 %
Nickel	5.5%
Tin	11.5%
Zinc	3 %

The adoption of solid outside big ends is further accelerated by the limited clearances available when long piston strokes coincide with coupled wheels of small diameter.   Irrespective of the form of big end employed, suitable allowances must in any case be made for the effects on vertical clearance of the weakening of springs and tyre wear occurring in service.

As the brasses are indeterminately stressed, they should be provided with deep flanges in order to secure rigidity.

The open type of big end with strap is at a disadvantage in that a mass of metal which should be beyond the big end centre, and not between the centres of the connecting rod, is unfavourably concentrated. When designing big ends of this type it is important that the centres of the big end bolts (the taper on the diameter of which may be $\frac{1}{8}''$ in 12") should be as far apart as possible in order to increase the bearing of the strap on the rod, a hole being bored through the connecting rod end to reduce its weight.

The straps or caps, as the case may be, can be conveniently considered as uniformly loaded beams. Unwin quotes 9,000 lb. per square inch as a suitable value of the working bending stress for mild steel. It was advocated in the *Railway Engineer* that the thickness of the strap at the corners should be made equal to ($\sqrt{2}$ × thickness of strap arm). With big ends of the marine pattern it is obviously advantageous so to arrange the bolt centres that they are as close together as possible.

A suitable taper for big end cotters is 1 in 16.

Outside cylinders permit of considerably more freedom as regards big end design than do those placed inside (on the assumption that two cylinders between the frames are being considered). In the former case the length of crankpin may be 6" or more, and in the latter, $5\frac{3}{8}''$ probably represents the extreme limit for the standard gauge. The provision of suitable bearing area therefore entails the adoption of a crankpin having a comparatively large diameter, with greater rubbing speeds in consequence, for inside cylinder engines; the diameter is primarily determined by the stipulation that the maximum fibre stress due to bending action shall not exceed 9-10 tons per square inch.

COUPLING RODS.

Inertia Loads.

The stresses to which coupling rods are subjected are similar to those in the connecting rod. Bending stresses are set up by centrifugal action and by the weight of the rod itself, whilst the load generated by the transmission of torque gives rise to direct, alternating stresses; the rod is further liable to buckle in the horizontal plane due to strains arising when the locomo-

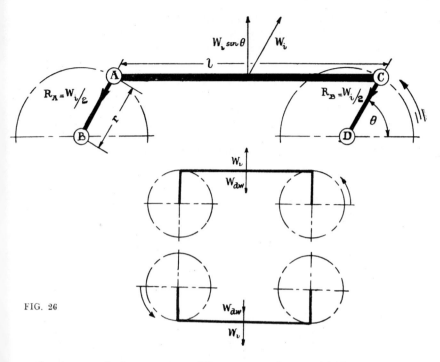

FIG. 26

tive is negotiating curves. The stresses due to this latter condition are not amenable to definite calculation.

Considering firstly the inertia stresses due to the centrifugal action, let rod $A\ C$ (Fig. 26) revolve at radius r feet about centres B and D respectively such that the mean crankpin velocity corresponding to the maximum rate of revolution is v feet per second. The radial acceleration of any point in the rod is then $\dfrac{v^2}{r}$ feet per second per second, its component normal to the rod being $\dfrac{v^2}{r} . \sin \theta$.

Then, if the average weight of the rod be m lb. per inch run and its length l inches, the total dynamic loading, normal to the rod, will be

$$W_i = \frac{m v^2}{g\ r}\ l.\ \sin \theta \text{ lb.,}$$

and the corresponding bending moment at mid-length, assuming the section of the rod to be parallel throughout and the loading uniformly distributed in consequence,

$$M_i = \frac{m\,v^2}{g\,r} \cdot \frac{l^2}{8} \text{—}sin\ \theta \text{ lb.-inches} \dots\dots\dots\dots\dots (178)$$

The maximum value occurs when $\theta = 90°$. Then,

$$M_i\,max. = \frac{m\,v^2}{g\,r} \cdot \frac{l^2}{8} \text{ lb.-inches} \dots\dots\dots\dots\dots (179)$$

When the rod is on top centre the actual bending stresses are reduced in extent, as the dead weight of the rod is then acting in a direction contrary to that of the inertia load, as shewn in Fig. 26. When on the bottom centre, however, both loadings have the same sense.

Since the maximum bending moment due to the dead weight, assuming uniform distribution, is

$$M_{dw}\,max. = \frac{m\,l^2}{8} \text{ lb.-inches} \dots\dots\dots\dots\dots (180)$$

then the maximum bending moment due to the combination of the inertia and dead weight loadings, occurring when the rod is on bottom centre, is

$$\Sigma\,M\,max. = \frac{m\,l^2}{8} \left(\frac{v^2}{gr} + 1 \right) \text{ lb.-inches} \dots\dots\dots (181)$$

and the corresponding maximum fibre stress due to this bending may be determined by alternative methods similar to those employed in (173) for connecting rods.

This stress may of course be either tensile or compressive, and to it must be added algebraically those due to $W_i\ cos\ \theta$ (the horizontal component of the inertia loading), and to the load generated by the transmission of the torque. The computation of the latter will be considered at some length in the succeeding section, together with the thrusts on the axleboxes, which may be conveniently evaluated concurrently.

Assuming for the moment that the longitudinally applied driving force in the coupling rod has been determined, then the stress due to the deflection only of the rod under its combined static and dynamic loads, which is additional to those arising from pure bending as previously determined, may be calculated from

$$f_{dl} = \frac{F}{A} \pm F \left(\frac{5}{384} \cdot \frac{W \, l^3}{E \, I^2} \cdot y \right) \dots\dots\dots\dots\dots\dots (182)$$

where F = sum of $W_i \, cos \, \theta$ and driving force,

   W = sum of inertia loads acting in the vertical plane
       and dead weight, the unit of mass adopted being
       of course uniform with F,

   E = Young's modulus for the material, and the re-
       maining symbols have the same significance as
       in (173).

It must be remembered, when determining the most unfavourable combination of stresses, that the effects of inertia
are greatest at high speeds, while the piston loads tend to fall
in value. Further, as with the connecting rod, the maximum
values of the various stresses concerned do not necessarily coincide at a given angular position of the coupling rod; the
most unfavourable combination must therefore be determined.

The calculated direct load in the coupling rod due to the
transmission of the torque generated, by inside cylinders only,
may be legitimately reduced by, say, 5%, to allow for the
partial absorption of its effective value by engine friction.

Direct (Horizontal) Loads on Coupling Rods and Axle-boxes.

The object of the following analysis is to determine the
maximum values of the direct loads, arising from the transmission of the driving torque, on coupling rods and axleboxes
for the specified arrangements of cylinders and drives. For
this purpose crank positions are taken at which maximum
torque is developed. It will be clearly understood that in
every case where the direction of a force is specified, that
direction is instantaneous, *i.e.*, its application is limited to the
crank position and direction of rotation under consideration;
all forces set up by the pull and thrust of the connecting rod
reverse in sense at each half revolution of the driving wheels,
and also when the direction of movement of the engine is
reversed.

In each case it is assumed for simplicity that the total adhesive weight, W, is equally distributed over n coupled axles,
and that each axle absorbs $\dfrac{\Sigma \, T}{n}$ torque, where $\Sigma \, T$ is the maximum value of the total applied torque. The theory is, of

course, equally applicable to cases where there are variations in the adhesive weights on individual coupled axles, the necessary adjustment being made by simple proportion. Thus:—

Let the weight on any given axle be W_A. Then, if the total adhesive weight be W_T, the torque absorbed by the axle under consideration will be $\dfrac{\Sigma T . W_A}{W_T}$.

It is also assumed in each case that extreme conditions of loading occur when an individual driving wheel slips, with the result that the whole of the applied torque, less the amount absorbed by that particular driving wheel, is transmitted by the coupling rod on the opposite side of the engine.

Let n = number of coupled axles,

P = load per piston,

Q = pull or thrust in connecting rod,

r = radius of crank,

r_{CR} = radius of coupling rod crank in those cases where this dimension is smaller than r, and

ΣT = maximum torque developed by engine.

Ton and inch units should be used throughout.

A graphical method of determining the approximate value of Q will be found by referring to Fig. 29H.

Case (i). Two outside cylinders driving end coupled axle.

With a two-cylinder engine the maximum torque is generated when both cranks make an angle of 45° with the engine centre line. Then

$$\Sigma T = 2\,Qr . \sin. 45° = \frac{2\,Qr}{\sqrt{2}} = \sqrt{2}\,Qr \quad \ldots\ldots\ldots\ldots (183)$$

Now, assume wheel A (Fig. 27a) slips. The whole of the applied torque, less that absorbed by wheels A and D, *i.e.*, $\dfrac{1}{n}\sqrt{2}\,Qr$, is then transmitted by the left hand coupling rod.

Let the load on the portion or section of coupling rod between wheels D and E be $F_{CR(DE)}$. Incidentally, it follows that this quantity is also the horizontal load on the crankpin at E.

Equating, we have

$$F_{CR(DE)}\ r\ sin.\ 45° = \sqrt{2}\,Q\,r\left(1 - \frac{1}{n}\right)$$

$$\text{whence } F_{c\dot{R}(DE)} = 2\,Q\left(1 - \frac{1}{n}\right) \quad \text{.............. (184)}$$

$$\text{Similarly, } F_{CR(EF)} = 2\,Q\left(1 - \frac{2}{n}\right) \text{................. (185)}$$

The horizontal load on the crankpin at F is also evaluated by this latter expression.

The load on any further portions or sections of coupling rod is successively diminished in each instance by $\frac{1}{n}$. $2\,Q$.

Since P is the horizontal component of Q, the horizontal load on the axlebox at D is equal to

$$F_{CR(DE)} - P \text{.. (186)}$$

and is a thrust on the back horn face for the crank position and direction of rotation shewn in the diagram. It should be noted that a driving axlebox will always be subjected to the maximum piston load when the connecting rod is on dead centre and the valve open to lead steam. In general, the coupling rod load is the greatest in magnitude of the horizontal forces acting on the axlebox; its direction is therefore that of the resultant force. The horizontal load on the axlebox at E of course acts in the same direction as that at D, and is equal to

$$F_{CR(DE)} - F_{CR(EF)} \text{.................................... (187)}$$

Stated generally, the horizontal thrust on any coupled axlebox other than the driving box is equal to the difference of the loads in the respective portions of coupling rod on either side of its crankpin. In other words, the thrusts on the coupled boxes throughout that side of the engine which is subjected to maximum coupling rod loadings are equal.

Case (ii). Two outside cylinders driving an intermediate coupled axle.

Assume wheel C (Fig. 27b) slips. Then the total load transmitted through the crankpin at G to the coupling rod is, as before,

$$F_{CR} = 2\,Q\left(1 - \frac{1}{n}\right)$$

This quantity F_{CR} is the force or load engendered in the **coupling rod** by the transmission of an applied torque equal to

$\sqrt{2}\,Q\,r\left(1 - \dfrac{1}{n}\right)$, and the distribution of this load throughout the length of the coupling rod, in any case where the driving axle occupies an intermediate position in the coupled group, is governed jointly by the total number of axles coupled, n, and by the position of the driving axle relative to them. Thus, in general terms, if there are x coupled axles to one side of the driving axle, say, that nearest the cylinders, and y to the other, so that $x + y = n - 1$, then the proportional direct loads transmitted by the coupling rod sections immediately adjacent to the driving crankpin will be $\dfrac{x}{x+y}.\ F_{CR}$ and $\dfrac{y}{x+y}.\ F_{CR}$ respectively. These loads are of opposite sign and, for the crank position and direction of rotation indicated in the diagram, are compressive and tensile respectively; as before, the loads on succeeding sections of coupling rod are diminished in each instance by $\dfrac{1}{n}.\ 2\,Q.$

For the position shewn, the thrust on the driving axlebox at G acts on the back horn face and is equal to

$$F_{CR} - P \dotfill (188)$$

The horizontal load on other coupled axleboxes may be determined by the principle enunciated in Case (i), and is equal to

$$\frac{F_{CR}}{x + y}.$$

Case (iii). Two inside cylinders driving end coupled axle (coupling rod phase angle, 180°).

In cases such as this the throw of the coupling rod cranks is almost invariably rather less than that of the main cranks.

Assuming that wheel A (Fig. 27c) is slipping, we have

$$F_{CR(DE)}r_{CR}\,sin\,45° = \sqrt{2}\,Qr\left(1 - \frac{1}{n}\right)$$

whence $F_{CR\ (DE)} = 2\,Q\left(1 - \dfrac{1}{n}\right)\dfrac{r}{r_{CR}}$ \dotfill (189)

The load on succeeding sections of the coupling rod is

reduced in each instance, assuming as always uniform distribution of the adhesive weight, by a constant amount

$$\frac{1}{n}\left(2\,Q.\ \frac{r}{r_{CR}} \right).$$ Therefore, by analogy with Case (i),

$$F_{CR\ (EF)} = 2\,Q\left(1 - \frac{2}{n} \right)\frac{r}{r_{CR}} \quad \text{.................... (190)}$$

With the conditions obtaining in the diagram, the horizontal load on the driving axlebox at D is thrusting on the front face of the hornblock, and equals

$$F_{CR\ (DE)} + P \quad \text{.. (191)}$$

Case (iv). Two inside cylinders driving an intermediate coupled axle (coupling rod phase angle, 180°).

Wheel B (Fig. 27d) is assumed to be slipping.   Force at crankpin F, due to coupling rod load, is given by

$$F_{CR} = 2\,Q\left(1 - \frac{1}{n} \right)\frac{r}{r_{CR}}$$

This is distributed in the coupling rod under consideration as follows:—

$$F_{CR\ (FG)} = \frac{y}{x+y}.\ \ F_{CR}\ \text{(compression)},$$

$$F_{CR\ (GH)} = \frac{y-1}{x+y}.\ \ F_{CR}\ \text{(compression), and}$$

$$F_{CR\ (FE)} = \frac{x}{x+y}.\ \ F_{CR}\ \text{(tension)}.$$

Horizontal thrust at driving axlebox F, acting on front face of hornblock,

$$= F_{CR} + P.$$

Case (v). Two inside cylinders driving end coupled wheels (coupling rods in phase with adjacent main cranks).

Assuming that wheel A (Fig. 27e) is slipping, the values (but not the direction, which is reversed) of the direct forces on the coupling rods are identical with those obtaining in Case (iii).   The resultant horizontal load on the driving hornblock at D is consequently equal, in this instance, to $(F_{CR\ (DE)} - P)$

and, under the conditions shewn in the diagram, is thrusting on the back face of the hornblock.

Case (vi). Two inside cylinders driving an intermediate coupled axle (coupling rods in phase with adjacent main cranks).

Wheel *B* (Fig. 27f) is assumed to be slipping. The values of the coupling rod loads are as in Case (iv). Their senses are, however, reversed, with the result that the direct load on the driving axlebox at *F* becomes $(F_{CR} - P)$ and is acting, with the conditions shewn on the diagram, on the back face of the hornblock.

Case (vii). Three cylinders driving one axle.

In this case the maximum torque developed, assuming all three cylinders to be open to steam when in the crank position shewn (Fig. 27g), is:—

$$\Sigma T = 2\,Q\,r.\,sin.\,30° + Q\,r.$$
$$= 2\,Q\,r.\,\tfrac{1}{2} + Q\,r.$$
$$= 2\,Q\,r. \quad\quad\quad\quad\quad\quad\quad\quad (192)$$

Assuming that wheel *A* is slipping, the total torque developed, $2\,Q\,r$, less that absorbed by the driving wheels, $\dfrac{1}{n}(2\,Q\,r)$, is transmitted to the coupling rod by the crankpin at *D*.

Equating,

$$F_{CR\,(DE)}\,r.\,sin\,30° = 2\,Q\,r - \frac{1}{n}\left(2\,Q\,r = 2\,Q\,r\left(1 - \frac{1}{n}\right)\right.$$

whence $F_{CR\,(DE)} = 4\,Q\left(1 - \dfrac{1}{n}\right)$ .... (193)

and, by a previous argument,

$$F_{CR\,(EF)} = 4\,Q\left(1 - \frac{2}{n}\right) \quad\quad\quad\quad (194)$$

On the assumptions that the piston loads are equal and that the inside cylinder is centrally disposed between the frames, the horizontal load on the driving axlebox at *D* is equal to

$$\left(F_{CR(DE)} - P_L + \frac{P_1}{2}\right) i.e.,\ F_{CR\,(DE)} - \frac{P}{2}$$ and, with the conditions stipulated on the diagram, is thrusting on the back face of the hornblock. Referring to the former expres-

sion, P_L is the piston load for the left-hand (outside) cylinder, and P_I that for the inside cylinder. As they are equal to one another, and to P, it follows that

$$- P_L + \frac{P_I}{2} = - \frac{P}{2}.$$

Case (viii). Three cylinders with divided drive.

The total applied torque, $\Sigma\ T$, is, as in Case (vii), equal to $2\ Q\ r$.

Two crank positions will be examined in this instance:—

(a) *As in Fig.* 27h.

Of the total applied torque, $2\ Q\ r.\ sin\ 30° = Q\ r$ is supplied by the two outside cylinders and an equal amount, $Q\ r$, by the inside cylinder. Each of the n uniformly loaded coupled axles absorbs torque equal to $2\ \dfrac{Q\ r}{n}$

Then, assuming that wheel A slips, the torque transmitted to the coupling rod through the crankpin at D is $Q\ r - \dfrac{2\ Qr}{n}$,

i.e., $Q\ r \left(1 - \dfrac{2}{n} \right)$

Equating,

$$F_{CR\ (DE)}\ r\ sin\ 30° = Q\ r \left(1 - \frac{2}{n} \right)$$

whence, $F_{CR\ (DE)} = 2\ Q \left(1 - \dfrac{2}{n} \right)$ .... (195)

and the thrust of the axlebox at D will be $F_{CR\ (DE)} + \dfrac{P_I}{2}$,

acting on the back face of the hornblock.

As torque is developed at the intermediate driving wheels in excess of what they can assimilate, $F_{CR\ (DE)}$ is transmitted through the length of the coupling rod to its trailing section. In other words, as the torque absorbed by the trailing wheels is $\dfrac{2\ Q\ r}{n}$, the horizontal load on the axlebox at F is

$$\frac{\dfrac{2\,Q r}{n}}{r\,sin\,30°} = \frac{4\,Q}{n} \qquad \dots\dots\dots\dots\dots\dots\dots\dots\dots\dots\dots \text{(196)}$$

acting, with the conditions shewn on the diagram, on the front horn face.

Consider now the axle $B\,E$. The torque developed by the outside cylinders is $2\,Q\,r\,sin\,30°$, i.e., $Q\,r$. Of this amount, $\dfrac{2\,Q r}{n}$ is absorbed by axle $B\,E$ itself.

On the assumption that wheel B is also slipping, the crankpin at E is transmitting the surplus torque from its own axle $B\,E$, i.e., $Qr - \dfrac{2\,Qr}{n} = Qr\left(1 - \dfrac{2}{n}\right)$, plus that from axle $A\,D$, which must also be equal to $Q\,r\left(1 - \dfrac{2}{n}\right)$, making a total of $2\,Q\,r\left(1 - \dfrac{2}{n}\right)$. Let the load on section $E\,F$ of coupling rod, and also on crankpin at F, be $F_{CR\,(EF)}$.

Then, equating,

$$F_{CR\,(EF)}.\ r\ sin\ 30° = 2Q\,r\left(1 - \frac{2}{n}\right)$$

whence, $F_{CR\,(EF)} = 4\,Q\left(1 - \dfrac{2}{n}\right)$ .... (197)

It should be noted that this expression applies generally, with the arrangement of drive under consideration, to that section of the coupling rod which is immediately to the rear of the second driving axle.

The horizontal load on the axleboxes derived from $F_{CR\,(EF)}$ is taken equally by the boxes at D and E respectively. The horizontal load on axlebox at E is therefore

$$2\,Q\left(1 - \frac{2}{n}\right) - P,$$

and, with the conditions shewn on the diagram, is thrusting on the back face of the hornblock.

(*b*) *Cranks in position shewn by Fig.* 27i.

The inside cylinder is at this instant developing zero torque but, assuming that it is open to lead steam, axleboxes A and D are each subjected to a horizontal thrust of magnitude $\dfrac{P}{2}$.

For the outside cylinders,

$$\Sigma T = 2\,Q\,r\,sin\,60° = 2\,Q\,r.\,\frac{\sqrt{3}}{2} = \sqrt{3}\,Q\,r \,\ldots\ldots (198)$$

Of this, $\dfrac{\sqrt{3}\,Q\,r}{n}$ is absorbed by each coupled axle. Assuming that wheel B is slipping, the torque transmitted by crankpin E is $\sqrt{3}\,Q\,r\left(1 - \dfrac{1}{n}\right)$. Let the coupling rod load on this crankpin be F_{CR}. Then:—

$$F_{CR}\,r\,sin\,60° = \sqrt{3}\,Q\,r\left(1 - \frac{1}{n}\right)$$

whence $F_{CR} = 2\,Q\left(1 - \dfrac{1}{n}\right)$ $\ldots\ldots\ldots\ldots\ldots (199)$

Proceeding as in Case (ii),

$$F_{CR\,(DE)} = \frac{x}{x+y}.\,F_{CR} \quad (\text{tension})$$

$$F_{CR\,(EF)} = \frac{y}{x+y}.\,F_{CR} \quad (\text{compression})$$

Horizontal loads on axleboxes are:—

At D: $F_{CR\,(DE)} + \dfrac{P_I}{2}$,

At E: $F_{CR} - P$,

At F: $F_{CR\,(EF)}$,

acting instantaneously on the back faces of the hornblocks at D and F, and on the front face at E.

Case (ix). Four cylinders (adjacent inside and outside cylinders at 180°), driving one axle.

$$\Sigma T = 4\,Q\,r.\,sin\,45° = 2\,\sqrt{2}\,Q\,r \quad\dots\dots\dots\dots (200)$$

Assume wheel A (Fig. 27j) to be slipping. The crankpin at D then transmits a torque of $2\,\sqrt{2}\,Q\,r\left(1 - \dfrac{1}{n}\right)$

Let the coupling rod load on this crankpin be F_{CR}.

Then, equating,

$$F_{CR}.\,r\,sin\,45° = 2\,\sqrt{2}\,Q\,r\left(1 - \frac{1}{n}\right)$$

whence,

$$F_{CR} = 4\,Q\left(1 - \frac{1}{n}\right) \quad\dots\dots\dots\dots (201)$$

This quantity also represents (a) the direct load on section $D\,E$ of the coupling rod, the instantaneous nature of the stress being tensile, and (b), since the piston loads on either side of the driving axleboxes mutually cancel, the horizontal thrust of the driving axleboxes on the horns which, with the conditions indicated by the diagram, acts on the back face.

Since $F_{CR\,(DE)} = 4\,Q\left(1 - \dfrac{1}{n}\right)$, it follows by previous argument that

$$F_{CR\,(EF)} = 4\,Q\left(1 - \frac{2}{n}\right) \quad\dots\dots\dots\dots (202)$$

the thrust on any succeeding sections of coupling rod being reduced *pro rata*.

The thrust on each coupled box, as distinct from the driving boxes, is given by $\dfrac{4\,Q}{n}$ and, in the circumstances under consideration, is acting on the front faces of the hornblocks concerned.

Case (x). Four cylinders (adjacent inside and outside cylinders at 180°), with divided drive.

The development of ΣT is as given in Case (ix), but its development is here distributed over two axles. The method of procedure is therefore analagous with that followed in Case (viii).

Assume wheel A (Fig. 27k) slips.   Axle AD will then transmit a torque of

$$\sqrt{2}\,Q\,r - \frac{2\sqrt{2}\,Q\,r}{n} = \sqrt{2}\,Q\,r\left(1 - \frac{2}{n}\right)$$

Let the direct load on the section of coupling rod between D and E be $F_{CR\ (DE)}$.   Then, equating,

$$F_{CR\ (DE)}\cdot r\,\sin 45° = \sqrt{2}\,Q\,r\left(1 - \frac{2}{n}\right),$$

whence $F_{CR\ (DE)} = 2\,Q\left(1 - \frac{2}{n}\right)$ .... (203)

The resultant horizontal load on the axlebox at D is equal to

$$F_{CR\ (DE)} + P \dots\dots\dots\dots\dots\dots\dots\dots\dots\dots\dots\dots\dots\dots\dots (204)$$

and, under the conditions indicated, is thrusting on the back face of the horn.

As in Case (viii), this load is transmitted to the trailing section or sections of the coupling rod, due to the fact that the torque developed in the axle driven by the outside cylinders is greater than can be assimilated by that axle itself.   Since the torque received by the trailing axle, at a radius of $r.\sin 45°$, is

equal to $\dfrac{2\sqrt{2}\,Q\,r}{n}$, the horizontal load on axlebox F, and on

all other coupled axleboxes, with the exception of driving boxes,

on the left-hand side of the engine, must be equal to $\dfrac{4\,Q}{n}$, and

is acting at the instant on the front faces of the hornblocks.

For the axle BE, driven by the outside cylinders, the torque generated is equal to $\sqrt{2}\,Q\,r$, and that transmitted to

$$\sqrt{2}\,Q\,r - \frac{2\sqrt{2}\,Q\,r}{n} = \sqrt{2}\,Q\,r\left(1 - \frac{2}{n}\right)$$

Now assume that wheel B slips.   Crankpin E must then

transmit a torque of $\sqrt{2}\,Q\,r\left(1 - \dfrac{2}{n}\right)$ due to the inside drive, plus the same amount arising from the outside drive; the torque transmitted at this pin is therefore

$$2 \sqrt{2} Q \, r \left(1 - \frac{2}{n} \right).$$

Equating,

$$F_{CR \; (EF)} . \; r \; sin \; 45° = 2 \sqrt{2} \, Q \, r \left(1 - \frac{2}{n} \right)$$

whence $F_{CR \; (EF)} = 4 \, Q \left(1 - \frac{2}{n} \right).$ .... (205)

As, however, this force is generated equally at crankpins D and E respectively, it follows that the resultant horizontal thrust on the axlebox at E is equal to

$$2 \, Q \left(1 - \frac{2}{n} \right) - P \; .... (206)$$

and, under the stipulated instantaneous conditions, acts on the back face of the hornblock.

COUPLING RODS.

General Remarks.

The working value of the total stress in the rod should not exceed ($\frac{1}{3}$ × elastic limit); the elastic limit in the case of mild steel approximates to 18 tons per square inch. With I sections, the thickness of the web need not exceed about $\frac{1}{2}''$ or $\frac{5}{8}''$ in the case of mild steel, or $\frac{3}{8}''$ for alloy steels, provided that sufficient strength be provided in the flanges.

The maximum desirable length between centres is about 10'-0" for single rods (*i.e.*, for four-coupled engines), and tapered sections are not usually justifiable for lengths below 9'-0" unless more than four wheels are coupled.

The distance between the coupling rod centres is in some instances made greater than that between the centres of the coupled axles by an amount ranging from 1/64" to $\frac{1}{16}''$, usually 1/32", to allow for the effects of strains arising in the frames when loaded, and also for expansion due to heat radiated from the firebox when the latter is adjacent to the coupled wheelbase.

The overall diameter of the rod round the crankpin customarily varies from 1.7d to 1.9d, where d is the crankpin diameter. The thickness of the bronze bush is usually either $\frac{5}{8}''$ or $\frac{3}{4}''$, of which up to $\frac{3}{16}''$ may represent that of a white metalled lining; this latter, as with big ends, is advisedly provided when intended to work in conjunction with crankpins of alloy steel.

The bush is preferably secured in the rod with a key, this effecting a more satisfactory fastening than either a grub screw or a tangential taper pin. In American practice use is occasionally made of a set screw which is integral with the oil cup; centrifugal action on the latter aggravates the tendency of the screw to slacken out as the bush endeavours to work loose in service. In some cases, where bushes are of heavy section and of hard bronze, no provision is made for registering the bush in the rod, although an external circumferential groove and additional radial oil holes are specified to ensure continuity of lubrication should the bush work loose. This practice is open to criticism; unless intended to be of the floating type, the bush should be definitely secured in the rod. Floating bushes used for coupling rods on the N.Y.C.R.R. are in three sections with $1/32''$ cuts between each segment to allow for expansion. Grease lubricated floating bushes of American design are usually bored out about $1/64''$ larger than the diameter of the crankpin; it is stated that the life of these floating bushes is about five times as great as that of fixed bushes.

To permit of sideplay, the length of the bush in the coupling rod is made less than that of the crankpin journal by an amount which varies, according to the length of the rigid wheelbase and radii of curves to be traversed, from $1/64''$ up to $5/32''$, a figure representative of British practice being $\frac{3}{16}''$. Some trailing bushes are fitted in a rectangular recess with curved ends to allow of relative movement between bush and rod when the engine is traversing a curve; this arrangement is used in combination with a horizontally articulated coupling rod.

In order to reduce the indeterminate strains to which coupling rods are subjected by track inequalities and uneven tyre wear, etc., it is usual in the case of inside cylinder engines to make the throw of the outside crankpins from $1''$ to $2''$ less than that of the main cranks; the path radius of the coupling rod crankpins should be determined by the magnitudes of the torque transmitted and the adhesion respectively. The outside cranks are customarily opposite, i.e., at 180° to their corresponding inside cranks, although in a few cases they are in

phase with them.   This practice was originated by the late
Mr. Stroudley, who argued that the thrust on the hornblocks
being the difference, as opposed to the sum, of the connecting
and coupling rod thrusts respectively, axlebox wear would be
reduced.   On the other hand, a considerably larger balance
weight thereby becomes necessary; the bending moment on the
crank axle is also appreciably increased.

OUTSIDE CRANKPINS.

It is no longer general practice to provide a collar adjacent
to the wheel centre on account of high localised stresses set up
at the radius between the pin and collar.   A collar may, however, be provided at the outer extremity of, and solid with,
the crankpin in those cases where the brasses are split.   Otherwise, a detachable collar must be adopted; this should
be pinned in preference to screwing, thus affording greater
security and at the same time facilitating the detection of incipient flaws in the crankpin.   The retaining pin may be of the
solid tapered pattern, screwed for a short length next the head
(*i.e.*, at the major diameter) in order to retain it in position,
or of the split type.   In any event the pin should be so fitted
that the smaller end, or end to be opened out, as the case may
be, is remote from the axle; the effect of centrifugal action
will then be to increase the hold of the pin.   Screwed taper
pins should be locked either by a nut on the head, outside the
collar, or by a split pin through the smaller end; alternatively,
both methods may be employed.   In some designs a hole is
drilled completely through the crankpin on its longitudinal
centre line; a pin, having a head of sufficiently large diameter
and thickness to function as a collar, is inserted in this hole
and secured by a nut and split pin at the end adjacent to
the main frame.

As crank pin failures are peculiarly liable to occur in the
portion within the wheel seat, the minimum diameter of this
part of the pin should be made such that the maximum fibre
stress due to bending occurs in the external portion of the pin.
The crankpin should be pressed into the wheel seat with a force
of approximately 10-12 tons per inch of diameter, and to enable
the pressure to be exerted uniformly throughout the length of
the seat it is advisable that the portion of the crankpin making
contact with the latter be turned taper;   the taper on the
diameter should not in any case exceed 1 in 50, and in some
instances is as little as 1 in 250.   As an additional precaution,
the end of the crankpin should finally be riveted over.

In British practice the length of journal is customarily made at least equal to, if not greater than, the diameter, thus avoiding excessive rubbing speeds.   American engineers, on the contrary, favour comparatively large diameters in conjunction with short journal lengths; although the life of the crankpin is shortened in consequence, it is claimed that greater lateral flexibility is obtained on curves and that the liability of coupling rods to fracture is correspondingly reduced.

The following formula, expressing the relationship of crankpin journal length to diameter, is quoted from the *Railway Engineer*:—

$$\frac{l}{d} = \frac{0.33 \sqrt{f}}{p} \quad \dots\dots\dots\dots\dots\dots\dots\dots\dots\dots\dots\dots (207)$$

where l = length of journal, inches,

d = diameter of journal, inches,

f = maximum bending stress in crankpin, lb. per square inch,

and p = average bearing pressure on crankpin in lb. per square inch of projected area.

Appropriate values of f and p for steel having an elastic limit of about 15 tons per square inch are given as 5 tons per square inch and $\frac{1}{2}$ ton per square inch respectively.

In general, crankpin design involves compliance with two conditions: firstly, the pin must present ample bearing surface, and secondly, it must have sufficient mechanical strength to resist the applied loads.   With regard to the former stipulation, suitable bearing pressures have already been quoted in the section dealing with big ends; the computation of the applied loads has also been considered previously.

In cases where consideration of bearing pressure is more important than that of mechanical strength and heat treated steel is employed, the practice of hollow boring is advantageous.

Mechanically, the crankpin must be treated as a cantilever. A frequently quoted convention for the determination of the bending moment is far too "roughly approximate" to be justifiable; the piston load is assumed to be the applied force, acting at a distance measured from the centre of the journal to the face of the wheel centre.   By this method the bending stresses actually obtaining are considerably understated.   The forces acting on connecting and coupling rods have already been considered at some length; for the present purpose the reactions due to them must be determined and the most unfavourable combination (in the case of inside cylinder engines the coupling rod reaction alone has to be considered) taken when calculating the maximum load on the outside crankpin. In either case the maximum applied loads, F tons, may be assumed to be acting at the centres of the appropriate journals, and capable of exerting bending action thence to the mid-length of the seated portion of the pin in the wheel centre, a total distance of l inches, and not merely to the face of the crank boss.

Then, the maximum bending stress in the crankpin, in tons per square inch, is given by

$$f_{max} = \frac{F \times l}{Z} \quad\text{..} \quad (208)$$

Z for solid circular section $= .0982\,D^3$

Z for hollow circular section $= .0982\left(\dfrac{D^4 - d^4}{D}\right)$

where D and d are the external and internal diameters respectively of the crankpin in inches.

Having thus calculated D for the crankpin, an addition must then be made for the effects of wear. A suitable increment is $\frac{1}{4}''$ for each $3\frac{1}{2}''$ to $4''$ of basic diameter; proportionate allowances may be made for smaller diameters, with a minimum of $\frac{1}{8}''$.

AXLES.

The method of stress determination given hereunder is based on the treatment formulated in an exhaustive series of articles, entitled "Modern Locomotive Engine Design and Construction," which were published in the *Railway Engineer* some few years ago. In acknowledging the source of this information the author wishes to record his indebtedness to the two anonymous writers of these articles, which have proved in many ways extremely helpful to innumerable locomotive engineers.

It will be understood that ton and inch units are employed throughout.

Case (i). Straight carrying axles with inside bearings.

Referring to Fig. 28, let G be the distance between the tread lines and L that between journal centres; further, let w be the

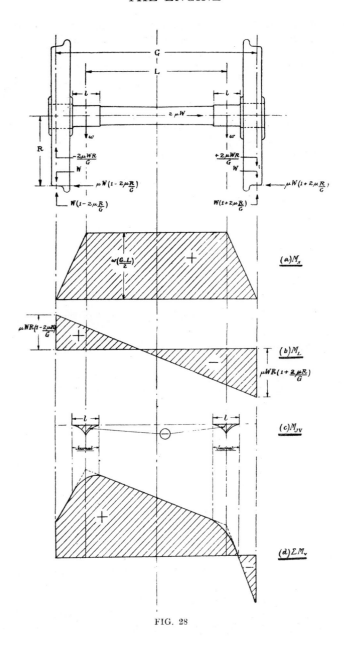

FIG. 28

spring borne load per journal, assumed acting at the centre of the journal, and W the gross load on the rail per wheel.

Consider firstly the bending moments arising from the spring borne loads. The bending moment M_S, due to the loads w, w, has a maximum value, which is constant between the journal centres, of

$$M_S = w \left(\frac{G - L}{2} \right) \quad\dots\dots\dots\dots\dots\dots\dots\dots\dots (209)$$

The positive bending moment therefor is shewn by diagram (a).

Next, consider the bending moment arising from the resistance offered by the axle to the tendency of the wheels to slide laterally across the rails. The total value of the reaction is $2\,\mu W$, where μ, the coefficient of adhesion, may be assumed for the purposes of calculation to have a maximum value of 0.25; this force acts horizontally along the centre line of the axle and, together with the external forces at the respective wheel treads, gives rise to a couple, of moment $2\,\mu W R$, acting, in the case under consideration, in a clockwise direction, R being the radius of the wheel measured to the tread. This couple is balanced by an equal and opposite couple $A\,G$, in which

$$A = 2\,\mu \frac{W R}{G}$$

Hence W, the normal load on the rail, is increased by $2\,\mu \dfrac{W R}{G}$ in the right-hand wheel and decreased by a similar amount in the left-hand wheel. The corresponding lateral forces at the tread are

$$\mu W \left(1 + 2 \frac{\mu R}{G} \right) \text{and } \mu W \left(1 - 2 \frac{\mu R}{G} \right)$$

respectively, and it follows that the bending moments due to them are:—

$$\text{Negative,} \qquad M_L = \mu W R \left(1 + 2 \frac{\mu R}{G} \right) \dots (210)$$

and positive, $M_L = \mu\ W\ R \left(1 - 2\ \dfrac{\mu\ R}{G} \right)$ .. (211)

The appropriate bending moment diagram is shewn at (b).

M_{JV}, the negative bending moment due to the distribution of the spring borne load over journal length l, has a general value of

$$M_{JV} = \frac{w}{2\ l} \left(\frac{l^2}{4} - x^2 \right) \dots\dots\dots\dots\dots\dots (212)$$

at any point distant x inches from the centre of the journal. The maximum value of M_{JV} occurs at the centre of the journal, where $x = 0$, and is equal to $\dfrac{w\ l}{8}$. This quantity is relatively large in the case of a heavily loaded narrow gauge engine. The diagram for this loading is shewn at (c), and the inclusive diagram obtained by adding the bending moments for all the loads previously enumerated is given at (d). The foregoing loadings, it is important to note, are basic and apply to all types of axle.

Reverting to the particular case under consideration, the twisting moments due to slip are:—

For left-hand wheel,

$$T_{LH} = \mu\ W\ R \left(1 - 2\ \frac{\mu\ R}{G} \right) \dots\dots\dots\dots (213)$$

For right-hand wheel,

$$T_{RH} = \mu\ W\ R \left(1 + 2\ \frac{\mu\ R}{G} \right) \dots\dots\dots\dots (214)$$

Lastly, for any given point in the axle, the equivalent bending moment is stated generally by

$$M_E = \sqrt{\ \Sigma\ M^2 + T^2}\ \dots\dots\dots\dots\dots\dots\dots (215)$$

In applying this equation it will be realised that, as the wheels have been assumed to be sliding from right to left, the maximum resultant values then occur on that portion of the axle which is to the left of the vertical centre line. The converse, of course, holds good when the direction of lateral sliding is reversed.

The required diameter of the axle at any given point may be determined, for solid axles, from

$$M_{\text{E}} = f\,Z = f \times \frac{\pi}{32}\,D^3 \quad\dots\dots\dots\dots\dots\dots \quad (216)$$

or for hollow axles, from

$$M_{\text{E}} = f \times \frac{\pi}{32}\left(\frac{D_1{}^4 - D_2{}^4}{D_1}\right)\dots\dots\dots\dots\dots \quad (217)$$

where D_1 and D_2 are the respective external and internal diameters.

In practice the usual maximum value of f is 10 tons per square inch for axles with wheels under 5'-0" in diameter, and with larger wheels, 9 tons per square inch. If possible, however, f should be so arranged as not to exceed ($\frac{1}{3}$ × elastic limit of the material) for the equal alternating stresses involved.

Case (ii). Straight carrying axles with outside bearings.

Procedure is as in the previous case, except that the direction of curvature due to the spring borne loads is reversed and the maximum value of M_S, in this case negative and effective over the distance between tread lines, as compared with that between journal centres in the previous instance, is obtained by transposing L and G in (209). Assuming the wheels to be slipping, as before, from right to left, M_S and M_L will both be negative in sense for the right half of the axle, which is therefore subjected to the maximum bending moment under this condition.

With this type of axle it is customary in American practice arbitrarily to increase the calculated spring borne load by 26%, thus allowing for vertical oscillation at high speeds. A similar allowance is made in British practice for tender axles and, in some cases, for carriage and wagon axles also.

Case (iii). Straight coupled axles with inside bearings (Fig. 29 A).

The bending moments due to loads applied in the vertical planes are determined as in Case (i) and the curve ΣM_V, obtained by the algebraic addition of M_S, M_L and M_{JV}, is drawn as shewn in Fig. 29 B.

There are three loadings to be considered in the horizontal plane (see Fig. 29 C). Consider firstly M_{CR}, which is the bending moment due to force F_{CR} in the coupling rod. The value of F_{CR} will have been obtained by the methods previously discussed. Assuming that the right-hand driving wheel is slipping, the total torque developed, less that absorbed by the left-hand driving wheel, gives rise to a load taken in its entirety by the left-hand rod, and the maximum bending moment due to this load is

$$M_{CR}\ max. = F_{CR}\left(\frac{X-L}{2}\right) \ \text{......................} (218)$$

This occurs at the mid length of the left-hand journal, diminishing to zero at the coupling rod centre on the left-hand side, and at the mid length of the axle journal on the right.

Secondly, there is a bending moment M_{DF} due to the driving force, $\mu\ W$, at the wheel tread. This force gives rise to the bending moment M_{DF}, which has a constant value between the journal centres calculated from

$$M_{DF} = \mu\ W\left(\frac{G-L}{2}\right) \ \text{..............................} (219)$$

Lastly, there is the negative bending moment, M_{JH}, due to the assumed uniform distribution of the loads over the length l of the journals. The total load, w_{JH}, is the algebraic sum of $\mu\ W$ and the reaction due to the coupling rod load. With reference to the latter, by the principle of moments,
Reaction of left-hand journal to coupling rod load =

$$\frac{F_{CR}\left(L+\dfrac{X-L}{2}\right)}{L} \ \text{..} (220)$$

The maximum value of M_{JH} occurs at the centre of the journal and is equal to

$$M_{JH}\ max. = \frac{w_{JH}\ l}{8} \ \text{......................................} (221)$$

The nett bending moment diagram, $\Sigma\ M_H$, due to the horizontal loads, is then drawn.

No serious error will arise if the loads in the vertical planes are assumed to act at right angles to those in the horizontal plane. Consequently, the resultant bending moments, M_R (see Fig. 29 D), may be determined for any given point in the axle from

$$M_R = \sqrt{\Sigma\ M_V^2 + \Sigma\ M_H^2} \ \text{..............................} (222)$$

The twisting moment diagram is also shewn in Fig. 29D. As under the postulated conditions the drive is being wholly transmitted by the left-hand coupling rod, the torque between the pin for this rod and the outer edge of the left-hand wheel seat is equal to $\dfrac{T}{n}$, and is reduced through the length of the wheel seat by the quantity absorbed by the corresponding wheel, *viz.*, $\dfrac{T}{2n}$. The centre portion of the axle is therefore subjected to a twisting moment of

$$\left(\frac{T}{n} - \frac{T}{2n} \right) = \frac{T}{2n}$$

This torque is equal to the amount absorbed by the right-hand wheel; the value of the torque at the right-hand extremity of the axle is therefore zero.

Finally, for any given point in the axle, the equivalent bending moment, M_E, is given by

$$M_E = \sqrt{M_R^2 + T^2} \quad \dotfill \quad (223)$$

The appropriate diameters of the axles are then calculated as in (216) or (217).

The above argument gives the most unfavourable combination of M_R and T, and may therefore be accepted for the purposes of design. The actual extent of the torque may, however, be considerably greater than is indicated above, although occurring in conjunction with relatively small bending moments in the horizontal plane. Consider a coupled axle next to an end driving axle, the right-hand wheel of which is slipping, and assume that this coupled axle is passing on the drive to both sides of the engine. The torque at the left-hand coupling rod crankpin will then be the difference between that required to drive $(2n - 2)$ wheels and that necessary for $(n - 2)$ wheels. Its nett value is therefore

$$T\left(1 - \frac{1}{n} \right) - \frac{T}{2n}(n - 2) = \frac{T}{2}.$$

Of this, $\dfrac{T}{2n}$ is absorbed by the left-hand wheel, giving a torque of $\dfrac{T}{2}\left(1-\dfrac{1}{n}\right)$ throughout the centre portion of the axle.

A similar quantity, $\dfrac{T}{2n}$, is abstracted at the right-hand wheel,

leaving $\dfrac{T(n-2)}{2n}$ to be transmitted at the right-hand crank-pin.

Case (iv).   Straight coupled driving axle with two outside cylinders and with inside bearings (Fig. 29 E).

For this type of axle the procedure for the determination of the bending moments due to vertical loading (Fig. 29 F) is identical with that adopted in the previous case.

In the horizontal plane (Fig. 29 G), the M_{CR} curve is also as before.   With reference to the M_{DF} curve, the maximum value is preferably determined, in the case of a driving axle, from

$$M_{DF}\ max. = \dfrac{T}{2nR}\left(\dfrac{G-L}{2}\right) \dotfill (224)$$

where T is the maximum torque developed and n the number of coupled wheels.

The bending moment due to the piston load is of opposite sign to that arising from the coupling rod load, and is therefore drawn on the opposite side of the datum line.   It has zero value at the crankpin centres and maintains a constant maximum value between the inner ends of the axlebox journals of

$$M_P\ max. = Q\left(\dfrac{C-L}{2}\right) \dotfill (225)$$

where Q is the thrust of the connecting rod. Q may be determined graphically (Fig. 29 II) by drawing the right-angled triangle $A\ B\ C$, in which $A\ C$ and $A\ B$ respectively represent the crank radius and length of connecting rod, between centres, to scale.   Then $A\ B$ is equal to Q to the same scale that $B\ C$ represents the piston load P.

Reverting to diagram G, the maximum load w_{JH} on the left-hand journal comprises (reaction due to F_{CR}, calculated as in previous case, plus driving force at wheel tread, minus load of one piston), and the maximum bending moment due

to it is $\dfrac{w_{JH}\ l}{8}$, acting at the centre of the journal.

Having drawn the resultant diagram of bending moments in the horizontal plane, $\Sigma\ M_H$, then, as before,

$$M_R = \sqrt{\Sigma\ M_V{}^2 + \Sigma\ M_H{}^2}$$

and $M_E = \sqrt{M_R{}^2 + T^2}$

The value of the torque to which the axle is subjected is the maximum torque generated, $\sqrt{2}\ Q\ r$, less that absorbed by one wheel, $\dfrac{T}{2n}$, assuming as heretofore that the right-hand wheel is slipping, and is therefore equal to $T\left(1 - \dfrac{1}{2n}\right)$

Case (v). Inside crank axle with inside bearings, driven by two cylinders (Fig. 29 I).

Bending moments in the vertical plane (Fig. 29 J) are again as in Case (i). M_{CR} and M_{DF}, acting in the horizontal plane (Fig. 29 K), are as in the previous case.

The bending moment due to the piston load is zero at the axlebox centres and has a maximum value, constant between the inner ends of the big end journals, of

$$M_P\ max. = Q\left(\dfrac{L - C}{2}\right) \quad\dots\dots\dots\dots\dots\dots\dots (226)$$

In the case under consideration the coupling rod cranks are assumed to be at 180° to the adjacent main cranks, as is usual; the bending moment due to piston load is then of opposite sense to that arising from the coupling rod loads, as in the previous case. Should, however, the coupling rod cranks be in phase with the contiguous main cranks, these bending moments are then of like sign and must therefore be added together, thus increasing considerably the bending stresses over the major portion of the crank axle.

For a crank axle with one centrally disposed cylinder (*e.g.,* for three-cylinder engines), the maximum bending moment due to piston load is

$$M_P\ max. = \dfrac{Q\ L}{4} \quad\dots\dots\dots\dots\dots\dots\dots\dots\dots\dots (227)$$

The diagram would of course be triangular, the maximum value occurring at the vertical centre line of the axle.

The maximum value of w_{JH} for the reverse bending moment is, with two cylinders,

{reaction at the left-hand axlebox due to F_{CR}, calculated as in (220), plus load of one piston, plus driving force at wheel tread}.

With one cylinder only, the above quantity would be reduced by one half piston load.

As before, $M_{JH} = \dfrac{w_{JH}\, l}{8}$,

$$M_R = \sqrt{\Sigma M_V{}^2 + \Sigma M_H{}^2}$$

and $M_E = \sqrt{M_R{}^2 + T^2}$

The fluctuations in the value of T throughout the length of the axle are shewn in Fig. 29 L. The values are:—

From left-hand coupling rod crankpin to outer edge of left-hand wheel seat,

$$T\left(1 - \frac{1}{n}\right).$$

From inner end of left-hand wheel seat to outer end of left-hand big end journal,

$$T\left(1 - \frac{1}{2n}\right).$$

Between inner ends of big end journals,

$$T\left(\frac{1}{2} - \frac{2}{2n}\right).$$

Note.—This latter quantity may be increased to $\dfrac{T}{2}$ with the right-hand wheel slipping freely, *i.e.*, when μ has zero value.

Between outer end of right-hand big end journal and inner end of right-hand wheel seat,

$$\frac{T}{2n}.$$

Thence to right-hand coupling rod crankpin, nil.

In these formulæ, as before,

T = maximum torque generated = $\sqrt{2}\, Q\, r$

and n = number of coupled axles.

Axlebox Journals.

In determining journal dimensions consideration must be given not only to the question of structural strength, but also to the provision of adequate bearing area. This latter subject will be dealt with subsequently when axleboxes are considered.

Side Thrust on Axles.

The side thrust, viz., $2\,\mu\,W$ plus, in the cases of bogie and pony truck axles, the load due to the side control springs, should be taken by a suitable projection of the box face pressing on the wheel boss, and not by an axle collar, the bearing area of the latter being totally inadequate for this purpose.

Stresses in Crank Axle Webs and Pins.

Crank axle failures usually occur at the junctions of the webs with the crankpin and axle journals, and may in most instances be attributed to the impossibility of providing sufficient thickness for the web, although it is significant that "breathing" action is greatest at these points.

With a rectangular web of width b and thickness h, the crankpin diameter being d, then, if the maximum bending stress in the web is not to exceed that in the crankpin, and h is equal to $\dfrac{d}{2}$, it may be shewn that b must equal $2.3562d$.

The value of the bending moment M in the web having been determined as indicated previously,

$$f = \frac{M}{Z},$$

and since Z for a rectangular section is $\dfrac{b\,h^2}{6}$, then, by transposition,

$$f = \frac{6\,M}{b\,h^2}$$

The value of f thus obtained is a mean, and its maximum

value is considerably greater.   The ratio of maximum to mean stress is

$$\frac{\left(r - \dfrac{\pi}{4}\dfrac{d}{k} \right)}{(r - d)} \quad\text{...} \quad (228)$$

in which r, as before, is the crank throw, *i.e.*, $\frac{1}{2}$ piston stroke, d the journal diameter, and $k\,d$ the width of web.

Webs of the Frémont type, in which metal between the axle and crankpin is removed, enable the high stresses between these points to be transferred to the outer portions of the web, these being relatively lightly stressed.

Built-up Crank Axles.

Since the distance between centres of the axlebox journal and crankpin, also the lengths of the journals, are customarily made identical with those for solid axles, it follows that the web thickness must also be the same in both cases, and stresses which are already high in solid crank axles are increased by residual stresses in built-up axles due to shrinkage of the web on to the respective pins.

The end radius of the web should be made equal to 0.866 d. Let the width of web $b = k\,d$.   Then

$$b = \frac{3\,\pi\,d}{16\,k^2} \quad\text{...} \quad (229)$$

If $k = \dfrac{2}{3}$, then $b = 1.325\ d$.

Crank Axles : General Remarks.

The preceding summary is of a logically developed argument and its application to axle design is therefore to be recommended in preference to that of empirical data; a certain amount of the latter will, however, now be advanced, but should be regarded only in the light of an approximate guide.

According to Kempe,

$$d = 0.375\ C + 1$$

where d = diameter of main bearings, inches, and
    C = cylinder diameter, inches.

Also, the diameter of the centre portion of the axle may be $(d - \frac{1}{2})$ inches, this dimension also applying to straight axles, that of the crankpins equal to d, and of the wheel seat $(d + 1)$ inches.

The following information is applicable to standard gauge engines of British design.

The maximum thickness of web which may be arranged is 5″; this is an extreme case and, with modern two-cylinder engines, the thickness usually ranges from 4″ to $4\frac{5}{8}$″. With solid axles the thickness of the outer webs should be from 0.6 to 0.65 d; this dimension is in some actual examples as low as $0.56d$, although $0.6d$ is the minimum thickness desirable. The thickness of the inner webs is usually made greater than that of the outer webs and, if there are no eccentrics to be accommodated, a thickness of about $0.7d$ may be provided.

The length of crankpins between webs is generally about $4\frac{1}{2}$″, although a length of $5\frac{1}{2}$″ has been arranged in some instances. The customary length of wheel seat is from 7″ to $7\frac{1}{4}$″.

The usual allowance for wear on the basic, i.e., calculated, diameters of both crankpins and main bearings is from $\frac{3}{8}$″ to $\frac{1}{2}$″; the allowance should not in any circumstances be less than $\frac{1}{4}$″.

Indeterminate stresses which may arise in axles are those due to uneven wear of tyres and of the axleboxes, both in the hornblock and on the journal, to the action of any water which may be trapped in the cylinders, and to transmitted shocks from the flanges when running over points and crossings. With regard to the latter, it is general experience that similar axles have a longer life with wheels of small diameter than with large.

Double bearings are rarely, if ever, adopted in modern design. Their use is not encouraged, as it leads to excessive rigidity, and consequently short life, of axles.

Changes of section must not be sudden, and generous radii must be provided where they occur. This principle is extended, e.g., on Midland section, L.M.S.R., solid crank axles to the big end pins, only 2″ of their total length being parallel, the remainder being turned to radii of $2\frac{1}{4}$″ and 1″ respectively. A similar construction may be observed in solid crank axles for the B12 type 4-6-0 engines of the L.N.E.R.

If keyways are unavoidable, they must be minimised in number, be shallow, and have all edges radiused. In this connection it is well to remember that, for purposes of calculation, the effective diameter of any shaft subjected to torsion or bending is that measured to the bottom of the keyways.

In some designs of crank axles carrying eccentrics the sheaves have been provided with lugs engaging with the web sides. Keyways are thus eliminated from the axle, but the adoption of this practice has in some instances caused excessive rigidity of the axle.

It is a peculiar phenomenon, for which no altogether satisfactory explanation has yet been offered, that when, say, the right-hand crank is arranged to lead, the liability to heating of the boxes and to failure of the crank axle, together, in the case of uni-directional traffic, with wear of rails, arise chiefly on that side.

Built-up crank axles are now largely employed in preference to solid axles for engines of large dimensions. In comparison, solid axles are lighter, cost less to maintain, and of course have no components liable to work loose. On the other hand, they are more likely to flaw, chiefly because the metal is not "worked" so extensively during forging, and have a shorter life when the piston loads to which they are subjected are high. For this latter reason, built-up crank axles are commonly employed when the cylinder diameter exceeds approximately 19″.

Failures of built-up axles are almost entirely due to the trunnions working loose in the webs, the causes being distortion, *i.e.*, bending, of crankpins, and heating of axleboxes. In this connection it is essential that each screw be tight in its thread and carefully fitted to register with the bottom of its hole prior to riveting. The former L.Y.R. experimented successfully with a composite axle, in which the axlebox trunnions and outside webs were forged solid, the remainder being built up.

It has sometimes been found that the use of balanced webs with built-up axles increases the "breathing" action, thus aggravating the liability of the crankpins to loosen, although theoretically their adoption should reduce the tendency of the axle to bend.

The shrinkage allowance for built-up cranks varies considerably in practice from about 1/500 to 1/330 of the nominal hole diameter. The pins should be further secured by screwed and riveted plugs, two being fitted per pin; the nominal plug diameter ranges from $1\frac{1}{4}″$ to $1\frac{3}{4}″$, the number of threads provided being from 8 to 12 per inch. It is desirable that the thickness of the web, where surrounding pins, shall be as uniform as possible.

Axles of hollow section are now sometimes adopted in order to reduce the weight necessary for given strength.

Inside journal collars are rarely provided in modern designs. Sudden changes of section with accompanying high local stresses are thereby avoided, the journal bearing surface may be increased, manufacturing costs are reduced, and the possibilities of boxes running hot are eliminated, either (a) when bearing hard on the radius of the collar, (b) on account of loss of lubricant by centrifugal action at the collar, or (c), due to an accumulation of foreign matter in the clearance between box and collar. On the other hand, steady riding qualities, especially when the engine has run a high mileage since repair, are to a certain extent sacrificed and, unless measures such as have previously been described are taken, side control is also less efficient; the wheels may make contact with the frames, or outside crossheads foul the coupling rods, when the engine is negotiating curves.

Considerable divergence of opinion has been expressed as to the most suitable steel for axles. Sir Henry Fowler stated (Proc. I. Loco. E.), that in his experience the greatest mileage is obtained from material having a low carbon content and of low tensile strength, but giving a relatively high elongation, and advanced the following particulars of crank axle steel used on the original M.R.:—

Open hearth acid steel: tensile strength 32-37 tons per square inch. Elongation of not less than 25% on 3″ with 32 tons, and 20% with 37 tons. $1\frac{1}{4}$″ square bar to bend through 120° without fracture when tested on 6″ centres.

Analysis:—Carbon, 0.22%.
Silicon, 0.16%.
Manganese, 0.69%.
Sulphur ⎫
Phosphorus ⎰ under 0.03%: maximum 0.04%.
Sulphur (in form of manganese sulphide), 0.029%.

Sir Henry's contentions were supported by the experience of the late L.Y.R., whilst results from the former S.E.C.R. shewed that they applied up to an elongation of 33%, but not beyond that limit. The experience of the quondam N.E.R., on the other hand, was that axle life increased with higher ultimate tensile strengths.

For built-up crank axles the late L.Y.R. used steel having

a tensile strength of 32-38 tons per square inch, and an elongation of 25-19% for the webs, and for the trunnions 35-40 tons
material having an elongation of 25-20%.

AXLEBOXES.

The forces acting on axleboxes may be summarised as:—

(a) The spring borne load.
(b) The resultant of the forces in the connecting and
coupling rods respectively. This is usually the
greatest in magnitude and acts approximately horizontally.
(c) A horizontal force arising from the tractive effort exerted at the wheel tread.
(d) The braking force, having a nearly horizontal line of
action, and
(e) The flange pressure, which acts horizontally in the
transverse plane.

Of these, (b) has already been considered in connection with
coupling rods, and (c) and (e) with axles; (d) will be dealt
with in Chapter XII.

In general, the position of the resultant line of action of
(a) and (b), or (a) and (d), as the case may be, determines
the necessary extent of the arc of contact between box and
journal. This ranges in practice from 60° to 90° for carrying
axleboxes. The chord of contact for coupled axleboxes com-
monly extends to within $\frac{1}{2}''$ or $\frac{5}{8}''$ of the horizontal centre line;
in some instances it coincides with the latter and, in extreme
cases of high piston loads, may be extended below the centre
line by means of auxiliary bearings.

Usual nominal bearing pressures due to static, i.e., spring
borne load, are 180-250 lb. per square inch for coupled boxes,
150-170 lb. per square inch for bogie and truck boxes, and
230-290 lb. per square inch for tender boxes. These pressures,
it should be noted, are based on the conventional projected
area, i.e., {journal diameter × (length minus radii)}. Where
coupled axleboxes are concerned the actual pressures therefore
approximate to the values given, but for carrying axleboxes a
more accurate basis would be to calculate the area on (chord
of the contact portion × nett length of bearing); in this event,
the actual pressure becomes 350-500 lb. per square inch. The
upper limit, viz., 500 lb. per square inch, should not in any
circumstances be exceeded, as otherwise the establishment of
the necessary oil film becomes impossible. It is inadvisable

to exceed a static bearing pressure of 350 lb. per square inch, either for coupled boxes, which are of course subjected additionally to forces of considerable magnitude in the horizontal plane, or for any other axleboxes where oil holes and grooves are present.

Axleboxes may either be cast solid in gunmetal or bronze, or of cast or forged steel, which should be fairly hard, with inserted brasses. If of the latter type, care must be exercised that the brass is securely held in the body of the box. The brass may be merely pressed in, provided that good fitting be guaranteed, or secured at the sides by grub screws or dowels; spigotting the brass into the crown of the box body is to be recommended. It is usual to provide the brass with collars; these register with corresponding recesses machined in the box. An inserted brass having a five-sided contour has been advocated as the ideal as regards prevention of movement in any direction (with the assistance, of course, of collars); although increasing the necessary weight of brass, a rectangular contour is, by comparison, cheaper to machine and fit, the latter process being considerably facilitated.

The first cost of the material for a solid "brass" box is higher than for steel; the scrap value, on the other hand, is correspondingly enhanced. Machining and fitting costs are also lower, largely due to the fact that detachable wearing pieces are not required on either the guides or the face adjacent to the wheel centre. "Brass" boxes are not so liable either to overheat, as the heat generated is more quickly conducted away than when dissimilar metals are present, or to " nip " when excessive heating actually occurs, and are capable of being recrowned. The argument frequently advanced against them that, for a given loading, a more extensive cutting away of the frames is involved, does not necessarily hold good when a good mixture is employed; phosphor bronze, for instance, may possess an ultimate tensile strength of approximately 27 tons per square inch, although an average value for gunmetal is admittedly only 15 tons per square inch and, for "antifriction" bronze, may be as low as 10 tons per square inch. Further, the frame gap dimension, for any axlebox with underhung springs, depends upon the thickness of the sides of the box, and this in turn is governed by the permissible bearing pressure on the ends of the spring hanger pin.

The chief disadvantage inherent to steel boxes lies in the tendency of the brasses to work loose and knock, ultimately breaking, fracture usually taking place across the crown. Play arising between a steel box and its brass also results, in many instances, in loss of lubricant. Nevertheless, many engineers prefer the steel box for the heaviest duties; maintenance, especially abroad, of this type of box is simplified by replacing the wearing pieces from stores.

In those instances where the brasses themselves are not arranged to provide a rubbing surface for the face of the wheel boss, a separate liner, either of brass or white metal and of generous area, must be fitted, similar provision also being made for the guide faces.

Unless either grease lubrication is adopted or the bearing is of anti-friction bronze (composition: copper, 72-77%, tin, 8%, and lead, 15-20%), the bearings must be provided with white metal pockets in order to minimise the friction at starting, prior to the establishment of the oil film. The low coefficient of friction of the white metal also lowers the resistance at high rubbing speeds, thereby reducing the heat generated, as actually the continuous maintenance of an unbroken oil film is impossible of attainment. The white metal pockets should not be more than about $\frac{3}{4}''$ deep and should preferably be serrated, with an undercut section to assist in the retention of the metal should it become warm. Such sections should not be located at the crown of the box, where they are a source of weakness. Further, the depth should not exceed the dimension stated, as any appreciable variation in thickness of white metal is undesirable; this causes practical difficulties in the form of uneven shrinkage when the box is metalled. The surface of the white metal should be as large as possible, consistent with the provision of sufficient area of brass to enable the engine to work home in the event of the white metal running out.

The composition of the white metal varies considerably. Since the acids present in oils have a detrimental effect on lead, a tin base is preferable, especially when working conditions are arduous. The mixtures adopted by the Association of Railway Locomotive Engineers are:—

A.R.L.E. No. 1 *Mixture* (*for coupled boxes*).		*A.R.L.E. No.* 3 *Mixture* (*for other boxes*).	
Tin	85	Lead	75
Antimony	10	Antimony	13
Copper	5	Tin	12

A mixture specified for heavy duties would conform to the following approximate composition:—

Copper	...	...	...	5-8%
Tin	...	...	...	81-85%
Antimony	...	...	...	10%
Lead	...	...	...	2-3%

A cheaper but less satisfactory mixture (quoted from the Proc. I. Loco. E.) is:—

Tin	...	...	...	46%
Lead	...	...	...	42%
Antimony	...	...	...	12%

Typical gunmetal and bronze mixtures for brasses and "brass" boxes are:—

Copper	85	86·5	86·3
Tin	10	13·5	13·2
Phosphor Copper	—	—	0·5
Zinc	5	—	—

The width of white metal pockets is usually less than that of the box, i.e., they exclude the radii; although not unknown, full width pockets are not to be recommended.   On some railways, bearings are occasionally built up in white metal for carrying axleboxes which have worn to the maximum extent.

In general, oil grooves should not be cut in the white metal.

Boxes which are not white metalled are liable to cause extensive scoring should excessive heating occur.

Pettigrew states empirically that the thickness of inserted brasses should be $0.2d$ at the crown, where d is the diameter of the journal.   When the boxes are of solid gunmetal, the crown thickness generally ranges from $0.38d$ to $0.4d$, the minimum thickness of metal on the horizontal centre line of the box approximating to $0.2d$.   The legs of coupled boxes must be rigid in order distribute the piston load, which is of a concentrated nature, and to counteract the "nipping up" tendency of the box in the event of overheating.

Axleboxes are sometimes bored to a diameter $1/32''$ or $\frac{1}{16}''$ larger than that of the journal.   This practice, prevalent in America and followed on some British railways, reduces the time required for bedding the box down, and is also beneficial from the point of view of lubrication.

The total longitudinal clearance of the axlebox brass on the journal is usually either $\frac{1}{16}''$ or $\frac{1}{8}''$, the latter amount being usual for large engines; in the past this play was increased to $\frac{1}{4}$″ in the cases of leading and trailing boxes of six wheels coupled engines, but in modern practice the necessary flexibility is in most cases secured by the adoption of thin flanged tyres for the intermediate pair of coupled wheels. For six-wheeled tenders this (total) clearance is about $\frac{1}{16}$″ for the leading and trailing axleboxes, and up to $\frac{5}{16}$″ for the intermediate boxes.

On engines a clearance of 1/64″ may be allowed between the box and the horn face, and 1/32″ between the flange of the box and the horn side. For eight-wheeled bogie tenders the sum of the clearances between box and journal and box and guides may be about $\frac{1}{8}$″ each way, i.e., a total of $\frac{1}{4}$″. In the case of the L.N.E.R. eight-wheeled non-bogie tenders, $\frac{1}{16}$″ play is allowed each way between box and journal and 1/32″ between box and guides, i.e., a total of 3/32″ each way, for the end boxes; the play between the box and the guides is increased to $\frac{1}{2}$″ in the case of the intermediate boxes.

In modern designs of engine axleboxes the flanges are frequently planed taper top and bottom so that the stipulated clearance between the flange and the horn side only holds good over a centrally disposed length representing one-third or less of the total depth of flange, the clearance at the extreme ends of the flanges being about 9/32″. To provide further flexibility, in the transverse plane, the rubbing surfaces of the box adjacent to the horn faces are sometimes similarly treated; in this particular case, however, the practice cannot be unconditionally recommended, as it has a detrimental effect on the riding qualities of the engine.

With overhung springs it is advisable to recess the box top and place therein a hard steel pad to act as a seat for the buckle spigot, thus preventing distortion of the box.

In the case of underhung springs the spring pin, which is usually about $1\frac{1}{2}$″ in diameter, should have well-rounded ends and be secured by set screws, recessed into the pin, to prevent scoring of the horn faces. Care must be exercised in locating the centre line of the pin that sufficient clearance is allowed for the underfeed oil pad. For "brass" boxes the minimum thickness of metal below the pin should be about $1\frac{1}{4}$″.

Keeps are usually of cast iron, having a ruling wall thickness of $\frac{1}{4}$″ or $\frac{5}{16}$″. Brass and malleable iron are also employed occasionally, and have the advantage that they are not so liable to break when dropped. The provision of an oil-filling spout is a distinct advantage.   The chief fault of most keep designs is inaccessibility, and a door or removable plate should be provided to facilitate examination of the pad.   In many instances the spring pin is arranged to pass through the keep, thus preventing easy removal of the latter.

The normal total range of movement of a box due to spring action varies aproximately from $1\frac{3}{4}''$ to $2\frac{1}{2}''$.   This latter amount may easily be attained when an engine is rolling at high speeds.   In addition to allowances for this movement, others must be made, when determining the necessary depth of gap in the frame to accommodate a given axlebox, for variations in the mean position of the box due to progressive tyre wear and also for sufficient clearance for packing used in the event of spring failure, when lifting, and so on.

LUBRICATION.

Valves and Cylinders.

Whether to employ a mechanical or hydrostatic lubricator is a controversial point, and comparison of various reports available on the extent of wear and carbonisation occurring with each type will shew contradictory results.   The following is a brief comparative summary of the salient characteristics of the two accepted methods of lubrication.

Hydrostatic Lubricator.	Mechanical Lubricator.
Operating force is that due to weight of column of water plus excess of boiler over steam chest pressure.	Positive pressure system, independent of steam pressure.
Oil delivery on time basis, independent of speed of revolution of engine. Feed dependent on setting adopted by individual enginemen and therefore not uniform.	Oil delivery directly proportional to speed of engine, continuous whilst engine is in motion and ceases when engine is brought to rest, with consequent prevention of waste.
Cheaper in the first instance, simpler and has no moving parts, with correspondingly reduced maintenance costs. Atomisation of oil completed without intervention of anti-carbonisers.	All moving parts work in oil; wear therefore minimised.

Hydrostatic Lubricator.	Mechanical Lubricator.
Lubricator under constant supervision and control of enginemen. Requires more attention, as regards adjustment when running, and therefore liable to distract enginemen's attention from road.	Is in some cases also located in cab, or provision made for adjustment of delivery therefrom. Less attention required on road.
Water of condensation may collect in delivery pipes, with the result that oil floats thereon, accumulates, and is only delivered to cylinders when suction tendency commences on shutting the regulator. Effects minimised by fitting chokes.	Condensate may also collect in delivery pipes in the event of anti-carboniser steam cock being left open when engine is standing for any length of time. Effects minimised by placing anti-carbonisers as near point of delivery as possible. Check valves are provided to prevent uncontrolled withdrawal of lubricant from feed pipes into valves and cylinders by suction when coasting with regulator shut.
Sight feed nipples may choke.	Valves may stick or driving pin joint fail.
The difference between boiler and steam chest pressure diminishes as the engine is worked more heavily, with the result that oil supply tends to fall off when most required. The chokes previously mentioned have also a beneficial effect in reducing this risk.	Delivery is independent of prevailing steam pressures.
Lubricator may be easily replenished when running.	Lubricator refilled more quickly (no water to drain off unless warmer pipe is defective or check valves stuck open, allowing steam to blow back).
Reduces temperature of steam at admission by about 20°F.	

Anti-carbonisers are now invariably used with mechanical lubricators. When so fitted it is probable that ultimately they give better results than a hydrostatic lubricator, the reason being that atomisation as a process may be carried too far. The extremely small particles of oil present a greater surface on which the heat may act and accelerate gasification, and further, they are more likely to be carried away before performing their intended function.

When adopting hydrostatic lubricators, separate delivery pipes should be provided for each feed. In certain examples of foreign practice, one pipe only is fitted from the lubricator to the immediate vicinity of the cylinders, where branch connections are provided for the various points of application; this method economises in piping but sacrifices uniformity of oil distribution, the branch nearest the main pipe taking the bulk of the supply. The delivery pipes must be arranged with a steady fall, the inclination being greater than that of the most severe gradient over which the engine has to run; pockets and horizontal lengths of pipe must be rigidly avoided. The chokes should be located as near as possible to the points of application.

Mechanical lubricators must not be driven from a valve spindle owing to the reduction occurring in oil delivery as notching up proceeds. Any convenient detail providing simple reciprocating motion through a constant distance may be utilised; a suitable point of attachment is the crosshead. A drive of light construction, with consequently no appreciable addition to the inertia forces, can then be arranged, although in some instances the connection is made at a suitable intermediate point on the connecting rod (the hole necessarily drilled in the latter is, however, objectionable). For certain inside cylinder engines a return crank has been specially provided for this purpose on the coupling rod pin; this arrangement usually involves a greater length of rod for the drive than is desirable.

The inclusion of feed water and/or air brake pumps with the points to be lubricated by the main hydrostatic or mechanical lubricator, as the case may be, is strongly urged.

Oil feed pipes are usually of copper and have an internal diameter of $\frac{1}{4}''$ or $\frac{5}{16}''$.

Check valves and chokes must be as near the points of application as possible. Check valves should preferably be spring loaded, to ensure positive action.

The effects of carbonisation are faulty steam distribution, broken piston rings, and scoring of valve bushes and cylinder barrels.

The steam supply to the anti-carbonisers for mechanical lubricators is usually taken from a cock located in the cab. The disadvantage of this arrangement is that, in the event of an engine standing in steam for some considerable time with this cock inadvertently left open, sufficient steam may accumulate in the cylinders to move the engine. Having regard to this and to the fact that an engine requires maximum lubrication when coasting at high speed with the regulator shut, with the result that there is then no horizontal force tending to lift the pistons off the cylinder barrels, the ideal control of anti-carboniser steam would be automatic and so arranged that the quantity of steam admitted would be directly proportional to the rate of revolution of the engine when running, increasing with closure of the regulator, and zero when standing.

The following tables, XXXVIII and XXXIX, are quoted

TABLE XXXVIII.
OIL DELIVERIES FROM WAKEFIELD No. 1 MECHANICAL LUBRICATOR (8 FEEDS).

Diameter of Driving Wheels.	Total Delivery from eight pumps (pints per 100 miles).						
	Position of Oil Regulating Plug.						
	Screwed home.	Unscrewed 1 turn.	Unscrewed 2 turns.	Unscrewed 3 turns.	Unscrewed 4 turns.	Unscrewed 5 turns.	Unscrewed 6 turns.
7'-0"	5·064	4·220	3·376	2·532	1·688	0·844	
6'-9"	5·259	4·383	3·506	2·630	1·763	0·877	
6'-6"	5·454	4·545	3·636	2·727	1·818	0·909	
6'-0"	5·904	4·920	3·936	2·952	1·978	0·984	nil.
5'-6"	6·456	5·380	4·304	3·228	2·152	1·076	
5'-0"	7·086	5·905	4·724	3·543	2·362	1·181	
4'-6"	7·926	6·605	5·284	3·963	2·642	1·321	

TABLE XXXIX.
OIL DELIVERIES FROM WAKEFIELD Nos. 7 AND 8 MECHANICAL LUBRICATORS (8 FEEDS).

Diameter of Driving Wheels.	Total Delivery from eight pumps (pints per 100 miles).					
	Position of Oil Regulating Plug.					
	Screwed home.	Unscrewed 1 turn.	Unscrewed 2 turns	Unscrewed 3 turns.	Unscrewed 4 turns.	Unscrewed 5 turns.
6'-6"	4·125	3·300	2·475	1·650	0·825	
6'-0"	4·160	3·568	2·676	1·784	0·892	
5'-6"	4·870	3·896	2·922	1·948	0·974	nil.
5'-0"	5·350	4·280	3·210	2·140	1·070	
4'-6"	5·955	4·764	3·573	2·382	1·191	
4'-0"	7·250	5·800	4·350	2·890	1·440	

from *Lubrication of Locomotives*, by the late E. L. Ahrons. In some instances the quantities as given are not strictly proportional, as, theoretically, they should be. This may perhaps be due to errors of calculation, or alternatively, the quantities may represent the results of actual experiments.

The next point to decide is whether to deliver the oil direct to the points of application or into the main steam pipe, and this again is a debatable question. It may be argued that steam pipe lubrication entails a considerable waste of oil as much of the latter, entrained with the steam, never makes contact with the parts to be lubricated, fails to fulfil its intended function and passes direct to exhaust, this resulting in considerable carbonisation at the blast pipe orifice. At the same time, such oil as is used is very completely emulsified and evenly distributed. Lubrication by this method frequently necessitates the presence of oil pipes in the smokebox, an extremely undesirable feature in that the high temperatures there obtaining induce carbonisation, and in any case cannot be applied to poppet valve engines in which lubricated steam should not pass the admission valves.

With lubrication direct to the points of application, on the other hand, carbonisation is greater on the valves and pistons but less in the blastpipe. The small drilled oil ducts are themselves liable to become carbonised and impede lubrication; nevertheless, the presence of oil pipes in the smokebox may be avoided.

When applying steam pipe lubrication the oil should be admitted as near the cylinder casting as possible and on the centreline of the steam pipe. The oil pipe end should be cut at an angle to increase the effective area presented to the oncoming steam; a sawcut should also be made on the horizontal centre line of the oil pipe to assist atomisation.

With direct lubrication, Mr. Kempt suggested (Proc. I. Loco. E., 1921) four small oil inlets per cylinder, *viz.*, two at the centre, spraying either up or down the cylinder walls, and one at each end directed towards the piston rod. During the pressure stroke delivery would then be retarded, but induced during the exhaust stroke when the steam temperature is reduced. With this arrangement the valves are lubricated by the oil entrained with the exhaust steam. In other applications, however, oil is admitted only at the centre of the barrel in order to reduce waste which may occur during the alternate exhaust strokes.

When provision is made for the direct lubrication of valves, the oil inlets should be so located, near the admission edges of piston valves, that they are not uncovered by the exhaust edges. Sometimes one feed only, delivering into the steam pipe immediately above the steam chest, is provided to lubricate piston valves, especially when hydrostatic lubrication is adopted.

Slide valves may give trouble, when used in conjunction with superheated steam, unless placed underneath the cylinders. The springs and strips of balanced valves may carbonise, stick and, consequently, blow through. The provision of oil grooves in the valve face is essential to secure even distribution of the lubricant for this type of valve.

As regards tail rods, when fitted, it is not usual to provide an anti-carboniser with mechanical lubrication. It is essential that the oil be conducted to the lower part of the bearing, and a positive pressure feed must be provided. Cast iron bushes should be used.

Mops usually give better results than forced oil feed to the piston glands, although liable to introduce dirt on the instroke unless changed at frequent intervals. Extensive carbonisation is liable to occur with forced feed of the lubricant to these details.

Graphite lubrication has in some instances been applied to the cylinders and valves. Since less oil is then consumed, carbonisation is reduced, but the experience on some railways is that the graphite tends to deposit on the walls of valve bushes and cylinder barrels, thereby causing ring seizures. Nevertheless, reductions both in wear generally and in fuel consumption are claimed for this method of lubrication, which is not applied direct but to the steam pipe, with discharge on the

TABLE XL.		
LUBRICANT DATA ("LUBRICATION OF LOCOMOTIVES" Ahrons)		
Type of Lubricant.	Specific Gravity.	Weight per pint, lb.
Mineral oil	0·86	1·075 ⎫
Mineral oil	0·9	1·125 ⎬ Average,
Rape oil	0·915	1·144 ⎨ 1·14
Cylinder oil	0·925	1·156 ⎭

centre line and sufficiently far from any junctions to ensure equal distribution to all cylinders. Colloidal graphite may be used with ordinary mechanical lubricators. Deflocculated graphite is, incidentally, capable of passing through worsted trimmings with but little loss of graphite. In general, however, special lubricators with mechanical stirring arrangements are employed in conjunction with graphite.

The quondam S.E.C.R. required compliance with the following specification for their superheater cylinder oil (Proc. I. Loco. E.):—

Specific gravity at 60° F., 0.902 approximately.
Flash point (closed): not below 500°F.
Viscosity (Redwood):
    At 140°F., 700-750 seconds.
    At 200°F., about 190 seconds.
    At 250°F., about 80 seconds.

To be free from suspended matter and all foreign impurities.

A heavier, more viscous oil is now favoured by some railways; the specific gravity at 60°F. is from 0.910 to 0.915 and the viscosity from 750 to 850 seconds at 140°F., and from 195 to 220 at 200°F. The minimum flash point specified is 550°F., the oil to flow at a stipulated temperature of 45°F.

It has been stated that superheater engines on the former G.N.R. consumed 5% more oil than those working with saturated steam, the cost being 29% greater.

General Remarks on the Lubrication of Bearings.

In a completely lubricated bearing the force of fluid friction is proportional to the speed of rubbing, to the area in contact and to the viscosity, or molecular friction, of the lubricant. The frictional force is independent of the pressure between the surfaces and of the materials comprising the opposing metallic surfaces. In this, the theoretically ideal bearing, the only friction is therefore that due to the viscosity of the oil forming the film between the two bodies concerned. Unfortunately, the conditions under which most locomotive bearings operate do not approximate to the ideal; the continued maintenance of an unbroken film of lubricant is difficult, if not impossible, and the loads may alternate in sense and fluctuate in extent throughout the revolution. Considerable attention to design is consequently essential in order to effect the most satisfactory compromise possible and thereby minimise internal resistance generally.

The nearest approach in practice to a theoretically satisfactory bearing is one which is simply loaded at the top, *e.g.*, that for an unbraked carrying axle, and lubricated by a pad in contact with the lower half of the journal. To prevent interruption of the oil film the bearing should be bevelled off, or preferably radiused, at the ends where the film enters and leaves the bearing respectively; an additional, or alternative method of attaining the same condition is to bore out the bearing to a slightly larger radius than that of the journal, thereby enabling the oil film to conform to the tapered formation essential to efficient lubrication. With pad lubrication oil holes and grooves are avoided; these not only affect adversely the continuity of the oil film but also reduce the bearing area and increase the average local stress in the material to the extent of from 200 to 300%. In the form of bearing under consideration the arc of contact should not exceed one-fourth, and may be as small as one-sixth, of the journal circumference.

Whether to obtain the requisite bearing area, such that the oil film may establish itself and possible extrusion be prevented, by providing a journal of small diameter and relatively great length, or *vice versa*, is a point which can be considered generally only with great difficulty ; each case must be considered in the light of its individual requirements and dimensional limitations. Mechanically, the short journal having a large diameter is obviously advantageous in that the bending moment is minimised, whilst the moment of inertia of the section has coincidentally a high value. It is also argued that the comparatively high speed of rubbing consequently attained assists the tendency of the lubricant to flow into the bearing, and that excessive length of bearing prevents easy access of oil to the crown when the latter coincides with the point of maximum pressure.

On the other hand, consider a journal d inches in diameter and l inches long, rotating at N revolutions per minute under a load of w lb. Then:—

Work expended in friction $= \mu\, w\, \pi\, \dfrac{d}{12}\, N$ ft.-lb. per minute.

And total heat generated per minute $= \dfrac{\mu\, w\, \pi\, d\, N}{12\, J}$ B.Th. U.

Now, if x B.Th.U. are conducted away per minute per

square inch of projected area,

$$x \, d \, l = \frac{\mu \, w \, \pi \, d \, N}{12 \, J}$$

whence $x = \dfrac{\mu \, w \, \pi \, N}{12 \, J \, l}$ .... (230)

It will be noted that d cancels out in (230), and accepting this argument, the bearing should be made as long as possible; such a bearing in actual practice gives the best results at high rotational speeds. The value of x for locomotive bearings exposed to currents of air is from 1.0 to 1.5 (Goodman). Sir J. Aspinall gives 0.009 as the value of μ for carriage journals with oil and pad lubrication; Professor Goodman suggests 0.012 for pad, and 0.02 for syphon lubrication. These values of μ may be applied to carrying axles; for driving boxes μ is usually assumed to be 0.05. These values agree with the findings of Henderson.

Brasses must be provided with end play to allow for expansion, apart from any considerations of clearance, and the radius at the end of the bearing must be greater than that at the root of the journal collar. This renders possible the formation of an oil film to resist end thrust. The process is further assisted by providing generous bearing areas for collars or wearing pieces.

When a surface of one material works over that of another, the most rapid wear occurs in the component made of the softer metal. The component which is the more difficult to replace should therefore be of the harder material.

Where angular movement is restricted and the bearing pressure low, both components should be of hard material.

Oil grooves must not be cut through to the ends of bearings or bushes unless it is intended to lubricate surfaces taking up end thrust; similarly, felt pads should not extend the full width of the bearing. In order to minimise the adverse effect of oil grooves on the continuity of the oil film, their cross and longitudinal sections should both be such that they merge gradually into the bearing. In those cases where the bearing completely surrounds its shaft or pin, a continuous circumferential groove at each end of the bearing will be found efficacious as regards prevention of leakage of oil.

Where bearings or bushes are either provided with pockets

of, or entirely lined with, white metal, care must be taken, especially in the latter case, that the compressive strength of the metal is sufficient to resist the loads involved, and that its cross sectional area is reasonably uniform throughout.

Fixed bushes which are not keyed or otherwise definitely secured should be provided with a groove, turned externally and provided with several circumferential oil holes, to ensure continuity of lubrication in the event of the bush creeping. For small ends, and other details in which the oil is thrown from end to end of the reservoir, provision must be made for the efficient trapping of the oil by the trimming. The best method of lubricating gudgeon pins is to drill a hole longitudinally through the pin to the centre line of the bearing surface, where suitable branches leading to the periphery are provided. This arrangement does away with oil holes in the small end of the connecting rod; these frequently originate fractures.

For floating bushes one oil hole should preferably be provided for each $4\frac{1}{4}$ square inches of surface; the bearing area served per oil hole should not in any circumstances exceed $5\frac{3}{4}$ square inches.

Oil holes for big ends, coupling rods and kindred details are usually $\frac{3}{8}''$ or $\frac{7}{16}''$ diameter.

It is advisable to provide two oil reservoirs for eccentrics (one per half strap). This prevents undue restriction or loss of lubrication which may otherwise occur when wear takes place and clearance becomes excessive as the joint opens.

In some designs little or no provision is made for the lubrication of bogie centres. An oil reservoir should be arranged therefor in an accessible position, *e.g.*, on the main frames, or on the smokebox tubeplate. If the bogie is of the swing link type, oil holes should be provided for the large pins.

Syphon lubrication is wasteful and should be avoided where possible. Some experiments with tail trimmings in use on a crosshead shewed the oil consumption to be 1.73 oz. per 100 miles.

All oil reservoirs must be so designed and located that the entry of water thereto is impossible; the presence of water soon causes lubrication failure.

Grease Lubrication.

Whilst oil has hitherto been universally used for lubrication, the adoption of grease lubrication has been encouraged by the intensive use of engines in modern traffic operation, involving the running of a greatly increased daily mileage. In these circumstances the use of oil may be costly and, further, troublesome as regards the extent of necessary attention to any trimmings which may be used and the comparatively frequent replenishment of oil reservoirs. Grease, on the other hand, requires little or no attention during the time the locomotive is in operation, the necessary greasing being done whilst the engine is in the shed; a grease block once applied to a coupled axlebox will run a mileage of from 15,000 to 20,000 without renewal. This facility with grease as a lubricant was first appreciated in the U.S.A., where many locomotives are now grease lubricated.

The use of grease generally offers the following advantages over that of oil:—

(1). Reduction in cost of lubricants.

(2). Little or no attention required by enginemen.

(3). Lubrication occurs only when the locomotive is in motion.

(4). Feed not controlled by the working of trimmings.

(5). Reduction in maintenance of details, due to the effective lubrication of points which with oil do not receive lubrication, either because the oil leaks away before performing its intended function or the oil holes have become blocked.

(6). In sandy countries grease, as it exudes from a bearing, automatically forms a dust shield, whereas oil under similar conditions attracts grit and forms an abrasive medium.

The adaption of engines, at present oil lubricated, to grease lubrication involves only minor alterations.

Two qualities of grease are used, *viz.*, a hard grease for coupled axleboxes, coupling and connecting rod bearings, and bearing surfaces of wheel bosses, and a soft grease, or solidified oil, for carrying axleboxes, valve motion, brake and spring rigging, and any other details normally lubricated with oil. It will thus be observed that, other than the special oil required for the cylinders and valves, it is now possible to lubricate a locomotive throughout with grease.

A representative type of hard grease lubricator for coupled axleboxes is that known as the " Ajax," designed and patented by Messrs. Whitelegg & Rogers. This lubricator can be applied to engines having the bearing springs either above or below the axlebox; hitherto, grease lubrication could not be adopted when underhung springs were employed. The lubricator itself is contained within a special form of keep or cellar, and it is a matter of a few minutes for this to be withdrawn and a new block of grease inserted.

The fittings for coupled axleboxes using hard grease are of a special spring feed type, and provided with automatic indicators which shew the extent of wear of the grease block and also, in consequence, when renewal of the latter becomes necessary. There are usually two designs of axlebox lubricators, one being suitable for application with overhung, and the other with underhung bearing springs.

For coupling and connecting rod bearings and wheel boss faces, Tecalemit Patent Giant Nipples are used. These nipples are of the button head form; they have a spring valve inside and are suitably threaded to screw into existing oil reservoirs. The grease is applied by means of a Tecalemit hard grease gun which is capable of exerting an extremely high pressure (4,000-5,000 lb. per square inch), thus ensuring the thorough distribution of the grease to every part of a bearing or bush. This grease gun has a screw feed working in conjunction with a small high pressure pump, and is charged with a specially supplied grease stick or cartridge, $1\frac{1}{2}''$ in diameter and having a length of $8''$. An alternative type of gun is the " Ajax " Patent Hard Grease Pump; this is of simple construction and is fed with hard grease sticks or candles.

The application of these grease nipples to the bearing surfaces of wheel bosses is important; many cases of hot axleboxes may be traced to shoulder, or boss, friction arising when the engine is negotiating curves.

For dealing with all the parts previously enumerated as using soft grease, Tecalemit Soft Grease Nipples are applied. These are quite small, although to the same design as the Tecalemit Giant Nipples, but are screwed with either a $\frac{1}{4}''$ or $\frac{3}{8}''$ gas thread shank. The soft grease for these is applied by a Tecalemit soft grease gun, capable of forcing grease in at the same pressure as the hard grease gun and generally of similar design, except that the grease is fed to the high pressure pump by means of a spring loaded piston.

Until recently, little attention has been paid to the question of lubricating bogie and other carrying axleboxes with grease, but Messrs. Whitelegg & Rogers, of Grand Buildings, Trafalgar Square, London, who are responsible for the supply in

Great Britain of the special equipment required for the grease lubrication of locomotives, and to whom the author is indebted for the foregoing information, have produced an automatic lubricator for this purpose, known as the "Ajax" Soft Grease Axlebox Lubricator.   It is of the spring feed type and is charged by means of a Tecalemit soft grease gun.   It is claimed that, by the use of this grease lubricator, considerably greater mileage can be run without attention than would be the case with oil and, further, that greater immunity from overheating is obtained.

Considering the subject generally, grease, although under constant feed, moves more slowly than oil, and therefore requires larger grooves.   The rate of feed increases, as for oil, with rise of temperature.   No white metal is needed in the brasses; careful fitting and highly finished bearing surfaces are unnecessary.

The lubricant used is a heavy mineral grease free from moisture; bearings may therefore run at temperatures in excess of the boiling point of water without affecting the delivery of the lubricant.   For the coupled axleboxes a stick of grease is, in most applications, applied under spring pressure to the journal.   This stick of grease is held up to a perforated steel plate conforming to the radius of the journal; when sufficient heat has been generated, the grease feeds through the holes in the plate and forms a film between journal and bearing.

As previously stated, grease is considerably cheaper than oil.   On the other hand, more rapid wear of brasses may be anticipated, as the bearing must warm up considerably and there is metallic contact before the grease commences to feed; the normal running temperature of the bearing is therefore raised.   Further, the internal resistance of the engine is increased with grease lubrication.   Some observations made in the U.S.A. shew that, from this point of view, there is no appreciable difference between oil and grease lubrication on goods engines which run at low speeds and continuously develop a high percentage of their maximum tractive effort. The superiority of oil is demonstrated in the case of engines working at high speeds and of which the mean tractive effort is less than about 45% of the maximum.

Floating bushes may be used in conjunction with grease lubrication for pins.

Oil Reservoirs for Rotating Bearings (Big Ends and Coupling Rods).   These must be of sufficient capacity for the longest run made non-stop or without opportunity for replenishment. The following capacities, measured to the top of the oil stand pipe, were given in the Proc. I. Loco E. as appropriate for a mileage of 300:—

Connecting rod big ends, 20 cubic inches, *i.e.*, 0.57 pint.
Coupling rods, 12 cubic inches, *i.e.*, 0.34 pint.

For a given capacity the cross sectional area of the reservoir should be as large as possible in conjunction with minimum height. By this means the effects of centrifugal force are minimised, and also, where worsted trimmings are employed, the maximum efficiency of syphoning is obtained.

The oil reservoirs should preferably be machined from the solid body of the rod and not be separate units; there is the possibility, in the latter case, that they may be detached by centrifugal action.

Provision must be made for the entry of air to replace the volume of oil as it is used; otherwise, a partial vacuum will form in the reservoir and the flow of oil be restricted in consequence. In those cases where the bearing is small, the pressure low, and the length of the oil pipe comparatively short, air will find its way up the pipe in a direction contrary to that of the oil flow and replace the volume of the consumed oil, but for the larger and more important bearings either a porous cork or cane must be arranged in the reservoir cap or, if buttons are used, a specific air hole provided.

Wire versus Worsted Trimmings for Rotating Bearings.

Wire trimmings are more economical in oil consumption, as they only feed when the engine is actually in motion; although a plug trimming does not feed continuously, as does a tail trimming, it may continue to pass the contained oil after the engine has come to rest. Wire trimmings, on the other hand, are more likely to pass dirt; with worsted the dirt is trapped in the trimming where, unless periodical cleaning is carried out, it accumulates until eventually the supply of lubricant is choked or entirely cut off.

Worsted trimmings must be altered if seasonal variations of atmospheric temperature are sufficiently marked to affect the viscosity of the oil. Necessary renewals are in any case more frequent than for wire trimmings, which should normally last from one shops repair to the next unless, as occasionally happens, they are mislaid during preparation of the engine.

The wires should be of very hard steel (up to 120 tons per

square inch tensile), 13 W.G. being usually employed for big ends and 12 W.G. for coupling rods.   The nipples should be of similar steel and cupped to trap the oil.   The wires should be of sufficient length to extend to within $\frac{1}{4}''$ of the journal, the bend at the top precluding actual contact; the holes through which they pass should be drilled 11 W.G. for one-third of their length, the lower two-thirds being broached taper.

The maximum lift of the wire should be about $\frac{3}{8}''$.   The top of the wire is either looped or bent through 90°, the upper surface of the bend controlling the lift by contact on the up stroke with a domed recess in the cap of the oil reservoir.

Comparison of Canes and Corks with Buttons.

Canes and corks are liable to be mislaid when the engine is being prepared.   They must be renewed should they lose their porous properties, and are also likely to break off in their holes.   Buttons, on the other hand, if the retaining springs are of sufficient strength to keep them in position when running, may cause the spout of the oil feeder to be burred over during engine preparation.

It is important that holes for canes or corks should not be recessed, as otherwise dirt will collect therein and be washed into the reservoir when the oil is next replenished.

Coupled Axleboxes : Mechanical Lubrication.

One of the most satisfactory and economical methods of lubricating coupled axleboxes is by mechanical lubricators. The oil can then be introduced at the point of maximum pressure, where it tends to separate the box from the journal with a film of lubricant, thus approximating to ideal conditions. Preparation of the engine is simplified; no oil is used when standing, and the feed is proportional to the speed, as distinct from the action of worsted trimmings.   The feed is capable of easy adjustment should an individual box tend to heat. The oil pressure may approximate to 300 lb. per square inch when running.   That the lubricator must be coupled to a reciprocating part having constant travel, and not to the valve spindle, applies with equal force to axleboxes as to valves and cylinders; a steam warming coil should be provided for use in cold weather.   When fitted, check valves should be as near the axleboxes as possible, but not actually on them, as they are then inaccessible for examination and cleaning.   They are, however, considered unnecessary by many engineers; it is stated that these valves are likely to fail owing to accumula-

tions of grit, with the result that the excessive pressure consequently generated causes the oil pipes to burst. It has been
proved that the oil pipes have no tendency to drain off when
the check valves are omitted.

Provision must be made for systematic lubrication of the
horn faces, which consume about 20% of the total oil for the
box. A small emergency reservoir should also be provided in
the crown of the box to enable the engine to work home in the
event of any failure of the mechanical system.

Flexible connections should be made with armoured hose and
must be so arranged that they are not unduly strained by the
normal range of movement of the box, say, $2\frac{1}{2}''$. The hose
should be protected with copper pipe if in the vicinity of the
firebox. Telescopic arrangements of ordinary pipe are universally preferable to flexible piping, provided that effective
arrangements be made for the exclusion of water and grit.

The average oil consumption may be as low as 2 oz. per box
per 100 miles.

Coupled Axleboxes : Gravity Oil Feed.

When oil is fed to the boxes by gravity an advantageous
position for the oilboxes is on the backplate of the firebox.
The oil is then maintained at a constant and fairly high temperature, independent of weather conditions, the reservoirs are
always accessible for examination and replenishment, the trimmings do not need to be altered with seasonal variations of
temperature and may easily be lifted shortly before the end of
each trip in order to reduce consumption; further, a good fall
is ensured from the reservoir to box. The oil reservoir should
not make actual contact with the backplate, but should stand
clear. Air insulation is thus provided which prevents the oil
temperature from becoming excessive; in the latter event the
rate of flow increases and the oil consumption becomes unnecessarily high. The disadvantages of this location are that
the necessary lengths of oil pipe may become undesirable in
extent, and that flexible connections to each box are unavoidable, although a simple and satisfactory form may usually be
devised.

Oil reservoirs placed on top of the splashers or footplate are
more accessible than when incorporated with the axlebox itself,
but are subjected to the extremes of atmospheric temperature
fluctuations.

The provision of oil stop cocks is not an unmixed blessing,

as enginemen may forget to open them prior to moving the engine.

General Remarks on the Lubrication of Axleboxes with Gravity Feed.

Oil reservoirs for gravity feed should have stand pipes of such length that the top is at least $\frac{3}{8}''$ below the underside of the lid; alternatively, the lid may be flanged around the edges in order to prevent the trimming being trapped by the lid. A continuous groove should in any case be machined round the underside of the lid, conforming to its contour, to obviate the entry of the water to the reservoir. The reservoir should be located, unless formed in the crown of the axlebox casting or situated as previously described, as near as possible to the box it serves and, if possible, on the vertical centre line of the box; it should be as shallow as can possibly be arranged, since the rate of feed through a trimming varies inversely as the depth of immersion of the tail.

It is well to repeat that the presence of water in any oil reservoir may have serious consequences; it may emanate from the condensate of a faulty steam joint or be introduced either during washing out, spray cleaning, or in the case of a tank engine, should the tank be allowed to overflow when ordinary care is not exercised whilst taking water. Other sources of danger are grit and sand. Provision must therefore be made for these contingencies by taking suitable protective measures, and in this connection the usual fibre dust shields and covers are generally not in themselves sufficient.

Oil channels should be in the brass and not in the white metal; their length should be less than that of the bearing, i.e., the latter should be sealed, in order to prevent leakage. The edges of oil channels should be gently bevelled or radiused; transverse grooves so finished do not seriously interrupt the continuity of the oil film. The depth of oil grooves must be sufficient to enable them to continue to function when the axlebox is worn to the maximum permissible extent; this may necessitate a depth of groove of $1''$ at the crown.

Considerable diversity is exhibited with regard to the location of the oil grooves, but the modern tendency is towards feeding at the point of maximum pressure. It has been found by experiment that this, in the case of a simple centrally-loaded bearing, occurs at an angle of about 47° with the horizontal centre line, in the upper left quadrant, with clockwise rotation. Compromise is necessary for all locomotive main bearings, as reversal of direction of rotation in the case of carrying boxes, or in the case of coupled boxes, reversal occurring in each revolution of the sense of the forces set up in the horizontal plane by the connecting rod, causes the points of maximum and minimum resultant pressure respectively to alternate in position. It would therefore appear that the provision of two grooves, one on each side of, and at about 45° from, the vertical centre line of the box is the best arrangement for coupled boxes; a similar location may be adopted for carrying boxes, the angle being, say, 30° in this case. It has been suggested that the lay-out of the oil grooves, as seen in plan, be made circular, or approximately so, to enable the feed to be delivered as closely as possible to the point of maximum pressure (*The Railway Engineer*).

With steel boxes having separate brasses, the oil pipe should be extended through the steel casting into either a screwed nipple or an enlarged countersunk hole in the brass, thus providing a register and ensuring continuity of lubrication. Similarly, in the case of axleboxes allowed considerable side play and working in steel stirrups, the oil way should pass through a nipple in the stirrup into a suitable elongated hole in the axlebox casting.

Carrying boxes do not require any oil holes when arranged with underfeed pad lubrication.

The provision of oil grooves on the sides of axleboxes for horn face lubrication should not be omitted.

WHEEL CENTRES.

These are now almost invariably of cast steel; avoidance of sudden changes of section is to be observed. The spokes are frequently inclined outwards towards the wheel centre in order to allow of increased axlebox bearing area. The extent of this dishing is from 3″ to 4″, measuring from the face of the wheel rim to that of the boss. The shrinking on of the tyre tends temporarily to increase the dishing of the wheel centre and, to counteract this, the width of the spoke section in the vicinity of the boss is increased by the provision of a large radius joining the spoke to the outside face of the wheel boss.

Approximately three spokes may be provided per foot of diameter. The elliptical spoke section may taper, between the radii at the wheel boss and rim respectively, from about $4\frac{1}{4}″$ × 2″ near the boss, the radius at the ends of the ellipse being

$\frac{7}{8}''$, to $3\frac{1}{2}'' \times 1\frac{3}{4}''$, end radius $\frac{3}{4}''$, near the rim, in the case of coupled wheels for express engines, or from about $3\frac{3}{4}'' \times 1\frac{3}{4}''$ to $3\frac{1}{4}'' \times 1\frac{1}{2}''$, with ellipse end radii of $\frac{5}{8}''$ and $\frac{1}{2}''$ respectively, for the carrying wheels.

In order to ensure a good fit throughout, the hole for the axle may be bored with a taper of about 1 in 250 on the diameter.   The key fitted as an additional safeguard to coupled axles may be of about $1\frac{1}{4}''$ by $\frac{3}{4}''$ section, the edges having a radius of $\frac{1}{16}''$ or $\frac{1}{8}''$.

The maximum diameter of the boss is from $2d$ to $2.25d$ for coupled wheels, and about $2d$ for carrying wheels, where d is the diameter of the axle at the wheel seat.

The rim of the wheel centre should be of substantial section, and is sometimes turned slightly taper (about 1 in 500), such that the maximum outside diameter is on the centre line of the section, in order to prevent lateral movement of the tyre. The maximum depth of the rim section at the centre is from $2''$ to $2\frac{1}{2}''$ when the section is roughly rectangular, the top surface being actually convex and giving a depth at the sides of the section of from $1\frac{1}{2}''$ to $1\frac{3}{4}''$.   Where a symmetrically disposed strengthening web of semicircular form is employed, the maximum depth of section is about $3\frac{1}{4}''$ or $3\frac{1}{2}''$.   The width of the rim section is governed by the section adopted for the tyre, and is of the order of $4\frac{3}{4}''$.

Side thrust is taken in American practice by a renewable liner on the wheel centre and not, as in this country, on the axlebox.

A departure from orthodox wheel design has been made on the N.Y.C.R.R. (*The Railway Gazette*, 25th May, 1934), in which the centre consists of a double disc, cast in steel and fitted with an ordinary tyre; the balance weight cavities are lead filled.   It is stated that there is a nett saving in weight of approximately 10%.   Clearance holes are provided to give access to pins and other details behind the wheels.   The material is A.R.A. Grade E steel, annealed to a temperature of about 1,650° F. and air cooled, its approximate analysis being:—

Carbon ...	...	...	0.3%
Manganese	...	...	0.8%
Silicon ...	...	...	0.4%
Sulphur ⎫		under	0.03%
Phosphorus ⎭			

The sections of metal are remarkably uniform for the purposes of casting, the ruling wall thickness being $\frac{3}{4}''$.   With ordinary spoked wheels the effect of shrinking the tyre on is to warp the hub outwards, in some cases by as much as $\frac{1}{4}''$; it is claimed that there is only 10% of this distortion with the disc wheels. It is stated that there is an increase in strength of about 50% with the latter, a further advantage being that it is possible, if desired, to increase the percentage of the reciprocating masses balanced.

TYRES.

The contours recommended by the British Engineering Standards Association have been universally adopted in this country (see Fig. 30, which is reproduced from the *Locomotive Engineers' Pocket Book*). The tyre thickness when new is commonly $3''$; re-turning may be performed until the thickness is reduced to $1\frac{5}{8}''$, scrapping taking place at $1\frac{1}{2}''$.

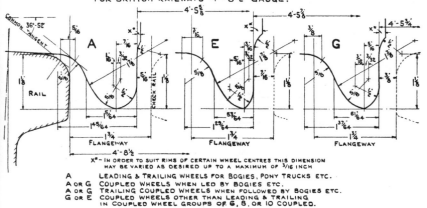

B.E.S.A. STANDARD TYRE CONTOURS (REPORT Nº 276-1927) FOR BRITISH RAILWAYS 4'-8½' GAUGE.

X° – IN ORDER TO SUIT RIMS OF CERTAIN WHEEL CENTRES THIS DIMENSION MAY BE VARIED AS DESIRED UP TO A MAXIMUM OF 3/16 INCH

A — LEADING & TRAILING WHEELS FOR BOGIES, PONY TRUCKS ETC.
A OR G — COUPLED WHEELS WHEN LED BY BOGIES ETC.
A OR G — TRAILING COUPLED WHEELS WHEN FOLLOWED BY BOGIES ETC.
G OR E — COUPLED WHEELS OTHER THAN LEADING & TRAILING IN COUPLED WHEEL GROUPS OF 6, 8, OR 10 COUPLED.

FIG. 30

Shrinkage allowance varies from 1/1200 to 1/750 of the diameter, with a tendency to increase to the latter amount. On some railways a sliding scale is in force, *e.g.*, the tyre is bored 0.001" smaller than the wheel centre per inch of diameter up to 5'-0", and .0625" smaller than the wheel centre for larger diameters.

Tyres are now rarely secured to the wheel centres with radial studs. Although it has been claimed that, in the event of a tyre fracturing, the effects of centrifugal action are sectionalised, each stud hole in itself represents a plane of weakness in which fracture is liable to occur. Further, the permissible amount of wear is limited with some applications of this design. The usual diameter of the studs was from $\frac{7}{8}''$ to $1\frac{1}{8}''$.

Transverse countersunk rivets, cold, turned, about $\frac{3}{4}''$ in diameter and placed between alternate spokes, are much to be preferred; in some cases hot rivets are used. With the Mansell ring type of fastening the rivets are usually located on the produced centre lines either of each spoke or of alternate spokes.

To provide sideplay in the rigid wheelbase of multi-coupled engines, the tyres for the wheels of one or more of the intermediate coupled axles may be either flangeless, set back or, as is usual practice in this country, thin flanged.

BALANCING.

Rotating masses are entirely balanced in the wheels and axles concerned; inside crankpins and webs are in some instances balanced by web extensions. The proportion of the reciprocating masses balanced is customarily from one-half to two-thirds, but may be as low as 0.4 for engines of which the total mass is great relative to that of the reciprocating parts, or as high as 0.8 in the case of narrow gauge engines. For engines having coupled wheels of small diameter, say, 3'-6" to 4'-0", and which normally run at low speeds, the proportion of the reciprocating masses balanced is usually comparatively high. Were the reciprocating parts completely balanced by revolving masses the unbalanced horizontal force, and therefore the swaying couple, would be non-existent, but the variation occurring in rail pressure throughout each revolution would be great. The converse holds good in the event of the reciprocating parts being entirely unbalanced, assuming the rotating masses to be completely balanced (as they are in practice), and although constant rail pressure would be obtained, the unbalanced horizontal force and swaying couple would have dangerous effects at high speeds of rotation. A compromise is therefore effected by partially balancing the reciprocating masses as above. Primary balancing only is applied in locomotive practice.

The principle rotating masses comprise:—
    Crank webs.
    All crank pins (including loose collars fitted to outside pins).
    Part of connecting rod.

Part of coupling rod allocated to wheel under consideration.

And the reciprocating masses:—

Piston head with rings, nut, rod and cotter.

Crosshead complete with slideblocks, gudgeon pin and nut.

Part of connecting rod.

The resolution of the total mass of the connecting rod into rotating and reciprocating components respectively is preferably carried out as advocated in an early section of this chapter. Assume the centre of mass of a connecting rod of length l between centres and mass M to be at a distance c from the big end centre. Then

Reciprocating mass assumed concentrated at crosshead =

$$m = \frac{M\,c}{l}$$

And rotating mass assumed concentrated at big end =

$$M - m.$$

In American practice the proportion of the connecting rod balanced is given by

$$M_{ER} = M\left(\frac{\kappa^2 - \dfrac{xr^2}{l}}{l^2 - r^2}\right) \quad\dotfill (231)$$

which reduces, as a general approximation, to

$$M_{ER} = M\left(\frac{\frac{1}{2}l^2 - \frac{5}{8}r^2}{l^2 - r^2}\right) \quad\dotfill (232)$$

In the foregoing,

M_{ER} = equivalent rotating mass of connecting rod, lb.,

M = mass of connecting rod, lb.,

κ = radius of gyration of connecting rod about crosshead pin, feet,

x = distance of centre of gravity of connecting rod from crosshead, feet,

l = length of connecting rod, feet, and

r = crank radius, feet.

Some engineers arbitrarily assume $\dfrac{M}{3}$ to be reciprocating and

$\frac{2}{3}M$ rotating. Other similar assumptions applicable to valve gear details are:—

Return crank with eccentric
pin ... ... $\frac{2}{3}$ weight assumed rotating at crank pin radius.

Combination lever ... ... $\frac{1}{4}$ weight assumed reciprocating.

Union link with pins ... Assumed reciprocating.

Eccentric rod (Walschaerts'
gear) ... ... Is about 90° out of phase with its own crank but practically, if not exactly, in phase (plus or minus) with one other, in the cases of two- and four-cylinder engines, and partly in phase if the engine has three cylinders.

Hammer Blow is the variation in the load transmitted by the wheel to the rail which is produced by the vertical component of the centrifugal force arising from that portion, m lb., of the balance weight which is allocated to the reciprocating masses. The general expression for the load on the rail at any instant is therefore given by

$$W \pm \frac{m}{l} \omega^2 r \sin \theta \text{ lb.} \quad \text{.....................................} \quad (233)$$

where W = static wheel load, lb.,

r = distance of centre of mass of balance weight from centre of axle, feet,

and θ = angle between horizontal centre line through axle and line joining centre of mass of balance weight with centre of axle.

$$\omega = 2\pi n = \frac{\pi N}{30}$$

where n = number of revolutions per second,

and N = number of revolutions per minute.

To minimise the hammer blow per wheel or axle, the reciprocating balance is distributed amongst the coupled wheels. There should be a minimum on the leading pair, as guiding action is required of them; in some instances the reciprocating balance in them is zero.

Typical allocations are:—

> For 0-6-0 engine: 0.25 to leading wheels.
> 0.5 to driving wheels.
> 0.25 to trailing wheels.
>
> For 0-8-0 engine: 0   to leading wheels.
> 0.5 to driving wheels.
> 0.5 to intermediate wheels.
> 0   to trailing wheels.

It is useful to remember that

$$\text{Centrifugal force} = \frac{Mv^2}{gr} = \frac{M\omega^2 r}{g} \text{ or, in absolute units,}$$

which are convenient for balancing calculations $= M\omega^2 r$

The maximum force causing horizontal disturbance is $\dfrac{m_u}{g}\omega^2 r$ per cylinder, and the value of the swaying couple due to it, $\dfrac{m_u}{g}\omega^2 rc$ for a two-cylinder engine with cranks at 90°.

In these expressions:—

> m_u = unbalanced mass of the reciprocating parts per cylinder, lb.,
> r = crank radius, feet,
> and c = distance between centres of cranks, feet.

In the following solution of a balancing problem the method employed is that introduced by Professor Dalby, and readers are referred to his book, *The Balancing of Engines* (published by Arnold), from which this example has been selected as being typical, for the complete development of his argument.

Conventions observed, without serious error, are:—

> The connecting rods are assumed to be of infinite length.
> Reciprocating parts are assumed to be concentrated at the crank pins.
> All masses are assumed in the first instance to be acting at a common radius, *viz.*, that of the driving crank pins; this involves in some cases, *e.g.*, coupling rods of inside cylinder engines, the calculation by the principle of moments of equivalent, or proportional, masses.

For the determination of the necessary balancing masses a vertical reference plane must be selected; this should be so

chosen as to contain the circle of revolution of the centre of
gravity of one of the balance weights.   The perpendicular distances from this plane to those of the various masses requiring
to be balanced (l_1, l_2, l_3 etc.) are then taken and couples of the
form Wrl calculated.   The couple polygon may then be drawn.
In this the vectors are drawn parallel to the cranks concerned,
and couples measured on different sides of the reference plane
must be of opposite sign.   Thus, if a couple on one side of
the reference plane be represented by a vector drawn *outwards*
from the axis of revolution, then a couple on the other side
must be represented by a vector drawn *inwards* towards the
axis.   In drawing the force (Wr) polygon, the vectors representing the forces are invariably drawn *outwards* from the
axis.

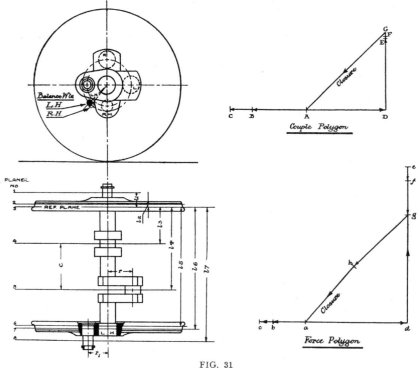

FIG. 31

Fig. **31** shews the elevation and plan, symbolically dimensioned, of a pair of wheels and axle for an engine with two
inside cylinders.   It is required to determine the mass and

location of the necessary balance weights. In the first instance, the known information is tabulated, the units being inches and pounds respectively.

Dimensions.

Piston stroke $= 2r$ inches
Radius of outside cranks $= r_1$ inches.
Cylinder centres $= c$ inches.
Coupling rod centres $= (l_1 + l_2 + l_7)$ inches.
Distance between mass centres of wheel cranks $= (l_2 + l_6)$ inches.
Distance between planes containing mass centres of balance weights $= l_5$ inches.

Rotating Masses.

Unbalanced mass at outside crankpins, comprising proportion of coupling rod, protruding portion of crankpin with washer, the whole being converted to an equivalent mass acting at inside crank pin radius:

$$Right = W_1 \text{ lb.}$$
$$Left = W_8 \text{ lb.}$$

Unbalanced mass of wheel crank, with included portion of crankpin:

$$R = W_2 \text{ lb.}$$
$$L = W_7 \text{ lb.}$$

Unbalanced mass of revolving parts at inside crank journals, comprising portion of connecting rod, inside crank webs and pins:

$$R = W_{4A} \text{ lb.}$$
$$L = W_{5A} \text{ lb.}$$

Reciprocating Masses.

Acting at inside crank journals and including piston head, rod, crosshead, and attachments previously specified, also portion of connecting rod:

$$R = W_{4B} \text{ lb.}$$
$$L = W_{5B} \text{ lb.}$$

The total masses to be balanced in planes 4 and 5 are then $W_{4A} + xW_{4B} = W_4$, and $W_{5A} + xW_{5B} = W_5$ respectively, where x is the stipulated proportion of the reciprocating masses to be balanced. The mass centres of the right- and left-hand balance weights are in planes 3 and 6 respectively, 3 originally being adopted as the reference plane.

Next, draw up a schedule in accordance with Table XLI, assuming those couples acting below the reference plane, as seen in the plan, to be positive. It will be noted that in the third column forces of the form Wr are tabulated, whilst the fourth column gives the Wrl couples.

TABLE XLI.

FORM OF SCHEDULE FOR BALANCING (*see* Fig. 31).

Ref No. of Crank or Plane.	Distance from Reference Plane.	Equivalent Mass at radius r, or absolute centrifugal force when $\omega^2 r = 1$.	Equivalent Mass Moment, or absolute centrifugal couple when $\omega^2 r = 1$.
1	$-l_1$	W_1	$-W_1 l_1$
2	$-l_2$	W_2	$-W_2 l_2$
3	0	(W_3 unknown)	0
4	l_3	W_4	$W_4 l_3$
5	l_4	W_5	$W_5 l_4$
6	l_5	(W_6 unknown)	Unknown
7	l_6	W_7	$W_7 l_6$
8	l_7	W_8	$W_8 l_7$

The quantities which at this stage are unknown are determined by constructions, the first being that of the couple polygon. Disregarding unknown quantities, the known couples are taken in order, working from the bottom of the plan upwards and, observing the conventions previously enumerated for the setting out of couple vectors, the polygon $ABCDEFG$ is drawn, so that $AB = W_8 l_7$, $BC = W_7 l_6$, $CD = W_5 l_4$, and so on. The closure, GA, is also drawn. Dividing the scaled value of GA by l_5, we obtain the value of $W_6 r$, or the equivalent balancing mass required in the left-hand wheel at radius r; as its sense and direction are given by the vector, $W_6 r$ may be drawn in parallel to the latter in the elevation.

Drawing next the force polygon, $abcdefgh$, the closure ha will be found equal to $W_3 r$.

It will be noted in the example given that, although gh and ha are not co-linear, the angle between the outside crank and centre line of balance weight is identical for R. and L. wheels; the same wheel casting therefore satisfies for both wheels.

Although disregarded in the example for the sake of simplicity, the valve gears would be treated in a similar manner in their planes between the cranks, the equivalent of their masses at the radius of the driving crank pins being determined.

An alternative method of solving balancing problems is that set out in the *Locomotive Engineers' Pocket Book*.

Finally, having determined by either method the value of Wr for the individual balance weight, its equivalent value when transferred to the wheel rim as a crescent must be found, and in this connection the following information may be of service. Referring to the diagram, Fig. 32 (a):—

Area of crescent $ABCEA$ = (area of segment $ABCDA$ — area of segment $AECDA$).

The area of a segment, see Fig. 32 (b), = (area of sector $AOCB$ — area of triangle ACO), and the area of a sector is given by $\left(\dfrac{\theta}{360} \times \pi r^2 \right)$, where θ is the number of degrees subtended by $\angle AOC$.

The distance of the centre of gravity of a segment from the centre of the generating circle is $\left(\dfrac{\text{chord}^3}{12 \times \text{area}} \right)$.

In practice the balance weight necessary to give the determined moment Wr is applied as near the wheel rim as possible

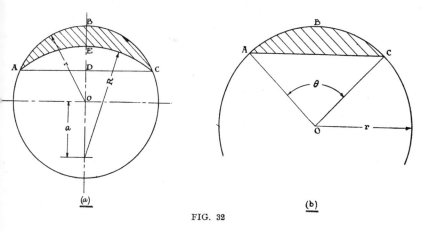

FIG. 32

in order to minimise the necessary mass of the balance weight, and consequently the hammer blow. The crescent form of balance weight is adopted in order to graduate the effect of hammer blow on the permanent way.

Reverting to Fig. 32 (a),
Balancing moment of crescent = area of segment $AECDA$
$\times$ distance a.

Also,

$$\frac{\text{Balancing moment of crescent}}{\text{Area of crescent}} = \text{distance of its centre of gravity from } O.$$

The deduction of the total weight of portions of spokes contained in the crescents must not be omitted.

Chapter X.

VALVES, PORTS AND VALVE GEARS.

TYPES OF VALVE.

Flat (or D) valves are now seldom employed for any but the smallest types of locomotive. The value of μ, for an unbalanced gunmetal valve working on a vertical cast iron port face, approximates to 0.068, and to 0.088 on a horizontal face (Aspinall). Two typical bronzes for valves are given below, the first composition being at one time used on the former L.Y.R.

Copper	80%	84%
Tin	10%	10%
Phosphor Copper ...	5%	6%
		(includes 15% Phosphorus).
Lead	5%	Nil.

Both mixtures have been used in conjunction with superheated steam. In the first case, considerable and uneven wear was reported; the second, used on another railway, has proved satisfactory with balanced valves.

Soft close-grained cast iron is a suitable material; friction, and therefore wear, is reduced. Care must be taken that the valve face, if surfaced on a planer, be machined in a direction at right angles to that obtaining for the port face. Irrespective of the material employed, holes or grooves should be provided in the valve face to retain the lubricant.

Trick (double-ported) valves are rarely adopted in British practice. They increase the port opening to admission steam but not to exhaust, where improvement is more frequently needed. Where this type of valve is used it is essential that the inner edges at the ends of the internal valve passage be so arranged that, when in full travel, they do not overrun the exhaust port edges, thus enabling live steam to pass directly to exhaust. With this form of valve it is important to remember that the actual lead is twice the apparent lead.

Under certain conditions, *e.g.*, low standard of mainten-ance, many engineers still prefer the **balanced slide valve** to the piston valve. A direct steam path may be arranged, wear is small, and it is possible to run between shoppings without in-termediate attention. A $\frac{3}{8}''$ hole may be drilled through the back of the valve to allow any live steam blowing past the balance strips or rings to escape to exhaust, thus preventing invalida-tion of the balancing effect. An alternative arrangement, which is far better and more generally adopted, is to eliminate the back wall of the valve in its entirety, thus providing a very direct exhaust which passes through an orifice in the pres-sure plate. The latter, incidentally, may conveniently be made integral with the steam chest cover. In a typical example of a balanced valve the grooves containing the balance strips are $2\frac{1}{4}''$ deep and $\frac{7}{16}''$ wide, the corresponding dimensions of the cast iron strips are $2\frac{1}{16}''$ and 27/64'' respectively, whilst the support-ing springs are $\frac{3}{8}''$ wide and are of sheet steel 3/32'' thick. Such springs have approximately the following unloaded cambers:— Long springs, $1\frac{3}{4}''$; short springs, 1''. The camber when loaded is about $\frac{9}{16}''$. In another case the grooves are $\frac{1}{2}''$ wide and have a depth of only $1\frac{9}{16}''$.

The area to be balanced is measured outside the strips, and in British practice is equivalent to 50-60% of the valve area. The area balanced by American designers, in the case of the Richardson type valve, is based on (1 steam port + 2 port bridges + exhaust port). Denoting this latter area by x, the areas customarily balanced for American valves of the single disc and double disc types are $1.08x$ and $1.15x$ respect-ively. For maintenance of steam tightness individual strips are preferable to a continuous frame or ring, owing to the fact that they are better able to adjust themselves to any irregulari-ties of surface.

It is usual in American practice to cast the steam chest, for all types of slide valve, separate from the main cylinder cast-ing. Although involving the manufacture and maintenance in steam-tight condition of an additional joint of considerable size, this arrangement nevertheless renders the port face very much more accessible for facing up. In this country, renew-able port faces of hardened steel have been successfully used in cases where the original surface has worn to the maximum extent. In view of the unequal expansions of the attachment and the main cylinder casting respectively, the former cannot be rigidly secured, and is therefore held in position by suspen-sion from a set bolt.

The frictional resistance of a **piston valve** has been variously estimated at from $12\frac{1}{2}\%$ to 20% of that for the equivalent slide valve, and may be appreciably less for piston valves fitted with restrained or narrow rings. In common with the motion details, however, the major forces are those due to inertia, and the weight of the piston valve, with its spindle and crosshead, must consequently be reduced as much as possible. In this connection it should be noted that the maximum inertia loads, on which the design must be based, occur when the regulator is shut and the engine placed in full gear whilst running at high speeds; the inertia effect is therefore affected by the extent of the maximum valve travel. A modern example of piston valve design for inside admission has light spider heads of drop forged steel on a spindle of small diameter, the portion between the heads being covered with seamless steel tube to which suitable belled ends are welded. This construction is of light weight, and at the same time enables the exhaust steam to pass freely from one end of the valve chamber to the other.

As weight restriction is so important, the use of aluminium alloys for the valve heads and spindles may be considered. It must be remembered, however, that the coefficient of expansion is approximately twice that for steel and, further, the metal is comparatively ductile; as the valve drops with wear the groove edges therefore tend to burr over, with an unfavourable effect on the action of the rings, and the use of tail rods which, in general, may improve the efficiency of the rings in service, must then be considered (Windle, Proc. I. Loco. E., 1933).

Compared with the slide valve, the piston valve is more complicated; although the cost of the material is less, it is ultimately more expensive to manufacture and is also more costly to maintain. Further, leakage past the valve is liable to occur and the path for the exhaust steam is more tortuous, notably when compared with the balanced type of slide valve. The possibility of rings breaking, particularly when the narrow (Knorr) pattern is adopted, is certainly no greater than that arising with balance rings and strips, although the effects of such mishaps are more disastrous with piston valves. In spite of the foregoing disabilities, piston valves are far superior to slide valves for the distribution of highly superheated steam, especially when the cylinder dimensions are large; the appreciably greater length of port obtained effects a corresponding improvement in the area of the port opening and, as previously mentioned, the frictional resistance of the piston valve is very small as compared with that of a slide valve. Special measures must be taken, particularly with valves having broad rings, to permit of the escape of trapped water from the cylinders, *e.g.*, by providing cylinder relief valves or ball valves in the piston valve heads.

Inside admission is decidedly preferable to outside. The spindle glands are then not subjected to the action of highly superheated steam at full pressure, the live steam itself is remote from the comparatively cool ends of the valve chamber and short, direct ports are more easily arranged. Further, in so far as loads due to the steam pressure are concerned, the portion of the valve spindle between the valve heads is virtually a tie, and not a strut.

With regard to the diameter of the valve, the conclusion reached from experiments carried out some years ago on the Pennsylvania R.R. was that it should not be less than 0.016 D^2, where D is the diameter of the cylinder. It was found that the condition of the valve, as regards freedom from leakage, was a factor of primary importance, and that the extent of leakage was proportional to the diameter of the valve. It was further established that a decrease in valve diameter necessitated a later cut-off in order to obtain a given power output at a given speed; this, incidentally, was obviously due to the effects of wiredrawing occurring with severely restricted areas of port opening.

Having regard to subsequent extended experience, and to the ultimate finding, it may now be taken that the diameter of a piston valve should approximate to one-half that of the cylinder it controls, the appropriate proportion being slightly less with long valve travels. It still does not appear to be generally realised that the efficiency of the circumferential port is variable, being naturally less at those parts of the periphery which are remote from the cylinder barrel; the gain from the fact that the effective length of port in the liner for a piston valve is roughly 50% greater than that for an equivalent slide valve is therefore by no means directly proportional. Further, to ensure ample port openings with early cut-offs, notably to exhaust, the area of the port should, within practical limits, be as great as can conveniently be provided. Lastly, due allowance must be made for the comparatively indirect path for, and, unless the exhaust bush is discarded (as is best), for the subdivision into small streams of, the exhaust steam; otherwise an undesirable increase in back pressure, and possibly in compression, may be anticipated. Since back pressure increases with speed, exhaust ports and passages must in any case be large in order to minimise its value, which ranges from 3 to 5 lb. per square inch gauge with good design, and may be as much as 10 lb. per square inch with a badly designed engine running at speed.

Table XLII gives some piston value dimensions, put forward by Mr. Selby in a paper read before the Institution of Locomotive Engineers, which may be recommended for consideration.

The longitudinal centre line of the valve must be as near that of the cylinder as can be arranged, and the valve heads at such a distance apart on the spindle that the passages thence to the cylinders are as short and direct as possible. An easy means of adjusting the position of the valve relative to the ports is provided by screwing and nutting the valve spindle on either side of its crosshead; the provision of this adjustment is essential in all cases where radial valve gears are employed.

Narrow (Knorr type) rings are very much more satisfactory than the broad pattern originally fitted. There is less friction, and therefore wear, with them, and the risk of breakage is considerably reduced; the reduction in wear may be partly attributed to the greater freedom with which the narrow ring can adapt itself to any irregularities in the surface of the liner. With the broad rings, should steam leak beneath them, pressure is exerted on a considerable area; the $\frac{3}{16}''$ holes customarily drilled through the rings to counteract this tendency are very liable to become choked as carbonisation occurs.   The claim that the broad ring prevented uneven liner wear may have held good when the ports in the latter were rectangular in form; ports of this shape are, however, rarely encountered in modern design.

Piston valve rings are turned initially to an outside diameter about $\frac{1}{8}''$ larger than the bore of the liner. A staggered slit, about $\frac{1}{2}''$ in width, is then cut through each ring at an angle of 45° to the end faces and the ring peened on the inside, diametrically opposite the slit, for a distance of about 2″, until the width of the slit has increased to $\frac{3}{4}''$.   The ring is next closed, placed in a jig or pad having a capacity of from 12 to 16 rings, and then finally turned to fit accurately the bore of the liner.   This method ensures a finished ring having uniform depth and spring throughout its periphery.   On some railways the final turned diameter of the ring is made 0.01″ larger than the bore of the liner.

TABLE XLII.

SUGGESTED DIMENSIONS OF PISTON VALVES (Selby, Proc.I.Loco.E.).

Cylinder Diameter, inches.	Diameter of Piston Valve, inches.	Steam Ports in Liner.			Steam Passage from Valve to Cylinder.			Exhaust Ports in Liner (where used).	
		Effective Length, inches.	Width, inches.	Area, square inches.	Length of Cross Section, inches.	Width, inches.	Cross Sectional Area, square inches.	Width, inches.	Area, square inches.
12-14	7	15	1	15·0	12	$1\frac{1}{4}$	15·0	$2\frac{1}{2}$	37·5
14-16	8	$17\frac{1}{2}$	$1\frac{1}{4}$	21·9	14	$1\frac{1}{2}$	21·0	3	52·5
16-18	9	20	$1\frac{1}{2}$	30·0	$16\frac{1}{2}$	$1\frac{3}{4}$	28·9	$3\frac{5}{8}$	72·5
18-20	10	$22\frac{1}{2}$	$1\frac{3}{4}$	39·3	19	2	38·0	$4\frac{1}{4}$	95·5
20-22	11	25	$1\frac{7}{8}$	46·9	21	$2\frac{1}{8}$	44·6	$4\frac{1}{2}$	112·5
22-24	12	$27\frac{1}{2}$	2	55·0	23	$2\frac{1}{4}$	51·7	5	137·5

Narrow rings may be about 9/32″ wide and 11/32″ deep in section; the split or gap is confined to reciprocation over a wide bridge at either the top or, preferably, the bottom of the liner, rotation of the ring in its groove being prevented by the turned head of a ⅜″ set bolt, placed between adjacent rings and registering with short recesses in the end faces of the rings. By placing the gaps at the bottom of the valve, the dropping of the latter as wear occurs tends to close the gaps. At least four narrow rings should be provided per valve head. When the valve is in position in the liner the gaps in the ring should not exceed $\frac{1}{16}$″ in width; owing to the influence of this dimension on the extent of valve leakage, 1/32″ is much to be preferred. On one railway the stipulated width of gap *in situ* is approximately 0.003″ per inch of valve diameter.

As the outer rings provide the steam and exhaust edges respectively of the valve, it is essential that they fit closely in their grooves; a side tolerance of about 0.004″ may be accepted. If of cast iron, which is the most satisfactory material for the purpose, the rings should be of the mixture specified for the cylinders.

When broad rings are used they must be restrained by clamp rings having suitable recesses in the faces to engage with lips turned on the valve rings to correspond, or by other means, in order to keep them in position during the erection of the valve, and also to prevent portions of the ring dissociating from the valve head in the event of breakage.

The outside diameter of the valve head is generally made 1/32″ less than the bore of the liner, although in some cases the diametral clearance is as small as 1/64″.

The valve liners may be so turned that the external diameter is from 0.003″ to 0.004″ larger than the bore of the valve chamber. They must be taper bored at the ends (the taper should not be more acute than 1 in 12 on the diameter) in order to facilitate the entry and removal of the valve with rings in position, and also to prevent the formation of ridges as wear takes place in service. The overall length of the parallel bore should be $\frac{1}{8}$″ less than the sum of the maximum valve travel and the effective width of the valve head, *i.e.*, the outside rings should overrun the parallel bore by $\frac{1}{16}$″ at each end when at full travel.

To ensure uniformity of wear on the rings, the ports in the liner may be approximately triangular in outline and so disposed that the admission line is demarked alternately by the base and apex of contiguous triangles. A purely triangular shape should not be adopted, as it gives an unduly restricted port opening at early cut-offs; further, carbonisation is prone to occur at the apex of each triangle. The width of the staggered, curved bridges should not be less than $\frac{1}{16}''$ on the inside of the bush (the port edges are machined radially), and at the top or bottom of the liner, according to the location of the set bolts retaining the valve rings, rectangular bridges, about $1''$ in width, should be provided. With the rectangular ports originally provided throughout the liner, the bottom bridge was in some cases as much as $3''$ in width, the maximum for the other bridges being about $1\frac{1}{2}''$. The maximum thickness of the liner wall (cast iron) may be $\frac{3}{4}''$.

An appreciable improvement in the freedom of the exhaust may be effected by machining a radius of about $\frac{1}{4}''$ around the edge of the exhaust apertures in the liner. It is, however, far better entirely to dispense with the exhaust liner, in which case projections are provided on the steam chest covers to act as distance pieces for the (admission steam) liner; the latter is pressed into the cylinder casting against a copper ring, of suitable section, which is fitted into a shouldered recess machined in the main casting.

The American practice of casting the valve spindle guide integrally with the valve chamber cover is excellent in that it ensures permanent alignment. Nevertheless, care must be exercised in adopting this procedure that the accessibility of the spindle glands is not sacrificed, and that the covers register accurately with the cylinder casting, by dowel pins or other means, in order that they may be replaced exactly in the position occupied prior to removal.

The basic, or calculated diameter of valve spindles for both slide and piston valves should be increased by $\frac{1}{8}''$ to $\frac{3}{16}''$ to allow for wear. The spindles may well be made hollow in order to decrease the effects of inertia, especially with long travel valve gears.

Although increasing pressures and dimensions, together with the incidence of superheating, necessitated the replacement of slide by piston valves, the inherent disadvantages of the latter have led to the application of **poppet valves** to locomotives, in some cases with a rotary drive. The latter drive absorbs from 1 to 1.5 horse-power for two-cylinder engines and about 2 horse-power for four-cylinder engines (Caprotti); the actuation of a

Lentz type gear with rotary drive for a three-cylinder engine is stated to absorb from 4 to 4.5 horse-power at 280 r.p.m.   In comparison, a conventional link motion or radial gear absorbs, under similar conditions, from 10 to 15 horse-power for a two-cylinder engine.   Wear is very slight with poppet valves and the use of separate admission and exhaust valves reduces the temperature range and, consequently, the extent of condensation; in this connection it must be remembered that with highly superheated steam the normal temperature range may be sufficient to crack the cylinder casting.   High rates of expansion are possible with poppet valves, the minimum suitable cut-off ranging from 3% to 5%, thus rendering compounding unnecessary from this point of view.   The cams may be so profiled as to give any desired arrangement of valve events.   With reference to the latter, it is well to remember that the port opening is relatively greater and considerably more rapid than with piston valves; opening to exhaust, for instance, should therefore be retarded, or loss of power, due to premature release, will be experienced.   There is no appreciable variation in lead as notching up proceeds ; all valve events are sharply defined and distribution losses minimised.   Valves of this type will be more fully considered subsequently.

Location of Valves.

The valves are now usually placed above the cylinders they serve, this position being eminently suitable for gears of the radial type.   In the case of engines with outside cylinders and link motion, with especial reference to direct drive, a convenient position for the valves is between the frames, the valve centre line being in or near the horizontal plane in which lies the cylinder centre line; a similar location is sometimes adopted for the valve controlling the inside cylinder of a three-cylinder engine.

Owing to their relatively great depth balanced slide valves are, in general, limited to positions either above or below the cylinder, the former being preferable.   If unbalanced slide valves are placed below the cylinders, they are at an advantage in that they fall away from the port faces when the engine is coasting; the release of water from the cylinders is also facilitated and, lastly, the centre of gravity of the boiler may be kept low if desired, especially with inside cylinders.   These advantages are, however, more than offset by the disadvantages of this position.   The arrangement of the steam pipes is frequently awkward and passages are not so direct as is desirable, as the centre line of the motion is of necessity steeply inclined to that of the cylinders, thus engendering excessive clearance volume, the steam chest is very exposed and losses by radiation and condensation are consequently high, with the result that effects similar to slight but continuous priming may be observed. Further, freedom as regards lay-out of the motion is unduly restricted and the connecting rods for inside cylinders are rendered inaccessible. Lastly, the ground clearance of the engine is reduced to a minimum and the risk of breakages by fouling thereby increased, especially in the event of derailment.

Since the introduction of the locomotive, the orientation of the unbalanced slide valve has been so varied at different periods that its locus completely circumscribes the periphery of the cylinder.

PORTS.

Must in general be as direct and free from bends as possible, and of generous cross-sectional area. The design is governed by the fact that the ports between the valve and cylinder are necessarily traversed by exhaust steam having a greater volume and lower natural velocity than the live steam admitted. In stationary practice it is usual so to proportion the ports that the velocity of flow lies between the limits of 4,000 and 6,000 feet per minute and, at the actual port opening, up to 9,000 feet per minute for slide valves and 12,000 for poppet valves.

Let V = mean velocity of steam, feet per minute,
S = average piston speed, feet per minute,
D = cylinder diameter, inches, and
a = cross-sectional area of port, normal to direction of steam flow, in square inches.

$$\text{Then } a = \frac{\pi D^2 S}{4 V} \quad\text{.. (234)}$$

It must be borne in mind that port area and clearance volume are interdependent; any increase in the former therefore involves an addition to the latter. In extreme cases, *e.g.*, cylinders of very large diameter, say 26″ and over, with poppet valves, the clearance volume may be as low as 4%-5%. With cylinders having dimensions common to British practice for three- and four-cylinder engines, a clearance of 6% is both desirable and attainable, although in many designs it ranges from 8% to 10%. The clearance volume is inclusive not only of the port between valve and cylinder, but also, of course, of the passages to drain cocks, relief valves, etc. Of the clearance, roughly $1\frac{1}{2}$% represents that between the piston head and the cylinder cover, and is only variable within narrow limits, but by careful attention to details such as the location of the valve heads and the distance of the centre line of the valve from that of the cylinder, it is possible to provide adequate port area without unduly increasing the clearance volume. As was shewn in Chapter II, the effect of clearance volume is to reduce the actual expansion as compared with the apparent ratio; other things being equal, increased clearance volume will result in a higher m.e.p. at the cost of augmented steam consumption.

Let D and A be the diameter and cross-sectional area respectively of the cylinder. Then suitable proportions of ports are:—

For Piston Valves:

Area of steam ports in liner = 0.15 A.

Area of exhaust ports in liner (where used) = from **0.36A** to 0.375A. The effective length of port, *i.e.*, exclusive of bridges, may be about (16 × steam port width), or equivalent to 1.28D.

A less empirical method of determining steam port area is based on the volume swept through by the piston, a suitable allowance being one square inch of steam port area per 200 cubic inches of working cylinder volume.

For Slide Valves:

Area of steam port = 0.095 A.

Area of exhaust port = from 0.19 A to 0.21 A.

Length of port, approximately (11 × steam port width). Is equivalent to about 0.85 D in British practice, and up to D in American.

One square inch of steam port area should be provided per 270 cubic inches of the volume swept through by the piston. Width of bridge is from 1″ to $1\frac{1}{4}$″ in British practice, but may be equal to width of steam port in American practice.

Length of port face should be less than maximum valve travel to minimise wear (grooving) in service, and a surplus thickness of metal of from $\frac{1}{2}$″ to $\frac{3}{4}$″ should be allowed for refacing.

Ports from Valve to Cylinder:

Cross-sectional area must be at least equal to, and preferably greater than that of steam ports, and further increased to compensate at curves.

VALVE CHARACTERISTICS AND EVENTS.

Lead, or the amount by which the valve is opened to admission steam when the crank is on dead centre, is determined by the extent of cushioning requisite for the normal running speed of the engine under consideration. With radial valve gears, giving a constant lead at all cut-offs, it ranges from $\frac{1}{16}''$ in the case of slow speed engines, *e.g.*, shunting engines or suburban tanks, to $\frac{3}{16}''$ or $\frac{1}{4}''$ for expresses. Where link motions, such as the Stephenson gear with open rods, are employed, and the extent of the lead varies inversely as the cut-off, the lead in full gear must be zero, as was common in American practice, or even negative in value (see G.W.R. example in Table XLIV), if it is desired to limit it to about $\frac{1}{8}''$ at running cut-offs of the order of 25%. With this procedure the best distribution is attained whilst running at all but the lowest speeds, the only disadvantage being that the initial acceleration of the engine is sacrificed somewhat. Excessive lead, on the other hand, although removing all possibility of over-compression, causes inordinate and premature cushioning, this resulting in reduced m.e.p. and possible overheating of the big ends.

Steam Lap regulates admission and cut-off, and is now usually made about $1\frac{1}{2}''$ or $1\frac{5}{8}''$ for piston valves, when in conjunction with a maximum travel of $5''$ to $5\frac{1}{2}''$, as compared with the customary $\frac{7}{8}''$ or $1''$ for slide valves. The smaller steam lap arranged for the latter is due to the following reasons:—

(a) The valve travel is appreciably less than that for modern piston valves, and

(b) By reducing the lap the port opening is increased, this being essential with the limited length of port available.

In an extreme case (Boston and Albany R.R., 2-8-4) the lap for the piston valves is $2\frac{7}{16}''$.

Late release in conjunction with full port opening to exhaust at the end of the stroke is desirable, and since the port opening to exhaust at the commencement of the exhaust stroke is equal to (steam lap + lead — exhaust lap), the required condition will be met if the steam lap equals the port width. Late release, however, involves early compression, and a compromise is therefore necessary.

Reduction of lap has the effect of increasing the lead and retarding the point of cut-off for any given setting of a valve gear; the converse of course holds good.

Exhaust Lap   controls the points of release and compression and rarely, if ever, has a positive value in locomotive practice owing to the excessive compression caused thereby at early cut-offs.   The usual, and generally the best arrangement, especially where a long steam lap is provided, is to make the valve *line on line* with the port; it should be noted that opening to exhaust increases with the valve travel.   However, should it be desired to hasten release, the inside lap may be negative or, in other words, **exhaust clearance** provided. This should not exceed $\frac{1}{16}''$ for slow speed engines, but in some cases is as much as $\frac{3}{16}''$ for expresses.   Generally speaking, exhaust clearance is more frequently used and a greater extent provided on American locomotives; for instance, $\frac{1}{4}''$ may be provided for piston valves, and $\frac{1}{8}''$ for slide valves, with radial valve gears.

Exhaust clearance has inherent disadvantages and careful consideration should therefore be given before adopting it. It has already been pointed out that it is hardly necessary with long valve travels; the extent of port area open to exhaust at the commencement of the exhaust stroke is more important than the position of the release point and, as stated, increases with the travel.   With exhaust clearance the toe of the indicator diagram tends to degenerate into a heel and, if carried to excess, may lead to appreciable loss of power.   With link motions the early release normally occurring with an early cut-off becomes premature.   Again, when the valve is in its central position, both ports are open to exhaust and intercommunication takes place; should the exhaust clearance be large, the exhaust from one end of the cylinder baffles that from the other, and the exhaust line of the indicator diagram will exhibit a rise or hump.   However, in cases where insufficient steam lap is provided or the lead is excessive, a small exhaust clearance, not exceeding $\frac{1}{16}''$, may be beneficial in reducing the risk of bearings running hot in the event of an engine with link motion being excessively notched up; the resultant premature point of compression is then delayed by the exhaust clearance.

Valve Travel is now usually 6″ or 7″ in full gear. The Boston and Albany locomotive previously cited has a maximum travel of 8¾″, whilst that for a large number of engines on the Chemin de Fer de l'Est is 10½″ (see Table XLVI).

Determination of the maximum travel is a matter of fundamental importance, and it is essential to secure full port opening to exhaust for all points of cut-off. To comply with this condition the travel in mid-gear, assuming opening to lead steam only in this position and that the movement of the valve is symmetrical about its central position, *i.e.*, neglecting the effects of angularity, must be 2 (steam lap + lead) and the maximum travel equal to 2 (steam lap + width of port opening to steam).

Increasing the valve travel, although involving greater inertia forces, accelerates the movement of the valve, with the result that all events are more sharply defined. The port opening to steam is increased and both release and compression delayed; also, the greater port opening to exhaust provides a free exhaust at high speeds of revolution with early cut-offs. In consequence, wiredrawing is reduced and the back pressure decreased. It is perhaps superfluous to mention that increased freedom of exhaust implies greater depth of indicator diagram, and that back pressure varies to a certain extent with the cut-off, falling off as the latter becomes earlier.

The term "long travel valve," although widely used, is somewhat misleading; "long lap valve" is a more accurate description.

Cut-off. Is stated with relation to the piston travel and not to the angular position of the crankpin. Chiefly since the introduction of the superheater there has been considerable controversy as to whether a restricted regulator opening in conjunction with a later cut-off, or full regulator opening with early cut-off, is ultimately the more economical. The arguments advanced by protagonists of the former method of working are:—

(*a*) The greater temperature range obtaining in the cylinders with an early cut-off absorbs the available superheat, thus invalidating the advantages which would otherwise obtain with a high initial temperature.

(*b*) Wiredrawing is beneficial in that it assists the flow of steam through the superheater.

(*c*) Where link motion is concerned, the steam consumption

is lower at high speeds with a late cut-off on account of the throttling in conjunction with freer admission and exhaust and later compression.

(*d*) The "missing quantity" increases as the m.e.p. falls.

(*e*) With an early cut-off there is greater fluctuation above and below the mean torque, with the result that the adhesion is not utilised in the most efficient manner.

On the other hand, the following advantages are claimed for early cut-offs and a full regulator opening:—

(*a*) Superheated steam is more elastic and enables greater expansion to be obtained without condensation and, with link motion, the greater fluidity of the steam allows it to negotiate the comparatively restricted exhaust port openings occurring with short travel valves at early cut-offs without baffling. (The method of increasing port openings to exhaust by lengthening the valve travel has already been discussed in this chapter).

(*b*) Steam chest pressure is more nearly equal to the boiler pressure; full advantage is therefore taken of the latter and there is less pre-admission wiredrawing.

(*c*) Restricted regulator openings cause wiredrawing, and therefore thermal loss.

(*d*) The demand for steam per stroke being less, water and fuel consumptions, together with boiler maintenance charges, are reduced and, further, the necessary velocity of steam flow through the superheater is correspondingly reduced and the degree of superheat consequently augmented. (As a generalisation this latter argument may be fallacious, in that the predetermined dimensions of the elements, extent of internal scouring action and reversal of steam flow, and extent of draught largely govern the degree of superheat attainable).

(*e*) The adhesion is in any event based on extreme conditions as regards cut-off and pressure; also, the torque fluctuation with early cut-offs is small with the majority of designs incorporating more than two cylinders.

(*f*) Lighter draught.

Many actual experiments, the results of a case in point being given in Table XLIII, have definitely proved that early cut-off working is ultimately the more economical, and most engines are now designed with proportions of valves and ports, such as have been previously advocated in this chapter, which enable them to be worked efficiently with an early cut-off.

TABLE XLIII.
COMPARATIVE EFFECTS ON COAL AND WATER CONSUMPTIONS OF VARYING REGULATOR OPENING AND POINT OF CUT-OFF (TESTS AT ALTOONA).

Engine developing 1,500 H.P.

Regulator Opening.	Partial Throttle.		Full Throttle.	Economy, %	
Reference.	1	2	3	3 over 1	3 over 2
Cut-off, %	40	30	20		
Dry coal, lb./I.H.P. hour.	2·52	2·25	2·02	19·8	10·2
Steam, lb. I.H.P. hour.	18·9	17·5	15·8	16·4	9·7

TABLE XLIV.
COMPARISON OF VALVE SETTINGS
(Fawcett, Proc.I.Loco.E., 1924).

Notch.	Steam Lap.	Lead.	Exhaust Clearance.	Cut-off.	Steam Port Opening.	Exhaust Port Opening.	Exhaust Closure.	Valve Travel
	inches.	inches.	inches.	%	inches.	inches.	%	inches.

STEPHENSON GEAR (TYPICAL).

Notch.	Steam Lap.	Lead.	Exhaust Clearance.	Cut-off.	Steam Port Opening.	Exhaust Port Opening.	Exhaust Closure.	Valve Travel
4	1	$\frac{1}{8}$	$\frac{1}{8}$	76	$1\frac{3}{16}$	$2\frac{15}{16}$	91	$4\frac{3}{8}$
1	1	$\frac{9}{32}$	$\frac{1}{8}$	27	$\frac{3}{8}$	$1\frac{1}{2}$	67	$2\frac{3}{4}$

WALSCHAERTS' GEAR (TYPICAL).

Notch.	Steam Lap.	Lead.	Exhaust Clearance.	Cut-off.	Steam Port Opening.	Exhaust Port Opening.	Exhaust Closure.	Valve Travel
4	1	$\frac{1}{8}$	$\frac{1}{8}$	72	$1\frac{3}{16}$	$2\frac{5}{16}$	94	$4\frac{3}{8}$
1	1	$\frac{1}{8}$	$\frac{1}{8}$	25	$\frac{1}{4}$	$1\frac{3}{8}$	74	$2\frac{1}{2}$

G.W.R. 18″ × 30″ CYLINDERS (MEAN OF FRONT AND BACK PORTS). STEPHENSON GEAR.

Notch.	Steam Lap.	Lead.	Exhaust Clearance.	Cut-off.	Steam Port Opening.	Exhaust Port Opening.	Exhaust Closure.	Valve Travel
Full	$1\frac{5}{8}$	−0·15	Nil.	77·5	1·5	3·12	94	6·25
Fast	$1\frac{5}{8}$	+0·12	Nil.	28·8	0·33	1·95	74·5	3·91

VALVE WITH 1½″ LAP AND 1½″ MAXIMUM STEAM PORT OPENING. MAXIMUM VALVE TRAVEL, 6″. WALSCHAERTS' GEAR.

Notch.	Steam Lap.	Lead.	Exhaust Clearance.	Cut-off.	Steam Port Opening.	Exhaust Port Opening.	Exhaust Closure.	Valve Travel
4	$1\frac{1}{2}$	$\frac{1}{8}$	Nil.	74	$1\frac{1}{2}$	3	92	6
1	$1\frac{1}{2}$	$\frac{1}{8}$	Nil.	25	$\frac{5}{16}$	$1\frac{13}{16}$	71	$3\frac{5}{8}$

TABLE XLV.

VALVE SETTING OF G.W.R. "CASTLE" CLASS ENGINES.

Four cylinders, 16″ × 26″. Piston valves, 8″ dia. Steam lap, 1⅝″ Exhaust lap, nil. Inside Walschaerts' gear; outside valves driven through rocking shafts.

The readings are as actually taken from an engine.

| Gear | | (A) IN FULL GEAR | | | | | | | | (B) IN FORWARD GEAR WITH CUT-OFF AT RUNNING POSITION. | |
| | | FORE. | | | | BACK. | | | | | |
Cylinder		L.O.	L.I.	R.I.	R.O.	L.O.	L.I.	R.I.	R.O.	R.I.	R.O.
Lead, inches	Front	·13	·22	·16	·08	·09	·16	·16	·11	·16	·08
	Back	·23	·14	·09	·18	·16	·12	·10	·19	·09	·18
Port opening, inches	Front	2·16	1·78	1·77	2·20	2·14	1·78	1·78	2·13	·27	·26
	Back	1·52	2·0	2·0	1·62	1·59	1·98	1·94	1·63	·24	·30
Travel, inches		6·93	7·03	7·02	7·07	6·98	7·01	6·97	7·01	3·76	3·81
Cut-off, %	Front			78·2	80·0					20·75	26·9
	Back			74·25	74·75					20·4	19·1
Exhaust, %	Front			93·3	93·1					70·9	72·75
	Back			85·0	92·75					68·5	67·6

TABLE XLVI.

SETTING AND EVENTS OF VALVES WITH ULTRA LONG TRAVEL, CHEMIN DE FER DE L'EST.

Maximum travel, 10½". Steam lap, 2". Gear, Walschaerts'. Dia. of coupled wheels, 4'-8". Maximum speed, 410 r.p.m. The following values are the mean of the front and back ports.

| | | Full gear | Notch. | | | | | | Mid gear |
			7	6	5	4	3	2	
Valve travel	inches	$10\frac{1}{2}$	$7\frac{5}{8}$	$6\frac{1}{2}$	$5\frac{13}{16}$	$5\frac{5}{16}$	$4\frac{7}{8}$	$4\frac{5}{8}$	$4\frac{5}{16}$
Steam port opening	inches	$3\frac{5}{16}$	$1\frac{7}{32}$	$1\frac{19}{32}$	$1\frac{1}{16}$	$1\frac{1}{16}$	$\frac{7}{32}$	$\frac{5}{16}$	$\frac{3}{16}$
					Percentage of Stroke.				
Steam Stroke:									
Duration of Admission		83·5	70	60	50	40	30	20	5
Duration of Expansion		10·5	20	27	33	38·75	44·5	48·5	44·5
Portion of Steam Stroke open to Exhaust		6	10	13	17	21·25	25·	31·5	50·5
Exhaust Stroke:									
Release		95·5	90·5	87	83	78·5	74·5	68·5	49·5
Compression		4·4	9·35	12·8	16·45	21·15	25	30·6	54·5
Pre-Admission		0·1	0·15	0·2	0·25	0·35	0·5	0·9	0·5

Small discrepancies are apparent in the above table; it may be surmised that they are due to the taking of averages from actual readings.

Compression. When determining a suitable point of compression it is important to remember that its location, and the extent both of lead and of clearance volume are all interdependent; these three factors must therefore be considered conjunctively.

The compression point should advance when the engine is running with early cut-offs at high piston speeds, in order that sufficient cushioning may be available to counteract the greatly augmented inertia forces then set up by the reciprocating masses.   Minimisation of thermal loss demands that the clearance volume shall be no more than is necessary to enable the final compression pressure to equal that in the steam chest when opening to lead steam commences.

An equation for compression steam has already been given $PV^{1.3} = C$, *vide* Chapter III), although many engineers consider it a sufficiently close approximation to assume that the compression steam follows the $PV = C$ law.

Actual Examples of Valve Settings are given in Tables XLIV, XLV and XLVI.

VALVE DIAGRAMS.

As this subject is fully treated in text books, brief mention only of the most suitable diagrams is made here, purely for the sake of completeness.   Valve diagrams are of very limited value to the locomotive engineer in that they neglect the angularity effects of connecting and eccentric rods and other unavoidable inaccuracies arising in practice with locomotive valve gears; further, a valve gear must first be simplified and reduced to an "equivalent eccentric" gear before being applied in principle to the following diagrams.

Provided the valve travel is known, the majority of problems may be solved, approximately only, either by the Reuleaux or the Zeuner diagram, the former being perhaps preferable; the "rectangular" valve displacement diagram will be found useful.   The oval diagram, sometimes used subsequent to the design of the valve, is not to be recommended; it does not define lead clearly.   The Bilgram diagram is to be preferred only when the valve travel is unknown.

Reuleaux Diagram   (Fig. 33).   Draw circle on diameter AB equal to the eccentric throw.   Next draw the valve displacement line *ab*, its inclination to *AB* being equal to angle of advance, $\theta°$.   *AB* represents, to a proportional scale, the piston

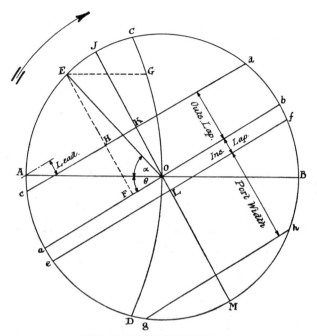

FIG. 33. REULEAUX DIAGRAM.

stroke; hence, A and B are the inner and outer dead centres respectively. With centre on AB produced and radius equal to distance between connecting rod centres, to same scale that AB represents piston stroke, draw arc CD passing through O, the centre of valve circle. Then, for any given crank position OE, i.e., when crank is $\alpha°$ from inner dead centre A, perpendicular EF drawn on to ab gives displacement of valve from middle of stroke, neglecting, of course, the effects of the angularity of the eccentric rod. Similarly, horizontal line EG, parallel to AB, gives to scale the displacement of piston from mid-stroke.

Next, draw cd parallel to ab and at distance equal to outside lap from it, also ef, if inside lap is provided, parallel to ab and at distance equal to inside lap from it as shewn.

$$cd = \text{steam line.}$$
$$ef = \text{exhaust line.}$$

Perpendicular such as EH, from E on to cd represents the valve opening to steam corresponding to given crank position, its maximum value being JK. Similarly, a perpendicular drawn from any given crank position between *ɟ* and *e*, below *ef*, will give the corresponding opening to exhaust. Should maximum opening *LM* exceed full port width, draw *gh* parallel to *ef* and at a distance equal to port width from it; then, for all crank positions between *h* and *g*, the valve is fully open to exhaust. The diagram as shewn applies only to the instroke, the direction of rotation being as indicated by the arrow on the diagram; for the outstroke, reverse positions of steam, exhaust and port lines relative to *ab*.

On the instroke as shewn, *i.e.*, with the crank rotating in a clockwise direction, admission occurs at *c*, cut-off at *d*, release at *f*, and compression at *e*.

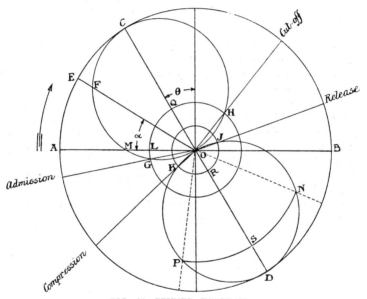

FIG. 34. ZEUNER DIAGRAM.

Zeuner Diagram (Fig. 34). Draw circle on diameter *AB*, equal to eccentric throw; as previously, *AB* represents the piston stroke to scale. Next, draw diameter *CD* inclined at the angular advance, $(90 + \theta)°$, to *AB*, and two circles on *CD* as shewn; it follows that the diameter of each is equal to ½ travel of valve.

Then, for any given crank position *OE*, *OF* gives displacement of valve from mid-position.

Next, with centre *O* and radius equal to outside lap, draw circle *GH*; also with same centre and radius equal to inside lap (if provided) draw circle *JK*.

Then draw radii to valve circle through:—

Point of intersection G.   This gives point of admission

,,   ,,   ,,   H.   ,,   ,,   ,,   cut-off

,,   ,,   ,,   J.   ,,   ,,   ,,   release

,,   ,,   ,,   K.   ,,   ,,   ,,   compression

as shewn on diagram, for outstroke only, when crank rotates in clockwise direction.

Length LM represents lead and CQ gives the maximum port opening to steam.

Lastly, draw arc NP from centre O with radius equal to (width of port + inside lap). Full exhaust opening then occurs for all crank positions from ON to OP.

$$RS = \text{port width.}$$

Rectangular or Wave Diagram.   Before proceeding to the diagram proper, *piston and valve displacement curves* must be obtained as a preliminary.   Considering the crank and connecting rod mechanism (Fig. 35), it is obvious that for any given crank position BC, if an arc BD be drawn with centre A and of radius AB, then the piston is at a distance CD from mid-stroke.

Alternatively, and more conveniently, draw arc ECF through C to radius AB; then draw BG parallel to AC.   Then $BG = CD$ = piston displacement from mid-position corresponding to given crank position.   The lengths BG appropriate to crank angles of 90° and 150° are shewn in the figure.

Repetition of either construction for various crank positions enables the displacement curves to be drawn.

Analytically, the displacement of the piston from mid-stroke is given in general terms (Inchley) by

$$x_p = r \cos a - \frac{r^2}{4l} (1 - \cos 2a) \dots\dots\dots (235)$$

where a = angle between crank and longitudinal centre line of engine,

r = half piston stroke,

and l = length of connecting rod.

Similarly, for valves, allowing for angularity effects,

$$x_v = r \cos a - \frac{r}{2n} \sin^2 a \dots\dots\dots (236)$$

where $n = \dfrac{l}{r} = \dfrac{\text{length of eccentric rod}}{\text{radius of eccentric}}$, and other symbols have the same significance as previously.

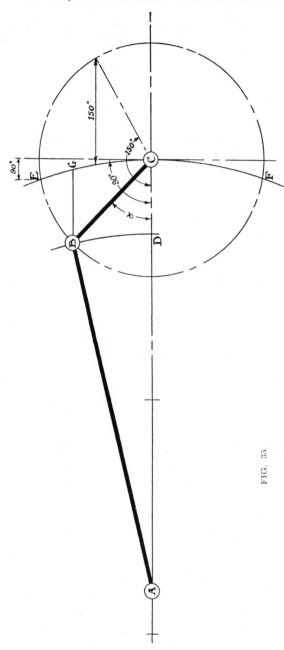

FIG. 35.

The *radius of the eccentric*, or *eccentricity*, is of course one half the throw and, with a simple eccentric gear, is equal to one half the valve travel.

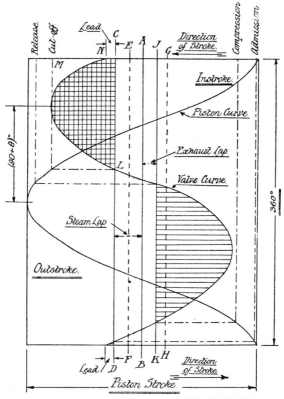

FIG. 36. RECTANGULAR OR WAVE DIAGRAM.

Considering now the rectangular diagram (Fig. 36), in which piston stroke is set off horizontally and one revolution, in degrees, vertically, first draw piston displacement curve and superimpose that for valve at a phase $(90 + \theta)°$ in advance of the piston, *i.e.*, maximum displacement of valve occurs $(90 + \theta)°$ earlier than that of piston. Set out steam lap line CD to left of mid-stroke line AB for stroke towards crank axle and a similar distance to the right for the out-stroke, the corresponding lines for inside lap (if positive) being to the right of AB at JK and left at EF respectively; the appropriate distances from AB in each of these cases must be to the same scale that is adopted for the valve displacement curve.   The latter, it may be noted, is usually drawn full size.

The procedure for each valve event is identical.   Take cut-off as an example.   This occurs at L.   Project thence horizontally to the point of intersection with the piston curve, thence vertically to give reading at M.   The construction for other events is shewn in the figure, shaded areas representing valve openings to steam during the in-stroke (cross hatched) and to exhaust during the outstroke respectively.   Distance $CN =$ lead.

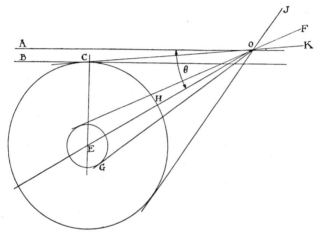

FIG. 37. BILGRAM DIAGRAM.

Bilgram Diagram.   (Fig. 37).   Draw any line AO to represent line of stroke of piston or valve.   The angular advance being $(90 + \theta)°$, set off $\theta° = \angle AOE$.   Draw BC parallel to AO at a distance from it equal to the lead. CE is drawn perpendicular to BC and of length equal to steam lap.   With centre E and radius EC describe circle.   With same centre and radius EG equal to exhaust lap describe another circle, and draw tangents from O.   Then:

$OK =$ crank position at admission,
$OF =$ crank position at release,
$OG =$ crank position at commencement of compression,
$OJ =$ crank position at cut-off,
$OE = \frac{1}{2}$ travel of valve, and
$OH =$ maximum opening to steam, H being the point at
           which OE intersects the steam lap circle.

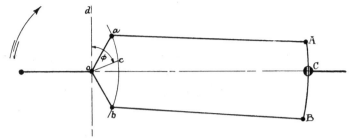

FIG. 38. EQUIVALENT ECCENTRIC: MACFARLANE GRAY'S
CONSTRUCTION.

Equivalent Eccentric: Macfarlane Gray's Construction.

(Fig. 38). To enable the preceding diagrams to be applied to Stephenson's link motion, in positions other than those in which the centre of the motion block lies on the longitudinal centre line of the eccentric rod produced, the equivalent eccentric must be determined, and one of the best known methods is given here; the results are sufficiently accurate for all practical purposes. With the motion block in any given position C, and crank on dead centre remote from cylinder, as indicated by the centre line diagram, Fig. 38, describe arc of circle, passing through a and b, of radius

$$\frac{ab \times aA}{2\,AB}$$

Next, take point c in arc ab such that

$$\frac{ac}{cb} = \frac{AC}{CB}$$

Then oc is the radius of the equivalent eccentric, its angular advance being

$$(90° + \angle\, doc) = (90 + \phi)°.$$

The arc ab as shewn in Fig. 38 applies to open rods; for crossed rods ab must be set out convex to the crank axle, the construction being shewn by Fig. 39.

Having obtained the "virtual" or "equivalent" eccentric for a given position of the motion, the valve diagram may then be drawn and the remaining unknown data determined therefrom.

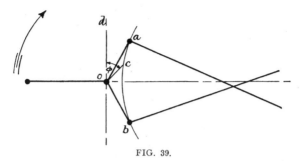

FIG. 39.

DESIGN OF VALVE GEAR COMPONENTS.

The inertia forces acting in each detail may be determined with the assistance of an acceleration image (for examples of which see Dalby's *Valves and Valve Gear Mechanisms*, Arnold), but the total forces acting are so numerous, variable and, in many instances, indeterminate, that design is largely empirical. It is quite possible for the inertia forces considerably to affect the valve timing at high speeds of revolution; the sections of components must therefore be stiff, in order to resist whipping, but light in weight.

Motion Pins must have ample bearing surface, the length of bearing surface being approximately twice the pin diameter. The pins should be finally ground to a diameter not exceeding the nominal diameter d, the minimum specified diameter ranging from $(d - .0005'')$ to $(d - .002'')$. The hole diameter should not exceed $(d + .003'')$. The use of nutted motion pins of more than one diameter is not to be recommended, as the nuts rapidly loosen in service and work off. All motion pins and bushes, if ferrous, should be case-hardened.

The bushing of holes for motion pins, the bushes being grooved externally to ensure continuity of lubrication should they rotate, is now frequently seen. The bushes in some cases are of phosphor bronze; where steel is employed for this purpose it should have a low carbon content to permit of case-hardening, mild steel so treated generally giving a longer life than hard steel.

Where one rod works in the forked end of another, the distance between the jaws may be width of rod plus an allowance of approximately 0.02''. In some cases side washers are provided; these are of phosphor bronze and drilled with several holes to retain the lubricant.

Reversing rods in American practice are tubular and are stronger, weight for weight, than the solid rectangular pattern common to British design. Further, the check nuts provided facilitate minor adjustments in length.

Weighbar shafts should be balanced by springs in preference to "bob" weights. Considerable reduction in weight is thereby achieved, and the possibility of the weights falling off is invalidated. Built-up shafts are more economical to manufacture than solid shafts, as work may proceed simultaneously on all units; case-hardening is also facilitated. A shrinkage allowance of .004″ on a 4″ diameter seat has been found satisfactory. Solid shafts are, however, more reliable in service, as there is no risk of components moving; in this connection, however, it may be argued that built-up crank axles are subjected to far more severe conditions of service.

Shaft journals should not be allowed to distort more than .01″ before re-turning, and the total initial allowance for wear on the diameter may be $\frac{3}{4}$″.

Eccentric sheaves must be as light and narrow as possible consistent with the provision of adequate bearing area; otherwise, the consequent rigidity will be found detrimental to the life of the crank axle. Double (or combined) eccentric sheaves may offend badly in this respect, but offer greater facility and accuracy in the maintenance of relative eccentric angularity. Straps should be bored not more than 0.015″ larger in diameter than the sheaves, and the total allowance for side play may be 0.03″.

The following treatment of eccentric design is due to Unwin.

Let total load on slide valve due to steam pressure be P lb.

Then force required to move valve $= \mu P$ lb.

Now let $W =$ weight of valve and associated components, lb.,

Then inertia forces at the ends of stroke, in pounds, are given approximately by

$$\pm \frac{W\,v^2}{g\,r}$$

where $r =$ radius of eccentric, feet, and

$v =$ velocity of sheave centre, feet per second.

Assuming the eccentric to rotate at n revolutions per second, then $v = 2\pi r n$.

Let the maximum thrust or pull on the eccentric be L lb.,

Then, for slide valves,

$$L_S = \mu\, P \pm \dfrac{W\, v^2}{g\ r} \quad \dotfill \quad (237)$$

And for piston valves,

$$L_P = \mu\, W \pm \dfrac{W\, v^2}{g\ r} \quad \dotfill \quad (238)$$

The projected area of the sheave periphery, when lined with anti-friction metal, may be such that the bearing pressure is from 100 to 120 lb. per square inch. According to Low, the effective bearing width, w, of the sheave on the strap may be about 0.0185 $\sqrt{lbp}$ inches, where l and b are the length and breadth respectively of the slide valve, inches, and p the steam-chest pressure in lb. per square inch. It is important that the sheave be so designed that its major diameter forms the bearing surface for the strap; centrifugal action then tends to confine the lubricant to this surface whilst the engine is running.

The width of the sheave where bearing on the axle may be from

$$\left(\frac{d}{6} + \frac{1''}{4}\right) \quad \text{to} \quad \left(\frac{d}{5} + \frac{1''}{4}\right),$$

where d is the crank axle diameter, inches; this width may be $\dfrac{d}{3}$ where d refers to the diameter of a jack shaft (Unwin).

The key used to secure the sheave to the axle may have a depth of about 0.4 w and a width approximately 0.6 w.

Considering next **eccentric straps,**

Let $t =$ minimum thickness of strap, inches,
   $b =$ width of strap, inches,
   $B =$ distance between bolt centres, inches,
and $L =$ load on eccentric, as before, lb.,
Then, for cast iron straps,

$$t = \frac{1}{60}\sqrt{\frac{L\,B}{b}} \quad \dotfill \quad (239)$$

and for steel,

$$t = \frac{1}{70}\sqrt{\frac{L\,B}{b}} \quad \dotfill \quad (240)$$

If the overall width of the sheave be w_1, then the diameter of the strap bolts may approximate to 0.4 w_1 (Low).

The depth of the **eccentric rod** in the vicinity of the strap end may be from 1.3 w_1 to 1.8 w_1; it is usual to taper the depth of the rod section to the small end. The width of the section may be about 0.4 w_1 throughout. In the absence of any means for adjusting the position of the valve at the valve spindle, it is most desirable to provide liners, the thickness of which may be varied as required, between the eccentric rods and straps on engines fitted with link motion. In order to prevent loss while running, drilled holes, as opposed to slots, should be provided in the liners for the strap studs.

VALVE GEAR CONTROL.

The valve gear may be operated manually or by power. In the former case control is effected either by screw or lever and in the latter by compressed air or steam, in conjunction with an oil and/or mechanical lock.

Lever reverse does not inherently permit of very fine adjustment. To counteract this disability as far as possible, the notches in the reversing quadrant or sector must be as small as can conveniently be made; a device sometimes adopted, particularly in American designs, is to cut alternate notches in the two sector plates and provide the lever with double clutches, one or other of which is always disengaged. The sector plates should be fairly short, as otherwise the lever, the effective length of which is determined by the moment necessary to lift the motion, may be a serious obstruction in the cab. Lever reverse should not be applied to passenger engines on account of the noticeable surging, felt throughout the length of the train, which occurs whenever the engine is notched up or the cut-off otherwise varied.

Although quicker in action than the screw, considerable muscular effort is necessary to operate the lever, even in conjunction with radial gears of which the weight of the radius rod only is taken; there is therefore a natural tendency to drive engines so fitted by varying the regulator opening in preference to the point of cut-off. Further, wear of the notches in the sector plates is rapid and a knock develops there far more rapidly than the corresponding vibration of the nut on the screw, although in the latter case there is a tendency for the cabside, or other superstructure to which the screw is bracketed, to loosen.

By reason of the rapidity of reversal afforded, lever control is mainly suitable for shunting engines, but the tendency constantly to allow the lever to fall into full gear, irrespective of the load hauled, gives rise to excessive fuel consumptions. The sector plates should therefore be fitted with an arrangement which necessitates the lever being held manually in the full gear positions, the lever being self-locking only at cut-offs of, say, 60% and under. A suitable arrangement is to ramp the ends of the sector curve against the locking tongue of the lever, thus eliminating the end notches in the sector plates.

Reversing screws are usually about $2''$-$2\frac{1}{2}''$ in diameter with a double or triple thread having a lead of $1''$-$1\frac{1}{4}''$. Provided the motion is suitably balanced, the screw should not be designed for slow operation; radial valve gears may be fitted with a screw having a coarser pitch than those for link motions. Some form of stop should be provided at either end to prevent overrunning, and consequently jamming, of the nut in its extreme positions. Care must be taken that the cut-off indicator plate is so located as to be clearly visible when the engine is running during the hours of darkness.

A definite lock should be provided on the weighbar shaft, for all fast running engines at least, in order to retain the motion in any desired position and to relieve the reversing gear of all vibration, shock and tendency to creep. The clutch should be attached to a rigid part of the engine, *e.g.*, the main frame, and may conveniently be operated by means of a pneumatic or steam cylinder of from $4\frac{1}{2}''$ to $6''$ diameter. The control of the valve for this cylinder must be located in the cab and so disposed, for the convenience of the driver, that it is in the immediate vicinity of the reversing wheel or lever.

With screw reverse a wheel is preferable to a double ended handle, as it facilitates operation and is less likely to lead to injury. The wheel should be provided with a hand grip at a radius of from $7''$ to $9''$.

Power reverse should be arranged horizontally, rather than vertically, in order to minimise possible creep. The action of the majority of power reverse gears is rapid, and a certain amount of judgment is necessary in order to effect the adjustment of the motion to any required intermediate position at the first attempt. This speed of operation, although of great benefit, for instance, when setting back, slacking couplings to detach, reversing to start when on dead centre, or for rapid notching up to check slipping, does not appear to be appreciated in the case of shunting engines, for which ease and rapidity of reversal are essential, and to which power gears are rarely fitted.

One of the most successful power reverse gears, which is peculiarly free from the weakness prevalent amongst many such mechanisms, *viz.*, liability to creep, is that operated by compressed air and applied as a standard to the express engines of the quondam G.E.R. Each end of the reversing cylinder of this gear is open to atmosphere immediately the motion has been set in any desired position, the reversing gear being mechanically locked to the hand screw with which the gear is also fitted.

VALVE GEARS.
Stephenson Gear (Fig. 40).

With slide valves, and also with inside admission piston valves indirectly driven through a rocking shaft, the eccentric in gear is always ahead of the crank, its angular advance being $(90 + \theta)°$. Should an inside admission piston valve be arranged for direct drive without the intervention of a rocking shaft, then the angular advance of the eccentric is in this case $(270 + \theta)°$, *i.e.*, the eccentric is $(90 - \theta)°$ behind the crank. The longitudinal centre line of the valve motion normally bisects the angle between the eccentrics, but in those cases where it is considered desirable to improve the steam distribution in one gear at the expense of the other, the eccentrics may be slightly displaced from this symmetrical position.

Referring to the outline diagram, Fig. 40, the radius of the link AC is made equal to $AH = CH$ in modern British designs, or to $AO = CO$ in American practice. The proportions of the weighbar shaft arm GE and hanger link ED are important. GE should be parallel to the longitudinal centre line of the valve gear when the motion is in mid-gear. Also, for this position, a line drawn through D, perpendicular to the centre line of the gear, should bisect the versed sine of the arc in which E moves. GE should be as long as possible, and certainly not less than $\dfrac{l}{4}$. The length of link ED must also be as great as can be arranged, in order that the locus of point D may be as nearly coincident as possible with the longitudinal centre line of the valve gear. In general, all links, rods

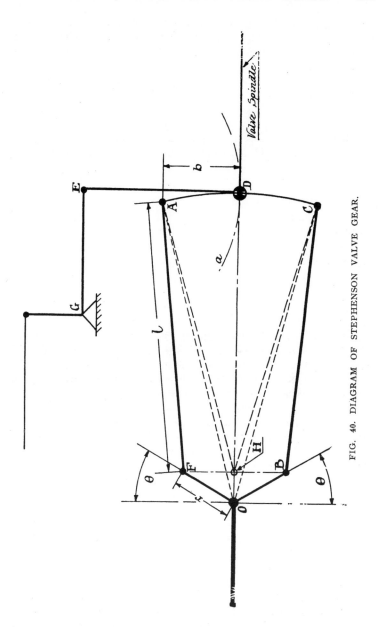

FIG. 40. DIAGRAM OF STEPHENSON VALVE GEAR.

and levers used in the design of the Stephenson gear should be as long as possible, excepting the extent of eccentric throw and length of the expansion link, in order that the adverse effects of angularity may be minimised.

The **slip** of a valve gear may be defined as the extent of the relative sliding, between the motion block and the expansion link, caused by the different paths in which the block and link are constrained to move. With the Stephenson gear, the actual amount of slip depends upon the position of the points of suspension of the expansion link and of attachment of the eccentric rods. As slip causes wear, these points should be so located that the slip is minimised with the gear in its normal running position.

In the absence of a model the variation in slip may be determined graphically from the diagram shewing a cycle of link positions. A template of the link radius with points A, C and D marked thereon is used. Draw two arcs of radius l, with centres F and B respectively, and correct relative to any given crank position; these arcs are loci of points A and C on the template. To determine the maximum slip, the link suspension arc of radius ED should be drawn for the full gear position; point D on the template must lie thereon. By taking successive crank positions the loci of A and C may be plotted. These loci take the form of an elongated figure " 8," roughly parallel to the valve stroke, and the length of any selected ordinate gives the extent of the slip at that point in the valve travel.

Purely from the point of view of minimising slip, the slot in the expansion link should be as short as possible for a given eccentric throw (since the extent of slip increases as the motion block is moved from mid-gear to full gear position), hanger link ED should be as long as possible and eccentric throw as small as possible, and pins A and C should be symmetrically disposed on the link arc with relation to pin D, which should also lie on the link arc. The consequent limitation of valve travel and of the displacement of the link would obviously have serious effects on the steam distribution; compromises are therefore essential.

The points of attachment of the eccentric rods at A and C are sometimes located behind the link arc, especially in American practice. By so doing the valve travel may be made equal to, or even exceed, the eccentric throw. In the latter case, the necessary throw for any given valve travel is minimised. In the former case, the line of thrust of the eccentric rod coincides with the line of valve stroke when the (direct) motion is in full gear, although this condition is not one of great moment in locomotive practice.

With offset eccentric rod pins, although the l/r ratio for the eccentric rods is increased for a given travel and the attendant angularity effects are therefore reduced, the extent of slip is increased and the resultant motion of the expansion link must be corrected by offsetting saddle pin D, the amount being such that not only these irregularities, but also those due to the angularity effects of the connecting rod are corrected.

As notching up proceeds with the Stephenson gear, the valve travel is reduced, all events occur earlier and the block slip decreases. The hastening of compression and of admission is, within limits, an advantage at high speeds in that the cushioning effect is enhanced. With crossed rods, an arrangement very rarely encountered in locomotive practice, the lead decreases as the engine is notched up, but with open rods the reverse obtains. This increase in lead as the cut-off becomes earlier is advantageous at high speeds for the reason given above ; the increase is accentuated when the eccentric rods are of short length. The argument that the earlier port opening to steam is beneficial, in that any excess compression is forced back into the steam chest, is theoretically fallacious, since this procedure involves the performance of negative work. Unless the measures emphasised in a prevous section of this chapter be adopted, the compression can only be kept within the desired limits by giving the valve exhaust clearance, a practice which, as was also pointed out, has serious disadvantages, the worst of which is premature release.

In mid-gear the valve is open to lead steam, the approximate displacement of the valve from its central position, neglecting the radial locus of the suspension links, being given by

$$r \sin \theta + r \left(\frac{b}{l} \right) \cos \theta$$

Dimensions r, b and l are indicated on Fig. 40.

Comparison of Link Motions with Radial Gears.

The advantage of the variable lead obtaining with link motions has been pointed out; with radial gears the lead is constant, and its extent must therefore be so determined as to be appropriate to the normal running cut-off. As with most compromises the results are not entirely satisfactory under all conditions of working, but at the same time no interference with the predetermined lead is possible. Considered *in toto* an improved distribution is obtained with radial gears.

Link motions for large engines assume very cumbersome proportions and render adequate transverse staying of the frames difficult; although simple and having a small number of pin joints in comparison with radial gears, the latter are considerably lighter in weight. The reduction may be as much as 50%, most of which, owing to the elimination of eccentrics, must be regarded as unsprung. The chief advantage of radial gears lies in this elimination of eccentrics with their great inertia and high rubbing speeds, imperfect lubrication, excessive friction, and concomitant wear to be taken up. For inside cylinders, radial gears of the Walschaerts' type are usually arranged with one small eccentric; with this exception, return cranks are now almost universally used in preference to eccentrics for the derivation of the valve travel component.

With most designs for radial gears the link moves through a relatively small angle, with the result that both wear and lost motion are reduced in extent. As a corollary, any liability of the block to wedge in the link is reduced. Further, the link trunnion is a fixed fulcrum, the movement of the link itself is derived from one eccentric rod only and the drive is more direct than that obtaining with a link motion; in this connection it may be mentioned that the trunnions must be of larger dimensions, in the case of radial gears, as they have to withstand the total reaction of the valve drive. From the engineman's point of view, radial gears are much easier to reverse than link motions, as the weight requiring to be moved by the weighbar shaft is appreciably lower.

Owing to their inherent simplicity link motions are still incorporated with new designs for many engines which are intended for industrial and other duties where the standard of mechanical maintenance may not be particularly high, and also for small shunting engines in orthodox railway service.

Walschaerts' Gear.

Relative Position of Return Crank or Eccentric. For engines running chiefly in fore gear the motion is usually so arranged that the motion block works in the lower portion of the link slot for this direction of running.   The drive is then more direct and, should there be a failure of the reversing gear, the engine is automatically thrown into full gear.

TABLE XLVII.
POSITION OF RETURN CRANK OR ECCENTRIC RELATIVE TO MAIN CRANK, WALSCHAERTS' GEAR.

Admission.	Position of Block in Link for full Fore Gear.	Position of Return Crank or Eccentric relative to Main Crank.
Inside.	At bottom.	Follows main crank.
Inside.	At top.	Leads main crank.
Outside.	At bottom.	Leads main crank.
Outside.	At top.	Follows main crank.

The phase angle between the main and the return crank is approximately 90°.   This angle should be adjusted to compensate partly for:—

1. Possible inclination of the eccentric rod, when the engine is on a dead centre, with relation to the longitudinal centre lines of the cylinder and of the valve motion respectively.
2. Any relative inclination between these two latter centre lines.
3. The error produced in the event of the centre line of the link foot pin being above the production of the cylinder centre line to the centre line of the driving axle.

Note.—The "centre line of the motion," in the case of Walschaerts' gear, is the line joining the respective centres of the driving axle and the eccentric rod pin joint with the link foot.

The phase angle should in any case be so determined, in conjunction with the length of the eccentric rod, that the expansion link is at its "central position" (see definition following) when the main crank is on either dead centre.

The phase angle only approximates closely to, or actually equals, 90° when the centre of the link foot pin swings symmetrically above and below the longitudinal centre line of the cylinder produced to the centre of the driving axle.

Eccentric Rod.   Must be as long as possible in order to reduce the effects of angularity.   The distance between the pin centres should be at least 7, and preferably 10 or 12 times the diameter of the return crank circle. The effective lengths of the eccentric rod and radius rod respectively are usually approximately equal; the length of the latter should not exceed that of the former.

Link. The radius is equal to the length of the radius rod between centres of the pin holes for the connections to the motion block and combination lever respectively. The total angle of oscillation of the link should preferably not be greater than 40°, and should in no circumstances exceed 45°.

The expansion link is said to be at its *central position* when a straight line drawn from one extremity of its slot arc to the other is normal to that drawn from the mid-point of the arc to the centre of the pin connecting the radius rod to the combination lever. When the main crank is on either dead centre the link should be at its central position, thereby allowing the motion block to be moved up and down the entire length of the link slot without moving the valve.

The pin hole in the link foot should be offset and so located as to ensure that (*a*) the link swings through an equal angle on either side of its central position, and (*b*), the centre of the link foot pin is as near the cylinder-axle centre line as possible.

Under ideal conditions the pivot, or trunnion centre of the link, would be in that same horizontal plane which contains the centre of the radius rod connection to the combination lever, and the arc in which the link foot pin swings would lie symmetrically above and below the production of the cylinder centre line to the centre of the driving axle. As, however, the diameter of the return crank circle should preferably be limited to 18″, and certainly should not in any event exceed 20″, the link pivot is frequently so located that the arc in which the link foot pin swings is at least 3″ above the cylinder-axle centre line.

The trunnion centre may be lower than the joint of the radius rod with the combination lever, provided the maximum inclination of the radius rod does not exceed 1 in 12. It is, however, better in such a case for the radius rod to be so arranged that the major portion of its length is normal to the straight line joining one end of the link slot arc with the other, when the link is at its central position, and for the remainder to be given a slight downward set in order to make connection with the combination lever.

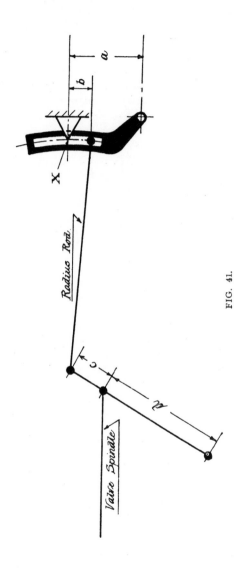

FIG. 41.

Referring to Fig. 41, as the link oscillates about a fixed pivot X, then

$$\frac{\text{movement of motion block}}{\text{movement of link foot pin}} = \frac{b}{a}$$

Dimension b is of course variable. Giving it its maximum value, *i.e.*, when the motion is in full gear, then, in those cases where the angle between the main and return cranks respectively is 90°,

Valve travel in full gear =

$$\sqrt{\left\{\left(\frac{c}{c+d}\right) \times \text{Piston stroke}\right\}^2 + \left\{\left(\frac{b}{a}\right) \times \text{Eccentric throw}\right\}^2} \quad \dots (241)$$

Radius Rod. The point of attachment of the lifting links to the radius rod has a direct effect on the extent of the slip of the motion block in the link. The slip may be minimised by extending the radius rod beyond the link and suspending it at the extremity. Should the suspension be arranged on the concave side of the link, the point of attachment should be as near the latter as can conveniently be arranged, as the slip, arising from the fact that the locus of the point of suspension is an arc, is proportionately increased at the motion block.

Combination Lever. Must be so located that it is perpendicular to the line of piston stroke at mid-stroke. Its length should be such that the point of connection to the radius rod allows the latter to be normal to the straight line joining the extremities of the link arc when the link is at its central position. The angle of oscillation of the combination lever should not exceed 60°, and should preferably not be greater than 50°.

The positions of the valve spindle and radius rod relative to the combination lever are shewn in Fig. 42 for inside and outside admission at (i) and (ii) respectively. These positions hold good irrespective of variations in the relative positions of main and return cranks mentioned previously, and are also independent of the selected location of the motion block in the expansion link for forward running.

For both inside and outside admission the total travel of point C must be equal to the piston stroke, and that of point A, due to the piston stroke, to 2 (lap + lead). Referring to the figure, the required proportions are obtained when,

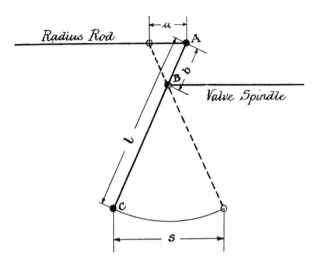

(i). *Inside Admission*

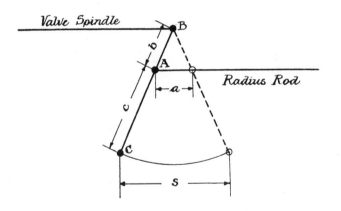

(ii). *Outside Admission*

In both diagrams :-
a = 2 (lap + lead)
s = Stroke of piston.

FIG. 42.

For inside admission,

$$\frac{b}{l} = \frac{a}{s} \quad \dots\dots\dots\dots\dots\dots\dots\dots\dots\dots \quad (242)$$

And for outside admission,

$$\frac{b}{c} = \frac{a}{s} \quad \dots\dots\dots\dots\dots\dots\dots\dots\dots\dots \quad (243)$$

where $a = 2$ (lap + lead)

and s = piston stroke.

When calculating dimension b to conform to the above proportions it is important to remember that its value must be such as to provide a working clearance for the end fittings of the valve spindle and radius rod respectively.

The travel of point A is given, approximately only, by:—

For inside admission,

$$2\left(\frac{R \sqrt{x^2 - a^2}}{R - a} \right) \quad \dots\dots\dots\dots\dots\dots\dots\dots \quad (244)$$

And for outside admission,

$$2\left(\frac{R \sqrt{x^2 - a^2}}{R + a} \right) \quad \dots\dots\dots\dots\dots\dots\dots\dots \quad (245)$$

where R = radius of main crank,

$x = \frac{1}{2}$ valve travel, and

$a =$ (lap + lead).

It should be noted that the radius rod has no movement in mid-gear; the valve spindle joint with the combination lever then becomes a fixed fulcrum for the latter.

Union Link. Should be so located that the vertical arc described by its swinging end is bisected by the straight line path of its fixed end or, in other words, this link should swing equal angles above and below a straight line which passes through the centre of its fulcrum pin on the crosshead, or crosshead arm, and is parallel to the line of piston stroke. The effective length of the union link may equal from one-half to three-quarters of the piston stroke.

Crosshead Arm. Is either bolted to, or integral with the crosshead, according to the exigencies of design; this detail becomes unnecessary when the distance between centres of the piston rod and valve spindle respectively is great.

Baker Gear (Fig. 43).

Is a variant of Walschaerts' gear which is now largely used in America; it incorporates a reversing mechanism developed from that of the Marshall gear and has the advantage that the principal parts are suitable for general application, and therefore standardised.   Variations in the desired maximum travel are obtained by altering either the proportions of the weighbar shaft arms or the travel of the reversing rod.   The manufacturers of the gear are the Pilliod Company, of New York and Swanton, Ohio.

The combination lever, union link, return crank and eccentric rod are as in Walschaerts' gear.   The link and block, however, are replaced in the Baker gear by a bell crank CAB (Fig. 43), the valve travel being derived from the horizontal component of the motion of arm AB.   All variations in valve travel, and reversal, are effected by modifying the angular position of this bell crank, the other arm, CA, being coupled to the "gear connecting rod" CDE at C.   An intermediate pin joint (D) in the latter accommodates dual hanger links, or " radius bars," DF, which are coupled at F to the "reverse yoke" and reversing rod by which the orientation of the range of bell crank oscillation is controlled.

As shewn diagrammatically by Fig. 43, the gear is arranged for inside admission ; the alterations necessary for outside admission are identical with those for Walschaerts' gear.

The valve settings recommended by the manufacturers for the "standard" gear are given in Table XLVIII, and those for the "long travel" gear in Table XLIX.

CONJUGATE GEARS.

Are now frequently applied to three- and four-cylinder engines, the latter design, when the adjacent inside and outside cranks are at 180° phase, providing the most favourable conditions for application.   There are three possible arrangements for four-cylinder engines ; these may be classified as follows:—

(1). Inside cylinders ahead of the outside.   Outside valves are indirectly driven from front end by rocking lever coupled to rear end of inside valve spindles.   The arms of the rocking levers are slightly offset, primarily to obtain similar angular movements of the rocking arms, and therefore of the valve spindles, relative to their respective pistons, and also to ensure that each arm is normal to its valve spindle when the valve is at mid-travel.

(2). Cylinders disposed as in (1), but outside valves directly driven by motion. Rocking shafts and levers are to rear of both valves, the inside valves obtaining an indirect drive therefrom. The advantage of this arrangement over (1) is that the valves and motion are more accessible, the valves in this case being withdrawn without stripping the rocking gear.

(3). All cylinders in line. Either inside or outside valves directly driven by motion, the rocking gear being located ahead of all the valves. This arrangement is the least satisfactory of the three.

For conjugate gears in general the indirect drive should be to the rear of the valves. Assuming the lengths of the valve spindles when subjected to the temperature of steam to be practically equal, they then expand, in the forward direction only, by an equal amount for which due allowance may be made when setting cold. There is, therefore, no cumulative effect on the gear due to expansion with this arrangement, which also provides maximum accessibility as regards the valves.

Friction may be reduced by the adoption, where possible, of ball or roller bearings. The use of such bearings for the centre pins of rocking levers, where it is essential that the fitting be accurate within close limits and that the security of the lever be ensured, is especially beneficial.

With three-cylinder engines having indirect motion it is not possible to set the cranks at equal phase angles of 120° unless all cylinder longitudinal centre lines are uniplanar, a condition which, having regard to the necessary clearance of axles by the inside engine, is difficult of achievement. This cylinder arrangement necessitates more complicated indirect drives than the four-cylinder cases previously cited, and may involve as many additional pin joints as are represented by a third set of Walschaerts' gear, although eliminating a possible inside eccentric. Further, all distortions, any errors, and wear occurring at pin joints are transmitted to, and magnified at, the indirectly driven valve spindle; the steam distribution suffers in consequence.

Satisfactory design of the components of all conjugate gears

is difficult in that, if of stiff section, the inertia effects cause
overrunning of the indirectly driven valve spindles at high
speeds, notably with gears for three-cylinder engines; this
engenders incorrect steam distribution, with resultant increases
in fuel and water consumptions and excessive wear at the main
bearings concerned. At the other extreme, lightly constructed
details decrease the effects of inertia, but are liable to whip
when working at high speeds, and this again leads to faulty
steam distribution.

Briefly summarised, the advantages of independent motions
for each cylinder, as opposed to conjugate gears in general,
are:—

    (*a*).   Each valve is accurately set individually, uniformity
of the valve events for all cylinders being in most cases
easily achieved.

    (*b*).   Setting of valves and correction of errors facilitated:
the adjustment of one valve does not affect that of
others.

    (*c*).   Effects of wear are not cumulative to the same degree,
and lost motion is less extensive.

    (*d*).   Components of each valve gear are comparatively
light in weight.

POPPET VALVES AND GEARS.

Brief mention has already been made of valves of this type,
to which more detailed consideration will now be given. Reductions in coal consumption of from 10% to 15% have been
recorded in comparison with piston valves, and may be attributed to:—

1. Less power required for drive: this, in the case of a three-
cylinder 4-4-0, with rotary cams actuating 12 valves,
absorbs only 4-4$\frac{1}{2}$ horse power at 280 r.p.m.
2. Improved steam distribution.
3. Ability to run with very early cut-offs.
4. Minimisation of valve leakage, and
5. Reduction in engine weight: this, for the 4-4-0 engine
previously mentioned, amounts to 1$\frac{1}{2}$ tons as compared
with similar piston valve engines.

The valves and gears designed by Messrs. Associated Locomotive Equipment Ltd., to whom the author is indebted for
the following information, conform to two basic types, *viz.*:—

    (*a*). **The "O.C." (i.e., oscillating cam) type,** in which
the cam shaft is rocked. This design is largely ap-

plied in cases of conversion, as it enables existing valve motions to be utilised, but also finds favour, especially abroad, in those instances where too radical a departure from conventional practice is not considered desirable. Fig. 44 comprises a general arrangement of the application of the " O.C." type gear to a 2-8-0 type engine with Walschaerts' motion, and indicates clearly how large a proportion of the existing motion may be utilised without modification. The maximum angular travel of the rocking lever in this particular instance is 84°, and it may be mentioned in this connection that the total swing is usually not greater than 90°.

(b). **The " R.C.," or rotary cam type,** in which the motion of the cam shaft is rotational, its speed of revolution necessarily corresponding with that of the driving axles. This arrangement represents a close approach to the valve actuating mechanism of the internal combustion engine.

The essential features of the " R.C." type equipment are the rotary cam shafts; one is provided for each cylinder, and each is fitted with a series of step cams, four sets of which are fitted to each cam shaft. Each set of cams is made in the form of a solid sleeve which fits on the shaft and is secured thereto by a key. Each step corresponds, in the case of the steam admission cams, to a predetermined cut-off, and in the case of those controlling the exhaust valves, to definite points of release and compression; the points of pre-admission are governed by the steam admission cams. The cut-offs provided in fore gear range from 10% to 85%, and three are provided in back gear, these being 30%, 50% and 85% respectively. The lead is progressively increased as the cut-off is reduced, and is zero in full gear. The valves, when in mid-gear, are so controlled by circular, or ring, cams that the steam valves are all closed and those for exhaust opened, thus effecting a bye-pass. Hence, when the engine is running in mid-gear, all the valves are stationary. An alternative arrangement is to hold all valves open in mid-gear.

The cam shafts must be capable of two forms of motion, these being the drive, which is purely rotative, and a transverse movement to enable any selected cam to engage; the means whereby these two motions are imparted may be clearly

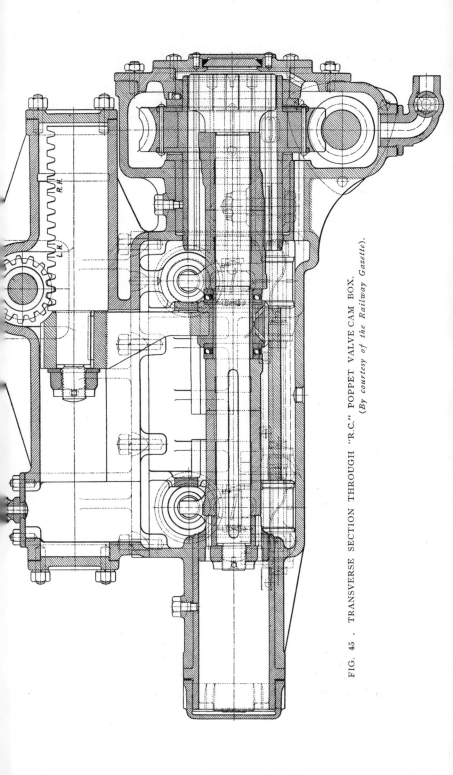

FIG. 45 . TRANSVERSE SECTION THROUGH "R.C." POPPET VALVE CAM BOX.
(By courtesy of the Railway Gazette).

seen in the accompanying figures. It will be observed from Fig. 45 that the drive is transmitted by a dog which is keyed to the end of the shaft and slides in a hollow sleeve, the latter running in bearings of large area. The sleeve is provided with splines which engage with solid keys cut in the driving dog. By this means the shaft can be moved transversely by the stirrup shewn, while it is at the same time rotated by the worm and wheel gearing located in the outer end of the cam box.

The valve arrangement is shewn by Figs. 46 and 47, these being sections through the steam admission and exhaust valves

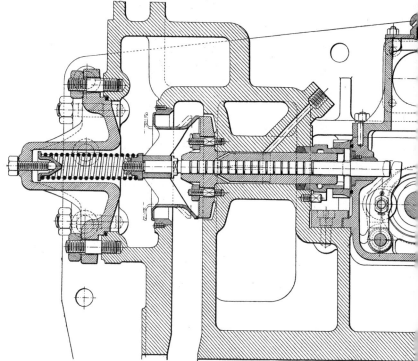

FIG. 46. SECTION THROUGH STEAM ADMISSION VALVE, "R.C."
POPPET VALVE GEAR.
(*By courtesy of the Railway Gazette*).

respectively. The combined valve spindle bushes and inner valve seatings, and also the renewable outer valve seatings, which take the form of rings held in the cylinder casting, should be noted. It will also be seen that the cams operate the valves indirectly through intermediate levers, thereby relieving the tappets and valve spindles of non-axial thrust; these levers are provided with suitably shaped rollers which

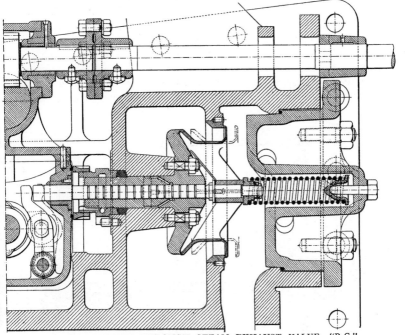

FIG. 47. SECTION THROUGH STEAM EXHAUST VALVE, "R.C."
POPPET VALVE GEAR.
(By courtesy of the Railway Gazette).

track on the cam profiles.   At their upper ends the levers make contact with tappets which in turn bear on the ends of the valve spindles.   The entire cam gear and also the driving wheels and worms are lubricated by the oil bath method, an oil level gauge being fitted to indicate the height of the oil in each cam case.

The main drive to the cam shafts (see Fig. 48) is, of course, so arranged as to synchronise the speed of revolution of the engine driving wheels with that of the cam shaft, and consists of gears and casings assembled on return cranks, the latter being carried in the usual manner on the main crankpins and so located that the centres of the return crank pins and the axles are coincident.   The gears housed in these casings are identical with those at the cam box except that those in

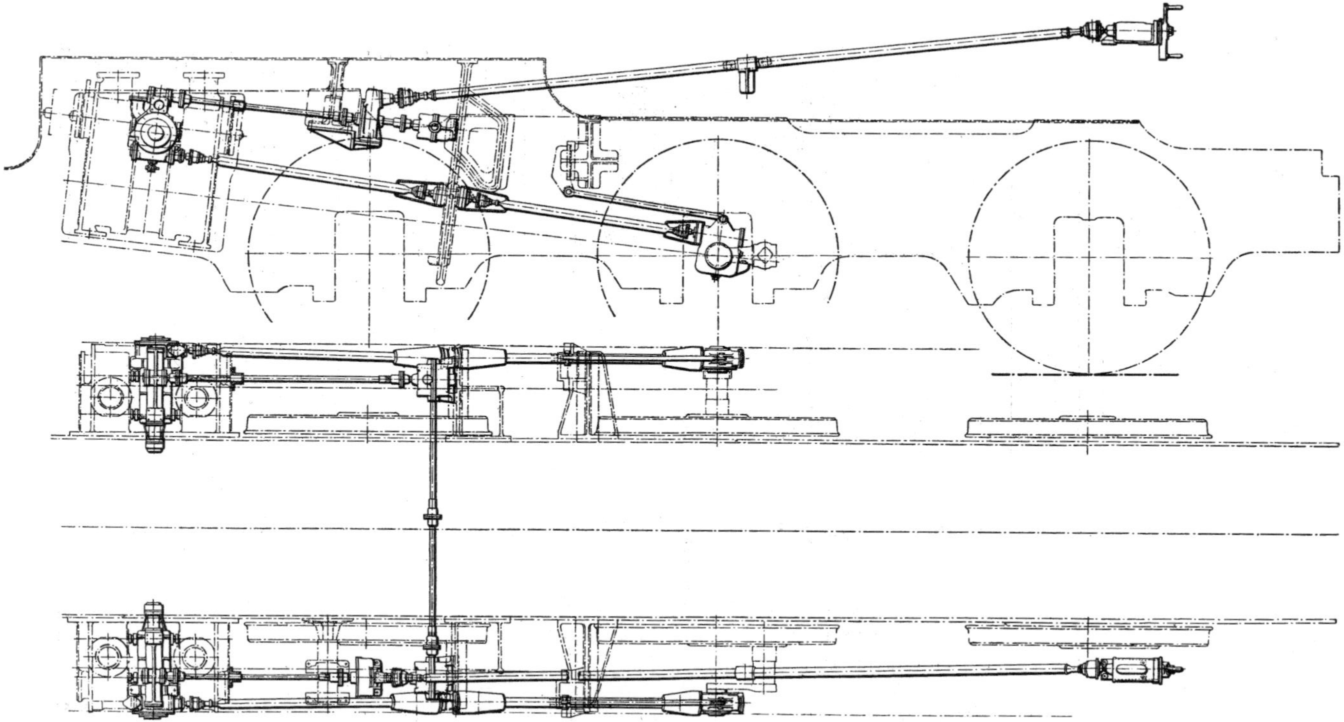

FIG. 48. ARRANGEMENT OF MAIN DRIVE AND REVERSING GEAR, "R.C." POPPET VALVE GEAR.

(By courtesy of the Railway Gazette).

the latter are reducing, whereas those at the return crank end are correspondingly increasing, gears; the gear ratio is usually of the order of 1:3.5. The gears in the return crank gear boxes run in oil baths; grease lubrication is applied to the worm shaft ball bearings. It will be noted that the return crank casing is provided with an anchor link; this takes the driving torque and is of such length that the gear box, as it rises and falls in synchronism with the movement of the axleboxes in their guides, is not perceptibly rocked about the crankpin.

The main drive, which is fitted to both sides of the engine, is through tubular shafting fitted with universal joints at each end, this feature being peculiar to the " R.C." equipment. The shafting is customarily assembled in two lengths as shewn, each being provided with one fixed universal coupling and one with a sliding end transmitting the drive through splines, the latter providing for telescopic movement of the shafting. Complete flexibility is thus provided for that section of the main drive shafting between the return crank gear box and the intermediate bearing located on the motion plate, and the provision of the universal couplings on the shaft between this intermediate bearing and the cam box eliminates any difficulties which might otherwise be encountered in the accurate alignment of these two bearing points. Ball bearings are used throughout for the main drive.

The reversing gear lay-out is illustrated, in addition to Fig. 48, by Fig. 49, which is a general arrangement of the application of the poppet valve gear to a 2-6-0 type mixed traffic engine. The bevel and reduction gears are entirely enclosed and self-lubricating; the driver's control in the cab conforms to an existing standard. As a general statement, the traverse by reversing wheel from full fore to full back gear may be from 2 to 7 revolutions; whilst it is desirable to restrict the number of turns arranged, the former figure should be regarded as a minimum.

The gear as a whole is favourably located from the point of view of accessibility. The poppet valves are arranged in pockets at the ends of the cylinders, and withdrawal involves only the removal of the end covers. The effects of expansion are counteracted, and steam tightness therefore maintained, by so arranging the section of the valve that the outer seating is provided with a measure of flexibility.

The valve spindles are each provided with several lubrication grooves; spindle lubrication may be effected either by

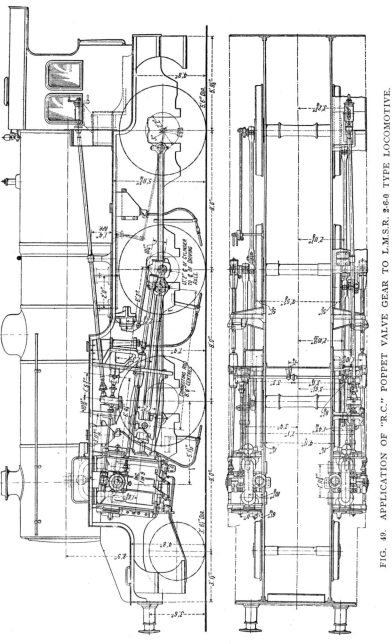

FIG. 49. APPLICATION OF "R.C." POPPET VALVE GEAR TO L.M.S.R. 2-6-0 TYPE LOCOMOTIVE.

(By courtesy of the Railway Gazette).

mechanical or hydrostatic means, according to which system is available. As the admission valves themselves do not require lubrication, absence of carbonisation troubles, and also their marked accessibility for examination, give them superiority over piston and flat slide valves in these respects, although a higher standard of workmanship is essential for their manufacture and setting. The clearance between the tappets and the rollers, it may be remarked, is approximately .03″.

The cam boxes are secured to the cylinders with fitted bolts, and are carried on suitable footings. A standard type of box has been evolved which is applicable to outside cylinders ranging from 16″ to 25″ in diameter with piston strokes of 24″ to 30″ or more. Similarly, the main drive and reversing gear details are also standard.

Table L is a typical example of the settings obtained with the " R.C." gear. The gear in this case was designed for an engine having cylinders 21″ in diameter with a stroke of 26″, the clearance volume being 9.5% ; the cylinder port area is 32.5 square inches. The valve diameters are $6\frac{9}{16}$″ for steam and 8″ for exhaust respectively, these dimensions referring to the internal diameter of the larger seating.

Caprotti Poppet Valves and Gear.   The basic principles of the Caprotti gear are comparable with those of the R.C. type gear previously described, but their application exhibits wide divergencies as regards the actual details. Four valves, in this case disposed vertically, are provided per cylinder, two of which are for admission steam and two for exhaust. These four valves are actuated by three cams, one of which controls the opening, and another the closure, of both admission valves; the third cam controls both exhaust valves. In some cases two exhaust cams are fitted, *viz.*, one for fast running and the other for low speeds. Variation of cut-off or reversal is effected by modifying the angular position of the cams relative to the cam shaft, and also, in the case of those for the admission valves, to one another. The transmission of the cam movements to all valves is through bell cranks. In the case of those actuating the admission valves, two rollers are provided, one running on the "opening" and the other on the "closure" cam; the motions of these two cams are thus compounded in order to obtain the desired movement of the bell crank.

The longitudinal driving shaft is operated through bevel

TABLE L.

SETTINGS OF THE "R.C." TYPE POPPET VALVE GEAR (MESSRS. ASSOCIATED LOCOMOTIVE EQUIPMENT, LTD.).

Gear.	Percentage of				Angle of				Steam.		Lead.	Exhaust.	
	Cut-Off.	Pre-admission.	Release.	Com-pression.	Cut-Off.	Pre-admission.	Release.	Com-pression.	Valve Lift.	Area through Valve (sq. ins.).		Valve Lift.	Area through Valve (sq. ins.).
Fore	85	0	95	20	134°	0°	26°	53°	·5"	20	0	·75"	36·8
,,	60	·1	90	25	102°	4°	37°	60°	·5"	20	1/32" B.	·75"	36·8
,,	45	·1	85	25	84°	4°	45°	60°	·5"	20	1/32" B.	·75"	36·8
,,	35	·5	80	30	72°	8°	53°	66°	·49"	19·6	3/32" F.	·75"	36·8
,,	25	1·1	80	30	60°	12°	53°	66°	·37"	14·8	3/32" F.	·75"	36·8
,,	20	1·7	80	30	53°	15°	53°	66°	·32"	12·8	5/16" F.	·75"	36·8
,,	15	1·7	80	30	45°	15°	53°	66°	·24"	9·6	5/16" F.	·75"	36·8
,,	10	1·7	80	30	37°	15°	53°	66°	·17"	6·8	1/8" F.	·75"	36·8
Mid	—	—	—	—	—	—	—	—	—	—	—	·5"	24·5
Back	30	·5	85	30	66°	8°	45°	66°	·25"	10	3/32" B.	·25"	12·3
,,	50	·1	90	25	90°	4°	37°	60°	·5"	20	1/32" B.	·5"	24·5
,,	85	0	95	20	134°	0°	26°	53°	·5"	20	0	·75"	36·8

gears mounted on ball bearings. The drive, for four cylinders, is stated to absorb a maximum of 2 horse power. Complete reversal, *i.e.*, from full fore to full back gear, is effected with rather less than one revolution of the handwheel. Alternatively, a lever may be used; the adoption of power reverse is in any case unnecessary.

The cams are housed in a self-contained portable gear box, and rotate in an oil-bath incorporated therewith. In the event of a failure, the construction of the gear box permits of its removal *en bloc* from the cylinder and replacement by a spare unit with minimum loss of engine availability. Dimensions of the two standardised cast steel gear boxes are as follows:—

Type			2 *C*.	4 *C*.
Width	...	...	2'-3$\frac{3}{16}$"	2'-3$\frac{3}{16}$"
Height	...	...	1'-6$\frac{1}{8}$"	1'-5$\frac{1}{2}$"
Length	...	...	2'-1$\frac{5}{8}$"	2'-11$\frac{1}{16}$"

Of these, the 2 *C* is designed for engines having two outside cylinders, one gear box being necessary for each cylinder; it is applicable to cylinders having diameters of from 14" to 33" and with strokes ranging from 20" to 30". The 4 *C* box may be applied either as a single unit to an engine having two inside cylinders only, or alternatively, two are employed for a four-cylinder engine. These latter boxes are normally set for cranks at 180° to one another, but may be used with but minor alteration for any other crank phase.

The valves are stamped from mild steel, the cages being of the same material. The standardised valve diameters are 5$\frac{1}{2}$", 6$\frac{1}{2}$", 7$\frac{1}{8}$" and 8" respectively, and all may be operated by the standard gear boxes previously described. The weight of the 6$\frac{1}{2}$" valve, complete with stem, is less than 4 lb. The valves are double seated, one seating being flat and the other conical, the apex of the cone lying in the plane of the flat seating in order to neutralise the effects of expansion. The springs provided to assist the valves to return to their seats are located in the steam spaces without, it is stated, any deleterious effect.

Observed trials carried out with these valves and gear on the Italian State Railways resulted in a steam economy of 17.4% over the piston valves and Walschaerts' motion they displaced.

Table LI compares the expansion and compression phases of the Caprotti with those of other gears at various cut-offs, and it will be noted that the Caprotti exhaust cam, giving constant release and compression, lengthens the period of expan-

TABLE LI.

COMPARISON OF EXPANSION AND COMPRESSION PHASES OF THE CAPROTTI GEAR WITH THOSE OF OTHER MOTIONS (MEASURED IN DEGREES OF THE SUBTENDED CRANK ANGLE).

Gear.	Cut-Off.	72%	60%	50%	40%	25%	15%
Caprotti	Expansion	24°	28° 30'	50°	61° 30'	80°	94° 30'
	Compression	60°	60°	60°	60°	60°	60°
Walschaerts'	Expansion	30°	32°	44°	51° 30'	57°	52°
	Compression	30°	32°	39°	43°	50°	56°
Stephenson	Expansion	26°	27°	34°	37°	42°	44°
	Compression	25°	26° 30'	45°	36°	41°	44° 30'
Joy	Expansion	27°	30°	40°	45°	48°	50°
	Compression	25°	29°	44°	36°	38°	42°

sion very considerably at early cut-offs. It should also be observed that, with the Caprotti valve gear, the extent of the compression phase may be varied as required.

Table LII comprises the valve settings actually obtained from an application of the Caprotti gear to an Italian State Railways engine.

The foregoing information has been extracted from the Caprotti brochure published by Messrs. Valve Gears Ltd., of Glasgow.

A recent development of French valve gear design effects an interesting compromise in that piston valves are cam actuated.

TABLE LII.

VALVE SETTINGS OF CAPROTTI GEAR, ITALIAN STATE RAILWAYS, FORWARD MOTION.

Position of the Reversing Shaft.	Angles of Admission.		Cut-Off, %		Lead Steam, %		Volumetric Ratios.			
							Expansion. 1 to		Compression. 1 to	
	Cut-Off.	Opening.	F.	B.	F.	B.	F.	B.	F.	B.
1	127° 20'	—10°	82·18	78·43	0·895	0·705	1·08	1·1	5·12	4·5
2	125° 20'	—10°	80·87	76·93	0·895	0·705	1·10	1·12	5·12	4·5
3	117° 50'	—10°	75·62	70·99	0·895	0·705	1·17	1·21	5·12	4·5
4	110° 20'	—10°	70·01	64·79	0·895	0·705	1·25	1·31	5·12	4·5
5	102° 50'	—10°	63·93	58·28	0·895	0·705	1·36	1·44	5·12	4·5
6	95° 20'	—10°	57·64	51·76	0·895	0·705	1·49	1·6	5·12	4·5
7	87° 50'	—10°	51·06	45·15	0·895	0·705	1·66	1·8	5·12	4·5
8	80° 20'	—10°	44·48	38·72	0·895	0·705	1·87	2·02	5·12	4·5
9	73°	—10°	38·11	32·70	0·895	0·705	2·13	2·35	5·12	4·5
10	66°	—10°	32·17	27·23	0·895	0·705	2·44	2·72	5·12	4·5
11	59° 10'	—10°	26·60	22·20	0·895	0·705	2·84	3·18	5·12	4·5
12	52° 40'	—10°	21·58	17·83	0·895	0·705	3·34	3·74	5·12	4·5
13	46° 30'	—10°	17·16	14·05	0·895	0·705	3·93	4·44	5·12	4·5
14	40° 30'	—10°	13·25	10·76	0·895	0·705	4·58	5·18	5·12	4·5
15	35°	—14°	10·07	8·13	1·68	1·32	5·52	6·1	4·70	4·22
16	30°	—18° 20'	7·45	5·95	2·8	2·2	6·5	7	4·17	3·8
17	25° 30'	—23° 10'	5·45	4·35	4·46	3·54	7·5	8	3·60	3·33

The following are constant throughout:—

Angle of Exhaust.   Opens at 140°   Closes at —70°

Exhaust Lead.   Opens: front, 10.5%, and back, 12.9%

Closes: front, 33.5%, and back, 29.3%.

Clearance Volume, 7.5%.

The reversing shaft positions range from full fore to rather more than mid gear, the angular interval between each being 4°.

Chapter XI.

COMPOUND EXPANSION.

As to whether simple or compound expansion is ultimately the more efficient is a question which, where the locomotive is concerned, has not reached finality. The various advantages claimed for one and two stage expansion respectively must therefore receive careful consideration, and in certain instances may only be accepted with more or less extensive qualifications. The advantages attributed to compound engines, together with their salient characteristics, will first be reviewed.

(1) *Reduction in cylinder condensation losses* due to the relatively small cooling area presented by the h.p. cylinders, to the lower temperature range per cylinder, and to re-evaporation of the steam prior to the second stage of expansion. This superiority over simple engines holds good at piston speeds below about 600 feet per minute (Hughes, Proc. I. Mech.E., 1910); more recent researches in Russia and the U.S.A. point to a critical speed of approximately 225 revolutions per minute. Further, the temperature fluctuations in the cylinders are determined not only by the position of cut-off but also by the piston speed, the range being reduced at high speeds, even with early cut-offs. It would therefore appear that compounding, from these points of view, shews to the greatest advantage when applied to locomotives working at slow speeds, *e.g.*, goods engines and passenger engines on arduous services.

(2) *More even torque with smaller piston loads and lower range of stress in engine details* on account of later working cut-offs and consequent lowering of pressure fluctuation per cylinder.

(3) *The horse power developed per unit of engine weight is increased* or, in other words, a greater power output is obtained from a given quantity of steam. This is tantamount to increased boiler capacity; easier mainten-

ance of full working pressure may therefore be expected. The value of this advantage is chiefly appreciated in those cases where axle loadings are severely restricted.

(4) *Improved indicator diagrams* by reason of two stage expansion. As the expansion per cylinder is not great, especially in the first, or h.p. stage, it is claimed that wiredrawing is reduced. Also, the h.p. cushion steam is available in its entirety for work in the l.p. cylinders.

(5) *Reduced valve and piston leakage* on account of lower pressure head. Further, any leakage occurring in the h.p. engines must do work in the l.p. cylinders, which are usually fitted with flat slide valves and therefore not prone to this trouble, before passing to exhaust.

(6) *The lighter blast* reduces the unburnt fuel loss and emission of sparks. Boiler and firebox maintenance costs are at the same time lowered. The heat loss in the exhaust is diminished, and the soft blast permits of the efficient combustion of low grade fuels thinly fired.

(7) *The necessary fuel and water capacity of the tender may be reduced,* for given work, in consequence of the preceding advantages.

The advantages of compounding enumerated above are both logical and feasible from the theoretical aspect, but it may prove difficult to produce a design such that they are realised in practice. The outstanding disadvantages to be considered, and eliminated where possible, are set out below.

(1) *Lack of flexibility.* Non-condensing compound engines only attain their maximum efficiency under constant conditions of operation, *i.e.,* when hauling uniform loads at a predetermined speed of revolution and developing a given power. The cylinder ratios and relationship of h.p. to l.p. cut-off (where the latter is unalterable) may therefore prove uneconomical on varying duties.

(2) *Increased cost of construction.*

(3). *Greater complication.* Reliability is consequently not so good, and availability for traffic reduced. Together with (2) and (4), this disadvantage naturally applies with less force when the compound engine is compared with three- and four-cylinder simples.

(4) *Increased costs of maintenance, repairs and lubricants.*

(5) *The l.p. cylinders and reciprocating parts are relatively heavy* and inertia forces increased accordingly.

(6) *The loads on the h.p. and l.p. pistons respectively may vary considerably in practice.*

(7) *A high m.e.p may not be actually obtained.* Excessive condensation may occur in the l.p. cylinders; this may reduce the velocity of the steam appreciably and increase the back pressure on account of the sluggish exhaust. The fact that the water consumption economies, due to compounding, are considerably lower than those in fuel supports the contention that improvements as regards the extent of initial condensation in the h.p. cylinders are more or less invalidated by subsequent condensation in the l.p. cylinders.

The compound engine does not exert such a high tractive effort when starting, and also at low speeds, as the simple engine; the initial acceleration is therefore not so rapid. An improvement in this respect is effected by fitting a starting valve; this procedure is now general, but tends partly to nullify the advantage of the decreased piston loads otherwise obtaining, with especial reference to the l.p. cylinders. At higher speeds, however, the tractive effort may be increased above that of a corresponding simple expansion engine, without unduly enhancing the steam consumption, by working with full regulator in conjunction with a late h.p. cut-off; this characteristic may be advanced as an explanation, for example, of the excellent work performed by the French compounds when working heavy loads on adverse gradients at high speeds and, at the same time, accelerating.

The progress of modern locomotive design has introduced certain factors which react unfavourably on compounding. Three of the more important will be cited; these are:—

(a) Long lap valves or poppet valves, in conjunction with appropriate cylinder and boiler dimensions, enable the simple engine to perform its work when running, for instance, on a level road and not accelerating its load, with a fully opened regulator and cut-offs of, say, from 10% to 15%, *i.e.*, with a corresponding true ratio of expansion, governed, of course, by the extent of clearance volume, of the order of 5:1. It is doubtful whether a compound engine operating under comparable conditions will give a greater number of expansions.

(b) Superheating does not increase the efficiency of the compound to the same extent that it does in the case of the simple engine because:

(i) Initial cylinder condensation losses have already been reduced.

(ii) Although the temperature drop in the l.p. cylinders may be low, the area of metal in contact with the steam is relatively great and the steam has lost much of its superheat, if not all, prior to the second stage of expansion, during which the extent of condensation is greatest.

(iii) The decrease in volume of steam occurring when all superheat has been extracted tends to lower the m.e.p. in the l.p. cylinders. This disability may be overcome, either by reducing the volume of the latter relative to the h.p. cylinders or by varying the cut-off ratio, for engines using superheated steam.

(c) Feed water heaters, when fitted to compound engines, are usually arranged to take receiver steam, as compared with exhaust steam in the case of simple engines. The delivery temperature of the feed is thereby enhanced, but the nett thermal gain to the engine is diminished in consequence.

The arguments advanced above, with reference to superheating, are not supported by some published information on the performance of French locomotives. It was there stated that losses, due to heat exchange between the steam and the cylinder walls and to leakage, represented 55.5% of the work done in the case of a goods engine using saturated steam with simple expansion, 41.5% for a non-superheater compound express, and 22.5% in the case of a similar engine fitted with superheater. Wood, on the other hand, quotes an example in his *Locomotive Operation* of a compound engine which shewed an economy of 13% over the corresponding simple when using saturated steam, this saving being reduced to 6% when a superheater was provided. Similarly, a 6% fuel economy achieved by compounding in the Argentine became a 9% loss when superheaters were introduced. There is no doubt that the characteristics peculiar to superheated steam are not always fully considered, but obviously should be, in connection with the design of compound locomotives.

Mention has been made of the possibility of excessive condensation occurring in the l.p. cylinders. In some instances, the author believes, steps have been taken to counteract this by the provision of interstage superheaters, but he has no information as to whether this practice effected the desired improvement.

Although the possible employment in future of ultra high boiler pressures may modify the position, compounding generally has never been so successful in this country as on the Continent. It may be suggested that the causes of this state of affairs are:—

(1) Our restricted loading gauges prohibit the employment of sufficiently large l.p. cylinders.

(2) The boiler pressures adopted were too low.

(3) Coal of good quality could be purchased cheaply. Although not altogether applicable to modern conditions, it should be noted that the ruling prices of fuel in this country, having regard to the calorific value, are still relatively low in comparison with those obtaining in many parts of the Continent.

(4) Steam ports were of inadequate area and valve gears unsuitable.

(5) Fittings essential to the most efficient working of compound engines, e.g., starting valves and independent valve gears, were sometimes omitted on the score of complication.

(6) Compound engines generally were not built in large numbers, with the result that the appropriate training of enginemen could not be thoroughly effected. This, apart from purely psychological considerations, resulted in unsatisfactory handling of the engines.

Types of Compound Engines.

Two Cylinder Compounds are not in general very satisfactory. If outside cylinders are employed, it is frequently difficult to accommodate an l.p. cylinder of adequate diameter. Another difficulty is to secure equality of the work done by the individual cylinders; this, in conjunction with the greater mass of the l.p. engine details, results in uneven distribution of stresses over the two sides of the engine. Further, there are only two exhaust beats per revolution, with the result that the draught is intermittent and combustion inefficient at all but the highest speeds of revolution.

Three Cylinder Compounds (two h.p. cylinders outside and one l.p. cylinder inside, or *vice versa*. Drive either to one axle or divided). Are also likely to suffer, but to a lesser degree, from unequal distribution of work in the cylinders.

Four Cylinder Compounds give the most satisfactory results and may be arranged with the h.p. cylinders either inside or outside, the drive being either to one axle or divided. The de Glehn compounds are arranged with a divided drive, thus reducing wear, the l.p. cylinders being inside the frames, where they are more protected from radiation losses and a free, direct exhaust to the blast pipe is afforded.

Starting, or Intercepting, and Relief Valves.

The provision of a starting, or intercepting, valve is now regarded as essential, and enables the compound engine to start as a simple. The decision as to whether both h.p. and l.p engines, or the l.p. cylinders only, shall be utilised for starting purposes determines the arrangement of the valve. In the former case, which is preferable, the valve must fulfil dual functions, *viz*.:—

1. Permit the h.p. engines to exhaust direct to the blast pipe when the engine is starting, and
2. Supply live steam at a reduced pressure to the l.p. cylinders.

The valve diverting the h.p. exhaust to the blast pipe must be so designed that the live steam supplied to the l.p. cylinders cannot act as back pressure on the h.p. engines. It is essential that this live steam be supplied to the l.p. cylinders at a reduced pressure, the reduction usually being effected by throttling, so that the mass of the l.p. engine details need not be unduly increased in order to withstand additional piston loads which occur only when starting.

When the l.p. cylinders only are utilised for starting, live steam is reduced in pressure and supplied to them as before, and the h.p. engines are bye-passed by permitting free communication between the ends of each cylinder, with the result that the h.p. pistons are balanced and perform no work. The disadvantages of this arrangement are that the l.p. engine details must be stronger, and therefore heavier, than they would be in the event of all cylinders being available for starting purposes, and that, in the case of a four-cylinder compound, for example, two cylinders are idle when the engine is starting.

An additional feature sometimes incorporated with intercepting valves is the automatic cessation of the reduced live steam supply when the pressure of the h.p. exhaust exceeds that obtaining in the receiver.

The receiver should in any case be fitted with a relief valve to prevent (1) excessive back pressures on the h.p. cylinders, and (2), overstressing of the l.p. engine details.

Factors affecting Distribution of Work over Cylinders.

These are the cylinder volume ratios and the relation of the cut-off in the h.p. cylinders to that in the l.p. cylinders. The two factors are interdependent, and must therefore be considered conjointly.

The ratio of the volume swept through by the h.p. pistons to that for the l.p. cylinders is governed by the boiler pressure and is also affected, as previously stated, by superheating. Whereas a maximum ratio of about 1: 2.7 was employed for saturated steam, modern passenger engines with superheaters and working at similar pressures, from 220 to 250 lb. per square inch, have cylinder ratios of from 1: 2.1 to 1: 2.5, a representative value being 1:2.25. A slightly lower ratio, say 1: 2.2, applies to goods engines working at these pressures. The ratio increases with the pressure ; for instance, the L.N.E.R. compound, No. 10,000, with a working pressure of 450 lb. per square inch, has a ratio of 1: 4.

Mr. Selby has suggested (Proc. I. Loco.E., 1930) the following ratios as suitable for superheated steam:

Ratio.	Pressure, lb. per square inch.
1: 2.0	225
1: 2.25	250
1: 2.5	300
1: 3.0	350-400

Those adopted by the P.L.M. (*ibid.*, 1931) are given below.

Ratio.	Pressure, lb. per square inch.
1: 1.62	170.67
1: 1.91	199.12
1: 2.17	227.57
1: 2.64	284.46

It should be noted that von Borries favoured lower ratios, varying from 1: 2 to 1: 2.2 (for saturated steam), than his contemporaries in other countries, but employed later l.p. cylinder cut-offs in order to avoid large cylinder clearance volumes and exhaust clearance for the l.p. cylinder valves.

Theoretically, the ratio of expansion in the h.p. cylinder, r_{hp}, should be equal to

$$r_{hp} = \frac{r_t}{R} \quad\dots\dots\dots\dots\dots\dots\dots\dots\dots\dots\dots\dots\dots\dots\dots \quad (246)$$

where r_t = total ratio of expansion required,
and R = ratio of l.p. to h.p. cylinder volume.

Note that R, in this case, is the inversion of the usual form of the cylinder volume ratio.

For a compound engine, the true value of r_t is given by

$$r_t = \frac{\text{volume of total l.p. piston displacement} + \text{l.p. clearance volume}}{\text{volume of h.p. piston displacement to point of cut-off} + \text{h.p. clearance volume.}} \quad \dots \quad (247)$$

In general terms, the effects of working a compound engine by varying the h.p. cut-off, the l.p. cut-off and regulator opening remaining constant, are:—

1. When the engine is working heavily, the greater proportion of the work is performed by the l.p. cylinders (especially in the event of the volume ratio being high).

2. When the engine is working lightly, little, if any work is performed by the l.p. cylinders.

On the other hand, with a constant cut-off in the h.p. cylinders, variation of the l.p. cut-off results in only a small proportion of the total work being done by the l.p. cylinders at late cut-offs, these conditions being reversed at early cut-offs.

Working with very early cut-offs in the h.p. cylinders should be avoided because:

(a) Early compression is especially undesirable in these cylinders, and

(b) The m.e.p. in the l.p. cylinders may be reduced excessively.

Partial closure of the regulator has practically no effect on the amount of work done by the l.p. cylinders, but diminishes that done by the h.p. cylinders.

Although the best results can only be obtained by suitable variation of the cut-offs in the h.p. and l.p. cylinders respectively, the provision of independent control of the valve gears is inadvisable unless the drivers have attained a high general standard of skill.

In some cases a constant point of cut-off is arranged for the l.p. cylinders.   For instance, the l.p. cylinders on certain French express engines cut-off at 66%, whilst the h.p. cylinders may be varied at will between approximately 45% and 85%. It is, however, more usual for the relationship of the respective cut-offs to be predetermined as in the example, also taken from French practice, given below.

| Cut-off, per cent. ||
High pressure Cylinders.	Low pressure Cylinders.
75.2	85.3
60	73
50	63
40	52
30	42
20	28

These variations are considerably greater than those advocated by the American Locomotive Company, who suggest that, for superheater engines with a cylinder volume ratio of 2.5:1, the l.p. cut-off should be approximately 5% greater than the h.p.   This divergence in cut-off falls to zero at a ratio of 2.75:1, and is increased for lower ratios, being about 10% for a 2.2:1 ratio.

Port Areas.

Von Borries and Worsdell provided the following port areas:
    For h.p. cylinders, equal to 8.1% of the piston area.
    For l.p. cylinders, equal to 6.4% of the piston area.
The above applied to passenger engines using saturated steam; the areas were reduced by one-tenth for goods engines.
Considerable increases on the foregoing are evidenced in modern practice, and the following are recommended as suitable for piston valves and superheated steam (Falconer, Proc. I. Loco.E.):
    For passenger engines, 17%—19% of h.p. piston area.
    For goods engines, 15%—17% of h.p. piston area.
The port area provided for the l.p. cylinders now commonly represents approximately 10% of the corresponding piston area.

Clearance Volume.

Representative clearance volumes at present provided are:—

	British Practice.	Continental Practice.
High pressure cylinders	15%	15%—20%
Low pressure cylinders	8%	9%—10%

Large clearance is necessary in the h.p. cylinders in order to avoid excessive compression, especially at cut-offs below 40%; compared with Continental practice, the clearance is not so great in most British designs, but alternative provision is made, in the shape of as much as $\frac{1}{4}''$ exhaust clearance on the h.p. valves, the advantage of this procedure being that the inequality of work distribution is not so marked.

Receiver.

Since the receiver is a reservoir of constant volume, the pressure therein is determined by the relation of the rate at which steam is supplied by the h.p. cylinders to that at which it is absorbed by the l.p. engines.   Should the demands of the latter exceed the supply from the h.p. cylinders, then a pressure drop will occur in the receiver.   Hence, " receiver drop " is due primarily to the relative valve events in the h.p. and l.p. cylinders respectively, and to the cylinder volume ratio, rather than to the volume of the receiver itself, although the latter, from this point of view, should be made small.

On the other hand, a receiver of small volume tends to increase the back pressure on the h.p. pistons to an undesirable extent.   In general, as the receiver volume increases, the areas of the h.p. indicator diagrams are augmented and those of the l.p. diagrams diminished.   It is therefore necessary to compromise in order to meet these opposing conditions as far as possible, and it has been found that the most suitable receiver volume for locomotives is the equivalent of from 3 to 4 h.p. piston displacements.   Steps must be taken to minimise radiation losses.

Tractive Effort of Compound Engines.

Some formulæ for the determination of the tractive force exerted by compound engines have already been given, see equations (2), (3) and (4), Chapter II.   Further formulæ, abstracted from the handbook of the American Locomotive Company, will now be quoted.

Let T = tractive effort, lb.,
  d = diameter of h.p. cylinders, inches,
  D = diameter of l.p. cylinders, inches,
  S = piston stroke, inches,
  P = working pressure of boiler, lb. per square inch,
  W = diameter of driving wheels, inches,
  R = ratio of l.p. to h.p. cylinder volume, and
  C = a constant (see Table LIII following).

Then, for a two-cylinder compound,

$$T_1 = \frac{D^2 SPC}{2W} \qquad \text{..} \qquad (248)$$

For a four-cylinder compound,

$$T_2 = \frac{D^2 SPC}{W} \qquad \text{..} \qquad (249)$$

It will be noted that in locomotive practice, as for other applications of compound expansion, power calculations are based on the assumption that the l.p. engine is of sufficient capacity to perform the total work required.

TABLE LIII.

VALUES OF CONSTANT " C " FOR COMPOUND ENGINE TRACTIVE FORCE FORMULÆ (AMERICAN LOCOMOTIVE COMPANY).

Cut-off, h. p cylinder, %	Ratio of l.p. to h.p. Cylinder Volume.						
	2·2	2·3	2·4	2·5	2·6	2·7	2·8
90			·571	·557	·542	·528	·513
89			·565	·550	·536	·521	·507
88		·573	·559	·543	·529	·515	·500
87		·567	·552	·537	·523	·509	·494
86	·575	·560	·546	·531	·517	·502	·489
85	·570	·555	·540	·526	·511	·497	·483
84	·564	·550	·534	·520	·506	·491	
83	·559	·544	·529	·515	·500	·486	
82	·553	·541	·524	·510	·496		
81	·548	·534	·520	·505	·490		
80	·543	·531	·515	·500	·486		

Taking C as .52, and assuming R to be 2.5:1, then, for a two-cylinder compound starting as a simple,

$$T_3 = \frac{85\ d^2\ SP}{W} = T_1 \times \frac{1.7}{CR} = 1.3\ T_1 \ \dots\dots\dots\ (250)$$

And similarly, for a four-cylinder compound under the same conditions,

$$T_4 = \frac{(2 \times .85)\ d^2 SP}{W} = T_2 \times \frac{1.7}{CR} = 1.3\ T_2 \ \dots\dots\ (251)$$

Quoting from the same source, it is stated that the value of T, when working with simple expansion at low speeds, is generally about 20% greater than that exerted if working compound.

It is essential that the total cross-sectional area of the main steam pipes to the h.p. cylinders be made ample; it should at least equal that provided for a corresponding simple expansion engine, and must not be reduced below this amount.

Tables LIV and LV give the leading dimensions of recent compound engines for passenger and goods service respectively.

TABLE LIV.

LEADING DIMENSIONS OF COMPOUND PASSENGER ENGINES.

Railway	L.M.S.	G.N. Ireland	Alsace-Lorraine	Nord	German State	P.O.	German State	Bengal Nagpur	Norte	Est.	P.L.M.	P.L.M.
Class or Type	Standard Compound	No. 87	T 20	3·1201	Series O4	No. 3566	Series 02	X.C. No. 792	No. 4601	No. 4·1001	241-A1	241-C
Wheel Arrangement	4-4-0	4-4-0	4-8-4 T	4-6-2	4-6-2	4-6-2	4-6-2	4-6-2	4-8-2	4-8-2	4-8-2	4-8-2
Cylinders, h.p. Number	1	1	2	2	2	2	2	2	2	2	2	2
Diameter (inches)	19	17·25	16·54	17·32	13·78	16·54	18·1	16·5	18·11	17·72	20·08	17·72
Stroke (inches)	26	26	25·59	25·98	23·62	25·59	26	26	26·77	28·3	25·59	25·59
Cylinders, l.p. Number	2	2	2	2	2	2	2	2	2	2	2	2
Diameter (inches)	21	19	24·8	24·41	20·47	25·2	28·3	25	27·56	28	28·35	26·77
Stroke (inches)	26	26	25·59	27·16	23·62	25·59	26	26	26·77	28·3	27·56	27·56
Cylinder Volume Ratio, h.p. : l.p.	1:2·445	1:2·426	1:2·248	1:2·085	1:2·207	1:2·321	1:2·445	1:2·3	1:2·31	1:2·5	1:2·16	1:2·458
Boiler Pressure, lb. per sq. inch.	200	250	227·57	227·7	355·75	227·57	227·57	250	235·2	235·2	227·57	284·46
Evaporative Heating Surface, (sq. ft.) Firebox	147·25	162	169·1	218·5	215·3	190·5	218·5	211	265·5	258	255·1	296
Tubes	1169·5	1089	1516·7	2457·3	2007	1797	2457·3	2228	2246·4	2080	2497·3	2373·5
Total	1316·75	1251	1685·8	2675·8	2222·3	1987·5	2675·8	2439	2511·9	2338	2752·4	2669·5
Superheater Surface (sq. ft.)	290·75	276·5	519·9	615·7	910	783	615·7	637	882·7	990	1223	978
Grate Area (sq. ft.)	28·4	25·22	33·26	37·68	44·1	45·9	37·68	51	53·82	47·3	53·82	53·9
Diameter of Coupled Wheels	6'-9½"	6'-7"	5'-5·36"	6'-2·8"	6'-6·74"	6'-2·8"	6'-2·8"	6'-2"	5'-8·9"	6'-4·7"	5'-10·47"	6'-6·74"
Weights (tons) Adhesive	39·2	40·95	66·95	53·2	54·15	56·1	53·2	64·35	62·9	72·8	73·8	77·7
Total Engine (working order)	61·7	65·05	121·3	92·8	102·4	97·5	92·8	105	101·25	109	114·95	122·7

TABLE LV.

LEADING DIMENSIONS OF COMPOUND GOODS LOCOMOTIVES.

Railway	Central Argentine	Belgian State	Delaware & Hudson	Delaware & Hudson	P.L.M.	Nord	German State
Class or Type	No. 849	Type 33	"John B. Jarvis"	No. 1403 "L. F. Loree"	1001	5-001	
Wheel Arrangement	2-8-0	2-8-0	2-8-0	4-8-0	2-8-2	2-10-0	2-10-0
Cylinders, h.p.				(Triple Expansion) h.p. 1 | 20, 32 ; i.p. 1 | 27.5, 32			
Number	1	2	1		2	2	2
Diameter (inches)	21	16.56	22.2		20.08	19.3	16.54
Stroke (inches)	26	26	30		25.59	25.2	25.98
Cylinders, l.p.							
Number	1	2	1	2	2	2	2
Diameter (inches)	31.5	23.63	38	33	28.35	26.8	26.77
Stroke (inches)	26	26	30	32	27.56	27.6	25.98
Cylinder Volume Ratio, h.p. : l.p.	1 : 2.25	1 : 2.04	1 : 2.93	h.p. : i.p. : l.p. :: 1 : 1.891 : 5.445	1 : 2.16	1 : 2.11	1 : 2.619
Boiler Pressure, lb. per sq. inch	200	227.57	400	500	227.57	227.57	367.5
Evaporative Heating Surface (sq. ft.)							
Firebox	165	202.5	1150	1026	168	187	
Tubes	1435	1727.5	1971	2325	2190	2522	
Total	1600	1930	3121	3351	2358	2709	2424
Superheater Surface (sq. ft.)	277	640.5	700	1076	760	670	1332
Grate Area (sq. ft.)	27.9	35	82	75.8	45.6	34.6	50.5
Diameter of Coupled Wheels	5'-2"	4'-11.875"	4'-9"	5'-3"	5'-3.9"	5'-1"	4'-7.12"
Weights (tons) Adhesive, Total Engine	60.8	73.75	131.7	139.7	68.4	86.9	100

Chapter XII.

FRAMES. SPRINGS. BRAKES. FLEXIBILITY ON CURVES. TANKS, BUNKERS AND TENDERS. SUPERSTRUCTURES.

FRAMES.

Comparison of Plate with Bar Frames.

Plate Frames.	Bar Frames.
Very rigid in vertical plane.	Weak in vertical plane. The single top rail over the horns may fracture on account of careless lifting in shops, or due to slackness of the hornstay.
Weak transversely. Flexibility enables engine to "give" when negotiating curves, but distortion of frames may lead to heating of axleboxes. A relatively large number of transverse stays are necessary.	Very rigid transversely; separate provision for flexibility of engine therefore essential. The necessary extent of transverse staying is small.
Comparatively strong at point of attachment of buffer beams. All brackets, gussets and cross stays easily attached.	Weak at leading end, and usually, in cases where a bogie is provided, behind cylinders also. Stays between smokebox and buffer beams customarily fitted.
With most designs the cylinder bolts are in direct shear.	Cylinders, if not cast integrally with the frames, are housed in recesses provided for them in the latter.
Coupled wheels of large diameter may be located under firebox	Diameter of coupled wheels, if under firebox, restricted; idle trailing wheels essential for engines with boilers of large capacity.
Inside motion and portion of firebox between frames inaccessible. Washing out facilities and side stay maintenance detrimentally affected.	Firebox and all details between frames accessible.

Comparison of Plate with Bar Frames—*(cont'd)*.

Plate Frames.	Bar Frames.
A deep firebox and efficient ashpan may be accommodated.	Distance between frames restricted ; ashpan and dampers narrow in consequence. Area of air intake therefore limited.
Narrow type firebox satisfactorily supported at a position remote from the level of the grate.	High boiler centre line necessary if ample depth provided at tubeplate for narrow type of firebox. For broad, shallow firebox, however, allows greatest possible width of shell between tyres with wheels of large diameter. If wheels are of small diameter, grate may overhang wheels without unduly raising boiler centre line.
The centres of axlebox guides and spring brackets are not uniplanar with the neutral axis of the frame ; all loadings are therefore excentric.	Points of application of loads coincide with neutral axis of frame, which has a substantial section. Axlebox guides are of simple channel form and comparatively easily replaced. The bearing areas of horns, being governed by width of frame section, are in some cases reduced.
	Very heavy construction.
	Springs and compensating gear favourably located ; spaces in frames utilised under firebox for this purpose. For other wheels, as the distance between tops of horn spaces and frame respectively is small, overhung springs may be employed. These are preferable to underhung springs, especially when used in conjunction with wheels of small diameter, as they may easily be examined or changed, even when no pits are available.
Frames easily joggled to clear cylinders, bogie side play, etc.	Frame sections proportioned to suit varying stresses in different parts of the frame.
Large number of bolts and rivets which may work loose.	Number of bolts minimised. No rivets employed.

From the foregoing it will be deduced that the wheel arrangement adopted and form of firebox employed are influenced by the type of frame used, and therein lies a partial explanation of the divergencies exhibited, for example, between British and American practice.

The thickness of **plate frames** varies from $\frac{3}{4}''$ to $1\frac{1}{2}''$; frames for heavy engines in this country are usually about $1\frac{1}{8}''$ thick, and for smaller engines of standard gauge a thickness of $1''$ is generally employed. There must be no sudden change in the frame section, and square corners are to be avoided; the top edge of the frame should as far as possible be uniplanar over the major portion of its length. Excessive local rigidity in the vertical plane will cause trouble, and must be eliminated either by reducing the depth of frame or by slotting holes. The provision of the latter is a common device for the reduction of weight; the dimensions must be determined with care as, if excessive, a local area of weakness, wherein cracks are prone to develop, is formed. Where possible, the holes should be so located that the accessibility of details placed between the frames, *e.g.*, motion parts, mud hole doors, etc., is improved. When the firebox is located between coupled axles, an allowance of $1/32''$ or $3/64''$ is sometimes made for longitudinal expansion of the frames between the centres of the axles concerned. Holes drilled through the frames at the leading end for the engagement of lifting tackle are very useful.

The frame surface should be faced up where required to form a bearing for cylinder bolt heads, etc. Where outside cylinders with inside steamchests are employed, the frames are cut away to receive them; keys may then be driven in at each end of the gap in the frame in order to relieve the cylinder bolts of shear stresses.

The inherent weakness of plate frames in the horizontal plane demands fairly extensive transverse bracing. In some designs, however, the required amount of rigidity is exceeded, and for this reason cross stays built up of plate and angle are generally preferable to steel castings. The cross stays are attached to the frames either with rivets, hot or cold, or driving fit bolts, and are sometimes provided with lips which register with the tops of the main frames.

Although the provision of two independent guides for each axlebox reduces the number of holes to be drilled in the frames, and also ensures more flexibility immediately above the axlebox, the adoption of the horse shoe shaped hornblock casting compensates for the weakness of the frame due to the cutting of the gap. In order to prevent initial stressing of the frame when driving fit bolts are put in, irrespective of the construction adopted, the bolt holes should not be too closely pitched; the centres should be zigzagged, and not in line. Similarly, bolts should not be located at the top corners of the hornblocks. It is important that the guide or hornblock be properly fitted to, and bear throughout its length on, the frame edge; the bolts must also bed down throughout their effective bearing length. The bolts may loosen by stretching, and the advisability of using steel having a fairly high ultimate strength, say, 33-36 tons per square inch tensile, may therefore be considered. The use of hexagonal heads, where possible, is preferable to that of the countersunk form.

The tops of the gaps cut in the frames for the horns should be generously radiused in every instance.

The provision of *wedge adjustment* for the guides is not altogether general; it is not so beneficial with steel as with "brass" axleboxes, as wear on the faces concerned is less rapid in the former case. A detrimental feature of wedges is that trouble may be experienced with the bolts working loose. Further, the taking up of wear by this method calls for a certain degree of skill, as it affects the cylinder clearance, and should therefore not be employed where the available labour is of a poor standard. On the other hand, a hot box in its early stages may be eased by slackening the wedges; moreover, this form of adjustment is more easily accomplished than the corresponding alternative procedure, *viz.*, the fitting of liners.

The incline of the wedge is from 1 in 10 to 1 in 14; it should be retained by a bolt 1″ in diameter, the permissible vertical movement of which may be approximately 2″. The tendency for the wedge to drop, owing to the slackening of the bolts, may be counteracted, subsequent to preliminary adjustment, by providing a fitted packing piece between the horizontal bolt and the bottom of the slot; plain packing is then added when it is necessary to raise the wedge, but the use of this additional packing should be limited to one piece. Ferruling of the vertical bolt is ineffective, as its intended action is invalidated in the event of the hornstay dropping. When the material is cast iron, the minimum wall thickness of the wedge may be about $1\frac{1}{4}″$ or $1\frac{3}{8}″$. The wedges are best located at the front of the boxes for engines with inclined cylinders, in order to neutralise variations occurring in the clearance as the engine settles down on the springs.

Buffer beams usually have a thickness of about $1\frac{1}{4}''$, and must be well stayed, with rigid gussets to take up the loads due to drawbar and buffing actions.

Bar frames manufactured in this country are in most cases cut from the solid slab, a process involving heavy machining costs and an excessive amount of scrap material. In America they are cast in steel, complete with cross stays and, in some instances, the cylinders also; alloys, *e.g.*, vanadium, are employed in order to reduce weight and also to facilitate the manufacture of the more intricate castings, at the same time reducing the proportion of faulty castings. Cross stays, where made independently, are secured to the main frames with turned driving bolts, the latter being tapered $\frac{1}{16}''$ per foot. Brake hanger and other pins are collared and bolted on.

MAIN FRAMES : LOADS AND FORCES.

Loads applied in the vertical plane comprise:—

(i). Spring borne loads. Attention must be given to the fact that the static weight distribution does not hold good

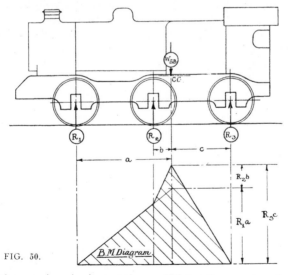

FIG. 50.

when the engine is in motion. When the engine is accelerating, the water tends by its inertia to mass at the end of the boiler remote from that of the engine which happens to be leading (the reverse of course holding good during deceleration), and the effect of track depression is to decrease the loads on the leading axles whilst increasing those at the trailing end. Shock stresses of an indeterminate nature also arise. It should be remembered that the static distribution is also modified when the engine is standing under repair with one or more pairs of wheels and axles removed, although, in these circumstances, the boiler would be empty.

Referring to Fig. 50, the total spring borne mass of the engine, W_{SB}, is assumed to be acting through its centre of gravity. In the example given the reactions at the points of suspension are R_1, R_2 and R_3 respectively, their sum naturally being equal to W_{SB}. The point of maximum bending occurs under the centre of gravity and, in the case under consideration, its moment is equal to R_3c. This moment is of course resisted by two frames.

(ii) Total weight of engine. Two cases will be examined:

(a) If lifted at extreme ends of frames by crane or engine hoist. This will probably be found to be the most severe case of vertical loading applied to the frames. Let W_T (see Fig. 51) be the total weight of the engine, assumed concentrated at its centre of gravity. The left and right hand reactions arising from it are equal to $W_T\left(\dfrac{l-x}{l}\right)$ and $W_T\dfrac{x}{l}$ respectively, the dimensions having the significance indicated on the diagram, and the maximum bending moment, occurring under the centre of gravity and taken by the two frames, is given by $W_T\left(\dfrac{l-x}{l}\right)x$.

When the engine is being lifted in the shops, the frames are then supporting the whole of the normally spring borne weight less water and, in the case of tank engines, fuel, with the possible addition of a proportion of the dead (*i.e.*, not spring borne) weight; coincidentally, one or more hornstays are necessarily removed, possibly at the point of maximum bending on the frame. In order to counteract the resulting tendency for the frames to fracture at the corners of those horn gaps which are located in areas subject to the greatest bending stresses, the frame section in these localities should be such that the

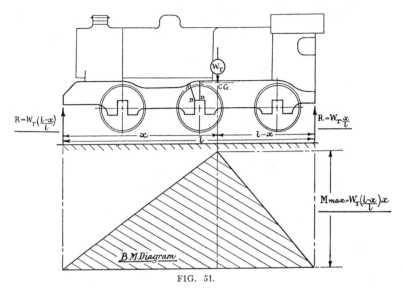

FIG. 51.

length of a line drawn from a gap corner to the nearest top edge of the frame is at least as great as, and preferably greater than, the distance between the top of the frame and the top of the gap. Again referring to Fig. 51, length of AB should at least equal that of CD.

(b) If lifted from one end only, e.g., by sheer legs. The most severe conditions obtain when the axle farthest from the end lifted is used as a fulcrum. The following approximate theory is based on the assumptions that the mass of the lifted engine, which may be the gross empty weight of the engine less that of one pair of wheels with axle and coupling rods, is concentrated at, and acting through, the centre of gravity, and that the longitudinal centre line of the frame is approximately coincident with the neutral axis of its section.

The engine is lifted through an angle of $(90—a)°$, the mass lifted being W_L tons. The maximum primary bending moment on the frames, due to the lifting, occurs at X (Fig. 52) and is

equal to $W_L \sin a \left(\dfrac{z—y}{z} \right) y$.

Let the force required to lift be L,
Then, taking moments,

$$L z. \sin a = W_L (z — y). \sin a$$

whence $L = W_L \left(\dfrac{z—y}{z} \right)$

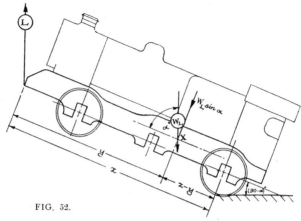

FIG. 52.

To the stresses arising from the primary bending must be added algebraically one or other of the following direct stresses, according to the position, relative to X, of the individual section of the frames under consideration:—

Compressive, to right of X:—

$$\frac{(W_L - L)\ cos\ a}{\text{Area of selected frame section.}}$$

Tensile, to left of X:—

$$\frac{L\ cos\ a}{\text{Area of selected frame section.}}$$

Thus, select a normal section AB (see Fig. 53) of the frame above a horn gap; this section is bisected at C and intersected at D by the frame centre line.   Let the primary bending moment at the selected section be designated M_1.   Further, if either of the foregoing direct stresses be called F, then the secondary bending moment due to it will be $F \times CD$; let this moment be M_2.   Then the total skin stress on section AB will be:—

$$\frac{M_1 \pm M_2}{Z_{AB}} \pm \frac{F}{\text{Area of section } AB} \quad \dots \dots \dots \dots \dots (252)$$

It will be understood that the strength of the frame must be considered with regard to the residual and resultant shear stresses which, arising in combination with the above load-

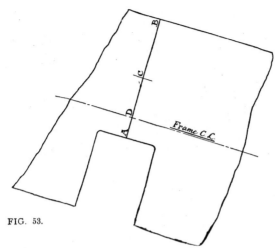

FIG. 53.

ings, may be determined by the ellipse of stress or by calculation. This consideration will give the maximum value of the
stress in the frame; this will be in the plane of resultant shear,
which is not a normal section.

(iii) Reactions of vertical thrust at the slide blocks. These
have already been considered in Chapter IX.

Loads applied in the horizontal plane.

In general, the stresses due to the loads applied in the vertical
plane are small by comparison with those arising from forces
acting horizontally on the frames and, with the exception of
the spring borne loads, do not occur in conjunction with them.
The frame should therefore be designed to withstand, with a
suitable factor of safety, the maximum stress produced by
the combined effects of the bending moments in the horizontal
plane and that in the vertical plane produced by the spring
borne loads.

The principal loads in the horizontal plane which, with the
exception of (vi) hereunder, are interrelated and must therefore be considered collectively, are those due to the reactions
of:—

(i)   Piston loads and connecting rod thrusts (see Chapter
       IX).
(ii)   Coupling rod loads *(ibid.)*.
(iii) Tractive force at coupled wheel treads.
(iv)   Pull at drawbar. (iii) and (iv) balance amongst
       themselves, since μW at the coupled wheel treads

equals internal resistance of engine plus drawbar pull, and give rise to a stress in the frames, between the points of application, which is tensile or compressive according to whether the engine is pulling or propelling its train.

(v) Buffing loads.
(vi) Braking loads, which will be considered in a subsequent section of this chapter.

In addition to the above, lateral loads due to resistance at the wheels to sliding across the rails, to flange action on curves,

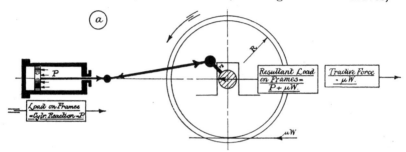

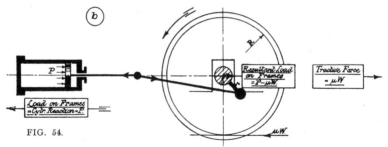

FIG. 54.

and to shocks experienced when passing over points and crossings, are taken by the frames and transmitted from one to the other by the cross stays and other transverse members.

Reactions of piston loads on frames.

The following argument is included to demonstrate the limitation of the effects of piston loads on the frame to that portion between the cylinder attachments and the driving hornblocks.

Let P = piston load,
  W = adhesive weight,
  R = radius of coupled wheels, and
  r = radius of crank.

Then, as a general case, for one cylinder in a pair of frames, the effects of angularity being ignored,

$$Pr = \mu\, WR$$

and $\mu\, W = \dfrac{Pr}{R}$

With the crank rotating in an anti-clockwise direction in the upper quadrants (Fig. 54 a), the resultant load per frame has a maximum value of $\frac{1}{2}(P + \mu\, W)$, and in the lower quadrants (Fig. 54 b) is equal to $\frac{1}{2}(P - \mu\, W)$.

BEARING SPRINGS.

Although from 50% to 66% lighter in weight and requiring less space, coiled springs are not often employed in modern locomotive practice for the main bearings. They are rather too sensitive, and further, fracture may have a more immediate effect on the availability of the engine; for these reasons semi-elliptic laminated springs are almost universally employed. The following formulæ and remarks on the design of laminated springs have been abstracted from *Laminated Springs* and *Springs and Suspension*, the works of Mr. T. H. Sanders (The Locomotive Publishing Co. Ltd.), to which readers are referred for a very complete treatment of the subject.

Let d = unit deflection, inches per ton,
  D = test deflection, inches,
  C = camber, inches,
  L = true (*i.e.*, curved) length of back plate of spring between centres of bearings, inches,
  L_S = length of short plate, inches,
  S = span, or full chord of spring between centres of bearings, inches,
  W = load on spring, tons,
  w = weight of spring, without hoop or fittings, lb.,
  n = number of plates, of uniform thickness, in spring,
  b = width of plates, inches,
  t = thickness of each plate, in one-sixteenths of an inch (example: $\frac{1}{2}'' = 8$),
  T = thickness of thickest plate in spring, inches,

TT = total thickness of plates of spring, inches. If the plates are of uniform thickness, then obviously $TT = nT$.

X = ratio of test load (or deflection) to working load (or deflection),

J = length of offset, or distance between adjacent plate ends, inches, and

h = width of buckle or hoop, inches.

Then the unit of deflection, which may vary in practice within the limits of 0.05″ and 0.5″ per ton, although a more representative range is from 0.14″ to 0.3″ per ton, is given by

$$d = \frac{0.1 \times L^3}{nbt^3} \qquad (253)$$

A typical value of d, for coupled axle bearing springs, is 0.25″ per ton.

The test load,

$$W_t = \frac{0.177 \; t^2 bn}{L} \qquad (254)$$

and working load,

$$W_w = \frac{Kt^2 \; bn}{L} \qquad (255)$$

The actual value of constant K is from 0.06 to 0.12, the recommended value being 0.08.

The standard maximum test deflection,

$$D = \frac{L^2}{900 \; T} \qquad (256)$$

The resiliency of laminated springs is given in inch-lb. per lb. weight of spring by

$$r = \frac{WD}{2 \; w} \qquad (257)$$

Taking r as 400,
Resiliency efficiency (%)

$$= \frac{1,000 \; W D}{3.5 \; w} \qquad (258)$$

Certain laminated buffing springs give the maximum

efficiency, which is of the order of 94%; the maximum efficiency which can be attained in the case of bearing springs is about 75%.

The approximate weight of the spring is given by

$$w = \frac{L \times b \times TT}{5.2} \qquad \text{............................} \quad (259)$$

The thickness of the plates may be determined from

$$t^2 = \frac{90 \times X \times W_w \times L}{16 \times n \times b} \qquad \text{..............................} \quad (260)$$

For $\frac{1}{2}''$ plates, $i.e.$, the U.S.A. standard thickness, $nb = W_w L$.

The increment for the true (arc) length L, according to the span and camber, is

$$\frac{2.65 \ C^2}{S} \qquad \text{...} \quad (261)$$

Then, as a rough approximation, accurate within 5%,

$$L = S \left(1 + \frac{2.65 \ C^2}{S^2} \right) \text{..........................} \quad (262)$$

The offset, or distance between adjacent plate ends, may be

$$J = \frac{L - L_S}{2 \ (n-1)} \qquad \text{...} \quad (263)$$

In the ideal design, J would be equal to $\dfrac{L}{2n}$.

The length of the short plate, L_S, may be $\left(\dfrac{L}{n} + h \right)$ for speared ends, or $\dfrac{L}{n}$ for squared ends. In the latter case, should the calculated value of $\dfrac{L}{n}$ be less than h, then L_S in practice should be made equal to $(h + 2'')$.

Points to be observed in design are:—

(a) Increasing the length of the spring results in improved riding of the engine and lengthens the life of the spring.

(b) The spring plates should be of uniform thickness throughout. The use of thick back plates leads to breakage on account of the high range of stress occurring in comparison with thin plates.

(c) Two or, at most, three full length plates are sufficient.

(d) All plate lengths should be multiples of the short plate length.

(e) The length of the offsets should be a uniform dimension throughout the spring, such as 1.5", 2.0", 2.5", etc.

(f) Not less than 8 plates should be employed for bearing springs (minimum for buffing springs of 70" or over, 10).

(g) Avoid the use of upward nibs for the centre fastening; downward nibs, i.e., with the depression on the tension side of the plate and the embossment on the compression side, if the plate thickness is greater than $\frac{3}{8}$", or cotter holes, are preferable. Efficiencies of various forms of centre fastening, the criterion being that of the solid plate, are as follows:—

Solid plate 100%
Sides flat (patented) 95%
Downward nib (depth of nib approximately equal to $\frac{T}{2}$, and that of depression, $\frac{5}{8} T$) ... 85%
Side notched 80%
Cotter hole 75%
Upward nib (special type, with nib generously radiused) 75%
Punched hole 70%
Drilled hole 70%
Upward nib (usual type, without external radius for nib) 60%

The following comparison may also be considered in conjunction with the foregoing:—

Type of Fastening.	Reduction in Cross Sectional Area of Plate.	Reduction in Efficiency.
Drilled hole	13%	30%
Cotter hole	7%	25%
Side notch	5%	20%
Sides flat	3%	5%

Where drilled or punched holes are employed, the steel for the rivets should preferably have an ultimate tensile strength of about 40 tons per square inch, the object being to reduce the number of failures by shearing.

(h) The suspension of the spring at the back plate ends should be through loose washers or small jumped ends. Welded or "solid end" back plates are to be avoided.

(i) The camber should be such that the spring is straight, or flat, when under full load. A reasonable tolerance for cambers is $+ \frac{1}{8}'' - 0''$.

(j) The plate ends may be square cut, especially if the off-set be less than 3", or speared; the "square spear" is preferable.

(k) Studs and slits may be provided to check lateral movement, and should be located where the material is in excess of theoretical requirements. Rib and groove steel is, however, distinctly to be preferred, but should not be used on plates of less thickness than $\frac{3}{8}''$. If studs and slits are used, they should be of the "open-slit" type, $i.e.$, with the slit at the plate end and the stud to suit; nevertheless, they are potential breaking points and much inferior for the intended purpose to rib and groove steel, or U-clips. Studs and slits are in any case unnecessary for springs less than 36" in length. Back plates in particular should never be studded, as this practice encourages fractures; the latter always commence on the tension side of plates. When U-clips are employed to check lateral movement, they should be fitted to the third or fourth plate.

(l) If possible, the thickness of band hoops should be uniform on all sides. The bottom should not be shaped internally to the bottom plate of the spring with the latter in the " unloaded " position. Lugged hoops should preferably be machined from the solid block.

(m) All qualities and treatments of steels give the same unit deflection, as the modulus of elasticity (E) has a constant value. Water hardened steels are satisfactory for springs; a sulphur or phosphorus content up to 0.07% is not deleterious.

(n) For the testing of completed springs, adherence to the requirements of the British Standard Specification is highly desirable.

Spring hangers are almost invariably so arranged as to be

vertical when under load. A simple method of determining the additional stress on the spring due to the inclination of

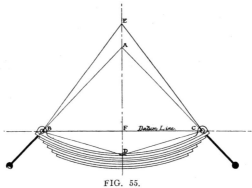

FIG. 55.

the hangers is that due to Professor Dalby. Draw the length, BDC, and camber, DF, of the spring to scale (Fig. 55); then extend the inclination lines of the hangers to meet the vertical centre line of the spring at A. On the opposite side of the datum line, join BD and CD. Then diagram BAC represents the nominal bending moment due to the applied load, and BDC the additional moment due to the inclination of the hangers. Diagram BDC may then be added algebraically to BAC as shewn, the complete bending moment diagram being given by BEC.

With restricted loading gauges there is little, if any, choice as regards the disposition of the bearing springs for engines of large dimensions, and they must be underhung; overhung springs are nevertheless preferable on account of their superior riding qualities and of the greater safety afforded when the engine is traversing a curve, by reason of the reduced displacement of its mass. Underhung springs are comparatively inaccessible, easily damaged in the event of derailment, and invalidate easy removal of the axlebox keep; they are also more liable to be subjected to intermittent transverse loads than overhung springs. On the other hand, they are more likely to preserve the direction of their line of action as wear takes place, and they are also lubricated to a certain extent by oil dripping from the axleboxes above them. This haphazard lubrication is beneficial in that it preserves the spring; it is, however, unnecessary from the frequently quoted point of view of interplate friction. The individual plates of a laminated spring form an entity which is constrained to move as such, and the lesser liveliness of such a spring, as compared with a coil spring having the same load characteristics, is fundamentally due to the fact that there is approximately three times the amount of steel in movement, this affecting the sensitiveness to shock and rebound. Interplate friction is the lesser check to liveliness and does not affect static deflection; should the spring be very rusty, however, it will affect the dynamic action.

It is essential that there should be at least 4″ clearance above rail level for underhung springs in the most adverse circumstances, *e.g.*, with tyres worn.

Resort is made to **compensation,** or **equalisation,** purely in order to relieve individual springs of shock and to improve the running qualities of the engine over indifferent permanent way. On the other hand, there is considerable inertia in the gear; the beams are necessarily heavy, as failure of any one member affects the entire group of which it is a member. Further, as wear occurs, there is a tendency for adhesive weight to be transferred to the carrying axles; the effects of wear are multiplied, with the result that trouble may be experienced with hot boxes, and the loads on the springs vary considerably from the predetermined amounts, becoming excessive in individual cases. It will therefore be seen that any initial improvement in the riding qualities of an engine is more than lost as the condition of the compensating gear deteriorates. Partial compensation is nevertheless advantageous in certain circumstances, and the principle should certainly be applied to bogies.

It should be noted that, in general, underhung springs are not so quickly affected as the overhung type when the compensating gear loses its alignment.

BRAKES.

By first principles, a train having a total weight of W tons and running at a speed of V miles per hour possesses kinetic energy, E, equal to xWV^2 ft.-lb.; when g is 32.2 feet per second per second, the value of the constant, x, is 74.82. Increasing this amount to allow for the rotational energy of the wheels, we have:—

Adding 10% for rolling stock of normal British design on the standard gauge,

$$E = 82.3 \ W \ V^2 \text{ ft.-lb.} \quad\quad\quad\quad (264)$$

Or, with an increment of 5% appropriate to American practice under similar conditions,

$$E = 78.56 \ W \ V^2 \text{ ft.-lb.} \quad \dots\dots\dots\dots\dots\dots\dots\dots\dots \text{(265)}$$

On shutting the regulator, this energy is eventually absorbed in its entirety by the various resistances acting on the train. Assuming these latter to total ΣR lb., then the distance in which the train can be brought to rest, S feet, is obtained from

$$\Sigma R.S = E$$

whence $S = \dfrac{E}{\Sigma R}$ feet $\dots\dots\dots\dots\dots\dots\dots\dots\dots\dots$ (266)

The rate of deceleration is customarily expressed as a percentage of the acceleration due to gravity, *i.e.*, 21.95 miles per hour per second, and in modern practice is of the order of 10%.

ΣR comprises the frictional resistances of the engine, tender and vehicles forming the train (determined from the mean speed during the process of deceleration), gradient resistance, which may be either positive or negative in value, resistances due to curves and wind, and the frictional resistance of the brakes. With the exception of this last item, the evaluation of these resistances has already been considered in Chapter II.

The frictional resistance of the brakes is given, in lb., by

(μ × total force exerted on the brake blocks).

In general, the value of μ, *the coefficient of friction between the brake block and the tyre*, falls with increase of speed and increases with rise of temperature; it also becomes higher as the unit pressure is reduced. Considering the influence of speed, μ for soft cast iron blocks on steel tyres varies from .167 at high speeds of rubbing to .269 at low speeds; the corresponding values for chilled cast iron blocks are .078 and .147. The results of other tests indicated that μ varied from .074 at high speeds to .242 at low speeds. As a general statement, the kinetic value of μ normally ranges from about .15 to .27, and .22 may be taken as a representative mean.

Two basic facts emerge from examination of the foregoing data: the brake blocks should (*a*) be of soft iron, and (*b*), be provided with a generous bearing area. The latter desideratum may in some instances be attained by providing two blocks per wheel. Reduction in bearing pressure should not be secured by the adoption of flanged brake blocks; with this form of shoe the dissipation of heat is far from uniform, with the result that hair cracks, possibly leading to serious flaws, develop in the tyres. For normal designs the area of the blocks is such that the maximum bearing pressure is in the vicinity of 8 tons per square inch.

The **brake force** is the total load applied to the wheels by the brake blocks, and must bear a fixed relation to the load transmitted to the rails by the wheels on which the blocks operate. Proportions recommended by the Westinghouse Brake Company are:—

For coupled wheels: 65% of minimum adhesive weight in working order, the brake force for any unbraked coupled wheels to be distributed amongst the remainder.

For bogie wheels: 50% of minimum weight on wheels in working order.

For tender wheels: from 85% to 100% of empty weight (all wheels to be braked).

The brake force is equal to

$$\frac{A \times P \times L}{2240} \text{ tons} \quad\dots\dots\dots\dots\dots\dots\dots\dots\dots\dots\dots\dots\dots (267)$$

where A = cross sectional area of brake cylinder(s), square inches,

P = available pressure in brake cylinder(s), lb. per square inch, and

L = leverage ratio of brake rigging.

TABLE LVI.
CROSS SECTIONAL AREAS OF BRAKE CYLINDERS.

Diameter (inches).	Area (square inches).
6	28·274
7	38·485
8	50·265
9	63·617
10	78·540
12	113·10
13	132·73
14	153·94
15	176·71
16	201·06
18	254·47
21	346·46
22	380·13
24	452·39

Where the Westinghouse brake is concerned, the use of brake cylinders over 16″ in diameter is not recommended; in such cases the necessary brake force should be obtained by the employment of two cylinders of smaller diameter.

Neither air nor vacuum brake cylinders should be located in the vicinity of the firebox or ashpan, as the heat radiated therefrom causes rapid deterioration of the leather packing in the one case and of rubber in the other.

The available pressure in the brake cylinders may be taken, for the purposes of calculation, as:—

For Westinghouse air brake .... 50 lb. per square inch.

For vacuum brake .... 0.5 lb. per square inch for each 1″ of vacuum maintained in normal working. Actually, a vacuum of 1″ of mercury at 50°F. is equivalent to a pressure of 0.48968 lb. per square inch, and at 32° F. to 0.49056 lb. per square inch.

For steam brake .... equal to working pressure of boiler. The pressure initially available in the brake cylinder may be less than the boiler pressure on account of the reduction occurring with the use of valves having restricted passages and of comparatively long lengths of pipe of small diameter; extensive condensation is a contributory factor which may be reduced by careful design. The diameter of the cylinder is usually from 8″ to 10″.

For hand brake,

Let R = radius of handle, inches,

q = pitch of screw, inches,

F = force applied manually to handle, lb., and

P = force transmitted by screw to brake rigging, lb.

Then, as a general expression,

$$P = \frac{2 \pi RF}{q} \qquad\qquad\qquad\qquad (268)$$

F is customarily taken at from 25 to 30 lb.; it is not justifiable to assume a value in excess of this latter figure.

When F is taken as 25 lb.,

$$P = \frac{157 \ R}{q} \qquad\qquad\qquad\qquad (269)$$

And when F is taken as 30 lb.,

$$P = \frac{188 \ R}{q} \quad\text{..} \quad (270)$$

The outside diameter of the screw is usually either $1\frac{3}{4}''$ or $2''$, the pitch of the square threads generally approximating to $\frac{3}{8}''$. The radius of the handle, which should be of about $1\frac{1}{4}''$ diameter material, may conveniently be made about $9''$.

Leverage ratios for brake rigging recommended by the Westinghouse Brake Company are:—

For brake cylinders having a total stroke of $6\frac{1}{4}''$...... $6\frac{1}{2}$: 1
For brake cylinders having a total stroke of $8''$ ...... 8 : 1
For brake cylinders having a total stroke of $12''$......10 : 1

The usual leverage arranged for steam brakes is about 7:1. The ratio for any form of brake should not greatly exceed 8:1, as otherwise, when wear occurs, the false or non-effective travel of the brake cylinder piston is excessively magnified. Ratios up to 14:1, although most undesirable, have sometimes proved unavoidable when clearances were insufficient to allow large brake cylinders to be used; with this ratio a piston travel of $7''$ provides for $\frac{1}{4}''$ clearance between blocks and wheels and $\frac{1}{4}''$ for wear.

The braking of bogie wheels, although increasing the available brake force on the engine, usually involves somewhat heavy maintenance charges.

The use of a steam brake on the engine in conjunction with continuous brakes for the train cannot be unreservedly recommended. With several of the arrangements coming under this category there is considerable disparity in the instantaneous relation between the brake force exerted on the engine and that obtaining on the train; the making of a smooth stop in these circumstances is very difficult, if not impossible.

Brake Rigging. The arrangement of the rigging is independent of the form of brake employed. Two brake blocks should be provided per wheel where possible, in order to increase the value of μ and at the same time eliminate the horizontal thrust to which the axlebox would otherwise be subjected; the "clasp" brake is, however, generally difficult to arrange when there are more than two coupled axles, owing to the limited clearance available between the wheels. The arrangement whereby the blocks (where one block only is provided per wheel) for adjacent coupled wheels act in opposite directions, usually toggle operated, is to be rigorously avoided, as this may subject the coupling rods to direct stresses of dangerous magnitude.

The brake force exerted by the blocks must act radially towards ihe centre of the wheel; the blocks must also be so disposed that their horizontal centre line is slightly below that of the wheels, with due regard to the necessity for the resultant of the spring borne load and the brake force to act within the arc of the axlebox bearing.   With this disposition the brake blocks are assisted to move clear of the wheels when released, this movement being further encouraged, not only by the provision of springs between the blocks and the hangers, but also by so inclining the brake hangers that they tend naturally to return to the "off" position under the action of gravity; it is important to observe that the necessary extent of this movement is increased as the engine bearing springs weaken in service.

The rigging must be so designed that the brake force exerted at the individual blocks is identical for all wheels which are equally loaded, in spite of possible uneven wear on the individual blocks.   Similarly, constant equality of the force must be ensured for each block when two brake blocks are provided per wheel.

The rigging should preferably be so arranged that its constituent members are as far as possible in tension when the brake is applied, thereby reducing weight.

The provision of two equalised pull rods has ultimately an advantage over the use of one rod centrally disposed. Although more care is necessary when taking up or adjusting with the former arrangement, bending moments on the cross beams are appreciably reduced; further, the pull rods may have a lower working stress, and are less liable to spring in practice.   The employment of turnbuckles for adjustment in place of the more usual multi-holed rod ends may be considered; in either case, accessibility must be studied.

When provided for use in conjunction with continuous brakes, the hand brake should be so arranged that it pulls on either the brake cylinder crosshead pin or its lever, thus ensuring that all levers move in the same direction irrespective of whether the brake is applied manually or by power.

The brake shaft should be so designed that the loads are transmitted to the pull rods in the immediate vicinity of the shaft bearings.   The bending moment on the shaft is then, in most instances, so small that it may be safely disregarded, and the shaft made sufficiently strong to resist torsion only.

Let d = diameter of shaft, inches,

f = maximum working shear stress at circumference, tons per square inch,

and T = twisting moment on shaft, inch-tons.

Then (Low)

$$d = 1.72 \sqrt[3]{\frac{T}{f}} \quad \dots\dots\dots\dots\dots\dots\dots\dots\dots\dots\dots\dots\dots \quad (271)$$

The solution of the overall leverage of the rigging and of the forces in its individual members, necessary to determine

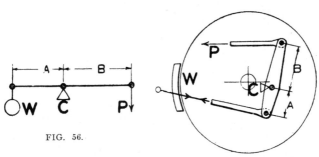

FIG. 56.

the appropriate proportions of the latter, merely involves a simple application of the principle of levers. As a basis, three types of lever must be considered; in each, P is assumed to be the force applied by the brake cylinder or hand brake screw, as the case may be, and W the force transmitted to the wheel by the brake block.

In the first case (Fig. 56), when fulcrum C is located between P and W,

the load on $C = W + P$.

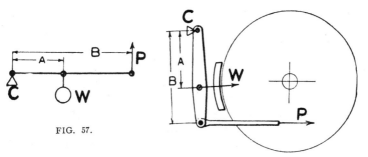

FIG. 57.

Secondly (Fig. 57), when W is interposed between P and fulcrum C,

the load on $C = W - P$.

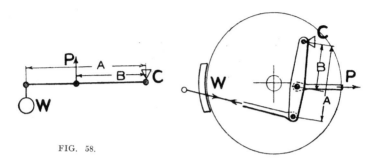

FIG. 58.

Lastly (Fig. 58), when P lies between W and fulcrum C, the load on $C = P - W$.

In each case,

$$W = \frac{P \times B}{A}$$

$$P = \frac{W \times A}{B}$$

$$A = \frac{P \times B}{W}$$

$$B = \frac{W \times A}{P}$$

Fig. 59 is an example of a compensated rigging. Assuming the brake force to be uniformly distributed over the axles,

$$W = P \times \frac{C}{D} \times \left\{ \left(\frac{1}{3} \times \frac{G}{H} \right) + \left(\frac{2}{3} \times \frac{1}{2} \times \frac{G}{H} \right) + \left(\frac{2}{3} \times \frac{1}{2} \times \frac{G}{H} \right) \right\} = P \times \frac{C}{D} \times \frac{G}{H}$$

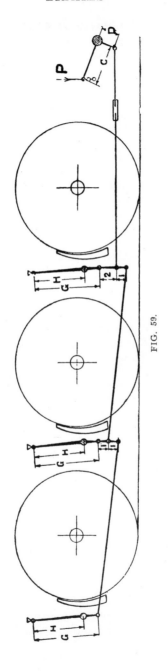

FIG. 59.

The Westinghouse Automatic Brake.

The author is indebted to Messrs. The Westinghouse Brake and Saxby Signal Co. Ltd. for information which has been placed at his disposal and is given below.

The following is an *inventory of the apparatus* on the engine:—

1. Steam stop valve.
2. Compressor governor.
3. Air compressor.
4. Main reservoir, having a minimum capacity of 12-15 cubic feet.
5. Driver's brake valve with regulating feed valve.
6. Brake valve isolating cock.
7. Equalising reservoir.
8. Brake (or train) pipe.
9. Triple valve.
10. Triple valve isolating cock (if not incorporated with triple valve).
11. Auxiliary reservoir.
12. Brake cylinder.
13. Hose couplings (normally 30″ long between engine and tender, and from 18″ to 42″, usual length, 24″ or 26″, at front of engine).
14. Coupling cocks.
15. Duplex gauge, indicating pressures in main reservoir and brake pipe respectively.
16. Drip cup (unless fitted to brake pipe on tender).
17. Release valve.
18. Release spring (only provided if hand brake is fitted in addition).

The tender requires to be fitted with items 8-14 inclusive, also 16 (if not already located on engine), and 18 (in those cases where a hand brake is also provided).

Internal diameters of pipe connections for Westinghouse brake with 8″ × 8½″ × 10″ compressor.

From steam stop valve to compressor .... 1″
Compressor exhaust .... 1¼″
From compressor steam cylinder drain cock to main drain pipe .... ⅛″
Compressor governor connections, including main drain pipe .... ¼″
(6″) Duplex pressure gauge connections .... ¼″
From tee piece to equalising reservoir .... ⅜″

From compressor to main reservoir .... 1″
From main reservoir to driver's brake valve .... 1″
Driver's brake valve exhaust .... $\frac{3}{4}$″
From driver's brake valve to brake pipe .... 1″
Brake (or train) pipe .... 1″
All connections from brake pipe to triple valve, brake
    cylinder and auxiliary reservoir .... $\frac{1}{2}$″

With regard to the last item, 1″ diameter piping is used in conjunction with $3\frac{1}{2}$″ triple valves, for both the ordinary and the quick acting pattern.

The internal diameters of the connections for other sizes of compressor may be found from Table LVII.

TABLE LVII.
INTERNAL DIAMETERS OF CONNECTIONS FOR
COMPRESSORS, WESTINGHOUSE BRAKE.

Compressor.		Steam Inlet.	Steam Exhaust.	Air Discharge.
Dimensions.	Type.			
10″ × $10\frac{5}{8}$″ × 10″	Single Stage	1″	$1\frac{1}{2}$″	$1\frac{1}{2}$″
8″ × $8\frac{1}{2}$″ × 10″	,, ,,	1″	$1\frac{1}{4}$″	1″
8″ × $7\frac{1}{2}$″ × 9″	,, ,,	1″	$1\frac{1}{4}$″	1″
6″ × $6\frac{1}{2}$″ × 9″	,, ,,	$\frac{3}{4}$″	1″	$\frac{3}{4}$″
8″ × $10\frac{5}{8}$″ × $10\frac{6}{16}$″	Tandem Compound	1″	$1\frac{1}{4}$″	$1\frac{1}{4}$″

TABLE LVIII.
OVERALL DIMENSIONS OF COMPRESSORS, WESTINGHOUSE
BRAKE.

Compressor Size.	Maximum Height.	Maximum Width, as seen in elevation.	Vertical C.L. of Compressor to bearing faces of lugs.	Maximum Projection, as seen in plan, from bearing faces of lugs.	Weight, lb.
10″ × $10\frac{5}{8}$″ × 10″	$4'-3\frac{1}{2}$″	$1'-11$″	$7\frac{1}{4}$″	$1'-2\frac{7}{16}$″	647
8″ × $8\frac{1}{2}$″ × 10″	$4'-2$″	$1'-6\frac{1}{2}$″	$6\frac{1}{4}$″	$1'-0\frac{1}{4}$″	408
8″ × $7\frac{1}{2}$″ × 9″	$3'-9$″	$1'-6$″	$6\frac{5}{8}$″	$11\frac{3}{4}$″ (+ $\frac{3}{4}$″ over-hanging lug)	364
6″ × $6\frac{1}{2}$″ × 9″	$3'-7\frac{1}{2}$″	$1'-6$″	$4\frac{13}{32}$″	$9\frac{5}{32}$″ (+ $\frac{3}{4}$″ over-hanging lug)	260
8″ × $10\frac{5}{8}$″ × $10\frac{6}{16}$″	$5-2\frac{11}{16}$″	$1'-8\frac{1}{4}$″	$7\frac{1}{4}$″	$1'-3$″	692

Table LVIII gives the leading dimensions of the various compressors.

Brake Cylinders. The following types of single piston brake cylinder will be considered:—

Type *V*, having lugs for bolting up the cylinder in a vertical position and having a piston of the trunk type, so designed that the piston rod can swing, and also move out, independently of the piston, thus permit-

TABLE LIX.

PARTICULARS OF WESTINGHOUSE BRAKE CYLINDERS, TYPE V.

Diameter (nominal).	Stroke.			Overall Diameter.	Height.	Nett Weight, lb.
	Total.	Maximum Working.	Minimum Working.			
7″				$11\frac{3}{8}$″	$1'-1\frac{1}{4}$″	84
8″				$1'-0\frac{3}{8}$″	$1'-1\frac{1}{4}$	95
10″				$1'-2\frac{3}{8}$″	$1'-1\frac{1}{4}$″	117
13″	$6\frac{1}{4}$″	4″	2″	$1'5\frac{5}{8}$″	$1'-1\frac{5}{16}$″	186
15″				$1'-7\frac{5}{8}$″	$1'-1\frac{5}{16}$″	220
16″				$1'-8\frac{7}{8}$″	$1'-2\frac{5}{8}$″	252
18″				$1'-10\frac{7}{8}$″	$1'-2\frac{5}{8}$″	318

TABLE LX.

PARTICULARS OF WESTINGHOUSE BRAKE CYLINDERS, TYPE VS.

Diameter (nominal).	Stroke.			Width of Flange.	Maximum Width over Cylinder.	Height.	Nett Weight, lb.
	Total.	Maximum Working.	Minimum Working.				
7″				$10\frac{3}{4}$″	$9\frac{1}{2}$″	$1'-1\frac{1}{4}$″	92
8″				$10\frac{3}{4}$″	$11\frac{3}{4}$″	$1'-1\frac{1}{4}$″	104
10″	$6\frac{1}{4}$″	4″	2″	$10\frac{7}{8}$″	$1'-1\frac{3}{4}$″	$1'-1\frac{1}{4}$″	135
13″				$1'-2\frac{1}{2}$″	$1'-5$″	$1'-1\frac{5}{16}$″	204
15″				$1'-7\frac{1}{2}$″	$1'-7$″	$1'-1\frac{5}{6}$″	261

ting the hand brake to be operated without moving the latter.

Type *VS*, similar to the above but provided with side flange for bolting up.

Type *H*, in which the cylinder is so arranged that the piston rod works in the horizontal plane and is constrained to move in a straight line; its attachment to a floating lever is therefore essential.

Type *J*, similar to Type *H*, but fitted with a trunk piston.

Of these cylinders, types *V* and *VS* are suitable for engines, and all are applicable to tenders.

TABLE LXI.

PARTICULARS OF WESTINGHOUSE BRAKE CYLINDERS, TYPES H AND J.

Dimensions.		Length from cr. of fulcrum bracket to cr. of (ordinary) crosshead.	Distance from bearing face of flange to longitudinal centre line.	Maximum Width.	Weight, exclusive of crosshead and fulcrum bracket, lb.	
Nominal Diameter.	Total Stroke.				From	To
6"	8"	$2'\text{-}4\frac{5}{16}''$	$3\frac{1}{2}''$	$8\frac{3}{4}''$	86	98
6"	12"	$2'\text{-}9\frac{1}{16}''$	$3\frac{1}{2}''$	$8\frac{3}{4}''$	93	138
8	8"	$2'\text{-}4\frac{3}{8}''$	$4\frac{1}{2}''$	$10\frac{3}{4}''$	109	125
8"	12"	$2'\text{-}9\frac{1}{8}''$	$4\frac{1}{2}''$	$10\frac{3}{4}''$	128	145
10"	8"	$2'\text{-}4\frac{3}{4}''$	$5\frac{5}{8}''$	$1'\text{-}1\frac{1}{4}''$	162	183
10"	12"	2'-9"	$5\frac{5}{8}''$	$1'\text{-}1\frac{1}{4}''$	172	193
12"	8"	$2'\text{-}4\frac{7}{8}''$	$6\frac{3}{8}''$	$1'\text{-}3\frac{5}{8}''$	219	241
12"	12"	$2'\text{-}9\frac{1}{8}''$	$6\frac{5}{8}''$	$1'\text{-}3\frac{5}{8}''$	237	260
14"	8"	$2'\text{-}4\frac{15}{16}''$	$7\frac{5}{8}''$	$1'\text{-}5\frac{3}{4}''$	255	282
14"	12"	$2'\text{-}9\frac{3}{16}''$	$7\frac{5}{8}''$	$1'\text{-}5\frac{3}{4}''$	304	330

Notes on Table LXI. With a total stroke of 8", the working stroke is 5" maximum and $2\frac{1}{2}''$ minimum. With a total stroke of 12", the working stroke is 8" maximum and 4" minimum. The dimensions of length, as given, obtain when the piston is in the "off" position and, should a slotted crosshead be substituted for the ordinary type, would be increased by 6" in each case.

Triple Valves. Particulars of the ordinary and quick acting types of valve respectively are given in tabular form. It is to be noted that, in the case of the quick acting pattern, the isolating cock is incorporated with it.

TABLE LXII.
ORDINARY TRIPLE VALVES FOR WESTINGHOUSE BRAKE.

Nominal Size.	Overall Height.	Length overall.	Weight, lb.	Suitable for use with Brake Cylinders :—
$2\frac{1}{2}$"	$10\frac{3}{16}$"	$5\frac{15}{16}$"	$14\frac{1}{2}$	6" *H. & J.* 7" *V.* 8" *V.* 8" *H. & J.* 10" *V.*
3"	$11\frac{7}{16}$"	$7\frac{1}{16}$"	$18\frac{3}{4}$	10" *H.* 10" *J.* 13" *V.* 2 × 10" *V.*
$3\frac{1}{2}$"	$11\frac{7}{8}$"	$8\frac{13}{16}$"	29	12" *H. & J* 15" *V.* 16" *V.* 14" *H. & J.* 2×13" *V.* 18" *V.* 16" *H. & J.*

TABLE LXIII.
QUICK ACTING TRIPLE VALVES FOR WESTINGHOUSE BRAKE.

Nominal Size.	Overall Height	Maximum Length (effective).	Width in end elevation.	Weight, lb.	Suitable for use with Brake Cylinders :—
$3\frac{1}{4}$"	1'-$4\frac{3}{8}$"	$9\frac{15}{16}$"	$6\frac{3}{8}$"	45	6" *H. & J* 7" *V.* 8" *V.* 8" *H. & J.* 10" *V.* 10" *H. & J.* 13" *V.* 2×10" *V.*
$3\frac{1}{2}$"	1'-$4\frac{5}{8}$"	$10\frac{11}{16}$"	$6\frac{3}{8}$"	48	12" *H. & J.* 15" *V.* 16" *V.* 14" *H. & J.* 18" *V.* 2×13" *V.* 16" *H. & J.*

TABLE LXIV.
AUXILIARY RESERVOIRS FOR WESTINGHOUSE BRAKE.

Outside Diameter, inches.	Overall Length, inches.	Weight, lb.	Suitable for use with Brake Cylinders :—
15	38	126	16" *H. & J.*
15	32	112	2 × 13" *V.* 18" *V.*
12	47	80	14" *H. & J.*
12	43	76	16" *V.*
12	36	66	15" *V.* 12" *H. & J.*
12	26	54	2 × 10" *V.* 13" *V.* 10" *H. & J.*
10	24	38	10" *V.* 8" *H. & J.*
10	15	28	7" *V.* 8" *V.* 6" *H. & J.*
10	11	25	Equalising reservoir for No. 4 driver's brake valve.

Auxiliary Reservoirs. Table LXIV gives the leading dimensions of auxiliary reservoirs. It should be noted that the auxiliary reservoir nipple increases the weights quoted by 2 lb. in each case.

The Vacuum Automatic Brake.

Much of the information which follows is given by the courtesy of Messrs. The Vacuum Brake Co. Ltd.

The necessary *equipment on the engine* comprises:—

1. Steam stop valve.
2. Combination vacuum ejector.
3. Duplex gauge, recording vacua obtaining in train pipe and vacuum chamber respectively.
4. Train pipe.
5. Brake cylinder(s) with hose connection(s).
6. Hose pipes connecting brake cylinder(s) to train pipe and also to vacuum chamber.
7. Vacuum chamber (if not accommodated on tender).
8. Drip trap with automatic ball valve.
9. Auxiliary maintaining pipe (with ball coupling between engine and tender).
10. End hose pipes, usually from 22″ to 27″ in length, with universal couplings and dummies.

The tender must be provided with items 4, 5, 6, 7 (if not on engine), 9 and 10.

It should be noted that release valves are not required for engine and tender brake cylinders, hand release being effected by means of a valve, immediately below the ejector, in the auxiliary pipe.

Owing to the limited clearances available, the use of the "combined" type of brake cylinder is not usual for engines and tenders. The provision of an independent vacuum chamber is consequently essential; it should not be located at the front of the engine, unless unavoidable, as excessive lengths of piping are thereby necessitated.

Ejector cone sizes are as follows:—

Type.	Small Ejector.	Large Ejector.
" Dreadnought "	20 mm.	30 mm.
" Super-Dreadnought "	Two 15 mm.	30 mm.

Ejector steam consumptions have already been quoted in Chapter VI.

Simple pumps, directly driven from one of the engine crossheads and having a bore of about 5″, are now employed, to an increasing extent, to assist in the maintenance of the required vacuum on express passenger engines, and an appreciable economy in steam consumption thereby accrues. The provision of a relief valve on the pump, set to open when the vacuum exceeds the normal by 1″ or 2″ of mercury, is essential, as otherwise the vacuum obtained at high speeds of revolution may be excessive.

Piping. In order to prevent delayed action of the brake, all piping must be as direct as possible. For the same reason, bends, where necessary, should be to generous radii and elbows as far as possible avoided. Both for accessibility and immunity from maintenance troubles, the ejector exhaust pipe should be external rather than arranged to pass through the boiler, and should have an internal diameter of at least $2\frac{1}{4}$″ or $2\frac{3}{8}$″. It must be as straight as possible and provided with a $\frac{3}{8}$″ drain hole for the removal of condensate at its lowest point, *i.e.*, in the pipe branch within the smokebox.

The internal diameter of the train pipe (iron piping) is 2″, its thickness approximating to $\frac{3}{16}$″. The auxiliary maintaining pipe on the engine and tender is of $\frac{3}{4}$″ pipe, the flexible pipe connections to the brake cylinders having also an internal diameter of $\frac{3}{4}$″.

Representative *dimensions adopted for copper piping on the engine* are:—

Location or Purpose.	Internal Diameter.	Thickness, W G.
Steam pipe from stop valve to ejector	$1\frac{1}{4}$″	10
Ejector drain pipe	$\frac{3}{8}$″	16
From vacuum gauge to train pipe and to vacuum chamber	$\frac{1}{4}$″	16

Wrought iron piping, having an internal diameter of 2″, is used for the connection between ejector and train pipe; the vacuum chamber pipe connections are of the same material and usually have an internal diameter of $\frac{3}{4}$″.

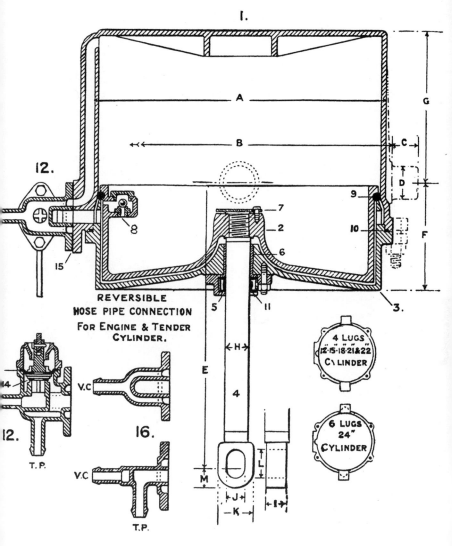

FIG. 60 (See Table LXV).

TABLE LXV.

DIMENSIONS OF SEPARATE TYPE BRAKE CYLINDERS, "F" CLASS, FOR VACUUM AUTOMATIC BRAKE.

Diameter	12″	15″	15″	18″	18″	21″	21″	22″	24″	24″
Stroke	6″	9″	8″	9″	8″	9″	12″	9″	12″	9″
A.	1′-0 1/2″	1′-3 5/8″	1′-3 5/8″	1′-6 5/8″	1′-6 5/8″	1′-9 5/8″	1′-9 5/8″	1′-10 5/8″	2′-0 5/8″	2′-0 5/8″
B.	1′-1 3/8″	1′-4 3/8″	1′-4 3/8″	1′-7 3/8″	1′-7 3/8″	1′-10 1/4″	1′-10 1/4″	1′-11 1/2″	2′-1 1/2″	2′-1 1/2″
C.	1 1/2″	1 5/8″	1 5/8″	1 5/8″	1 5/8″	2″	2″	2″	2″	2″
D.	1 3/4″	2″	2″	2″	2″	2″	2″	3″	3″	3″
E.	11 7/8″	1′-5 7/16″	1′-3 15/16″	1′-5 7/16″	1′-3 15/16″	1′-5 9/16″	1′-10 1/16″	1′-6 11/16″	1′-10 1/16″	1′-7 5/16″
F.	4 11/16″	6 1/2″	6″	6 1/2″	6″	7″	8 1/2″	7″	9″	7 1/2″
G.	5 7/8″	9 3/16″	7 11/16″	9 1/4″	7 11/16″	8 3/4″	11 3/4″	8 3/4″	11 1/4″	8 1/4″
H.	1″	1 1/2″	1 1/2″	1 1/2″	1 1/2″	1 1/2″	1 1/2″	1 3/4″	1 3/4″	1 3/4″
I.	7/8″	1 1/4″	1 1/4″	1 1/4″	1 1/4″	1 1/4″	1 1/4″	1 1/2″	1 1/2″	1 1/2″
J.	1 3/16″	1 3/16″	1 3/16″	1 3/16″	1 3/16″	1 3/16″	1 3/16″	1 3/16″	1 3/16″	1 3/16″
K.	1 9/16″	2 1/4″	2 1/4″	2 1/4″	2 1/4″	2 1/4″	2 1/4″	2 1/4″	2 1/4″	2 1/4″
L.	1 1/4″	1 3/4″	1 3/4″	1 3/4″	1 3/4″	1 3/4″	1 3/4″	1 3/4″	1 3/4″	1 3/4″

For the significance of Table LXV see Fig. 60, which also shews the individual parts numbered as follows:—

1. Cylinder.
2. Piston.
3. Cylinder casing.
4. W.I. piston rod coated with brass.
5. Piston rod packing box.
6. Piston rod guide bush.
7. Piston rod cap.
8. Ball valve.
9. Rolling ring.
10. Joint ring.
11. Piston rod gland packing ring.
12. Reversible release valve.
13. Diaphragm for release valve.
14. Seating ring for release valve.

TABLE LXVI.
DIMENSIONS OF SEPARATE TYPE BRAKE CYLINDERS, "E" CLASS, FOR VACUUM AUTOMATIC BRAKE.

Diameter	12″	15″	18″	21″	22″	24″
A.	$12\frac{1}{2}''$	$1'\text{-}3\frac{5}{8}''$	$1'\text{-}6\frac{5}{8}''$	$1'\text{-}9\frac{5}{8}''$	$1'\text{-}10\frac{5}{8}''$	$2'\text{-}0\frac{5}{8}''$
B.	$13\frac{3}{8}''$	$1'\text{-}4\frac{3}{8}''$	$1'\text{-}7\frac{3}{8}''$	$1'\text{-}10\frac{1}{4}''$	$1'\text{-}11\frac{1}{2}''$	$2'\text{-}1\frac{1}{2}''$
C.	$1\frac{1}{2}''$	$1\frac{5}{8}''$	$1\frac{5}{8}''$	$2''$	$2''$	$2''$
D.	$1\frac{3}{4}''$	$2''$	$2''$	$2''$	$3''$	$3''$
E.	$11\frac{7}{8}''$	$1'\text{-}3\frac{15}{16}''$	$1'\text{-}3\frac{15}{16}''$	$1'\text{-}3\frac{1}{2}''$	$1'\text{-}6''$	$1'\text{-}6''$
F.	$4\frac{11}{16}''$	$6''$	$6''$	$6''$	$7''$	$7''$
G.	$6\frac{7}{16}''$	$8\frac{3}{16}''$	$8\frac{3}{16}''$	$8\frac{3}{16}''$	$9\frac{5}{16}''$	$9\frac{5}{16}''$
H.	$1''$	$1\frac{1}{2}''$	$1\frac{1}{2}''$	$1\frac{1}{2}''$	$1\frac{1}{2}''$	$1\frac{1}{2}''$
I.	$\frac{7}{8}''$	$1\frac{1}{4}''$	$1\frac{1}{4}''$	$1\frac{1}{4}''$	$1\frac{1}{4}''$	$1\frac{1}{4}''$
J.	$\frac{13}{16}''$	$1\frac{3}{16}''$	$1\frac{3}{16}''$	$1\frac{3}{16}''$	$1\frac{3}{16}''$	$1\frac{3}{16}''$
K.	$1\frac{9}{16}''$	$2\frac{1}{4}''$	$2\frac{1}{4}''$	$2\frac{1}{4}''$	$2\frac{1}{4}''$	$2\frac{1}{4}''$
L.	$1\frac{1}{4}''$	$1\frac{3}{4}''$	$1\frac{3}{4}''$	$1\frac{3}{4}''$	$1\frac{3}{4}''$	$1\frac{3}{4}''$
M.	$\frac{7}{8}''$	$1\frac{1}{4}''$	$1\frac{1}{4}''$	$1\frac{1}{4}''$	$1\frac{1}{4}''$	$1\frac{1}{4}''$

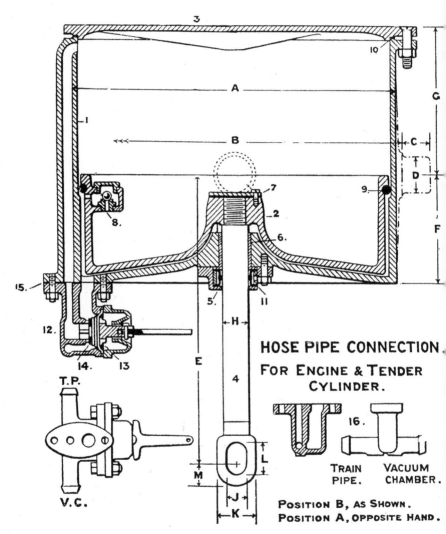

HOSE PIPE CONNECTION.
FOR ENGINE & TENDER
CYLINDER.

TRAIN PIPE.   VACUUM CHAMBER.

POSITION B, AS SHOWN.
POSITION A, OPPOSITE HAND.

FIG. 61 (See Table LXVI).

15. Insertion joint for release valve.
16. Reversible hose pipe connection for engine and cylinders.

For the significance of Table LXVI reference should be made to Fig. 61, which also shews the individual parts numbered as follows:—

1. Cylinder.
2. Piston.
3. Cylinder casing.
4. W.I. Piston rod coated with brass.
5. Piston rod packing box.
6. Piston rod guide bush.
7. Piston rod cap.
8. Ball valve.
9. Rolling ring.

TABLE LXVII.

EFFORTS OF VARIOUS SEPARATE TYPE VACUUM BRAKE CYLINDERS, TOGETHER WITH APPROPRIATE VACUUM CHAMBER DIMENSIONS.

Brake Cylinder.		Effort (cwt.) with initial vacuum of 20″		Total maximum leverage of brake rigging.	Vacuum Chamber.	
Diameter (inches).	Stroke (inches)	Actual at half stroke.	Theoretical.		Diameter.	Length.
12	6	8	10	7 : 1	12″	3′-0″
12	8			9 : 1		
15	6	14	16	7 : 1	16¼″	3′-3″
15	8			9 : 1		
18	6	20	23	7 : 1	17″	4′-0″
18	8			9 : 1		
21	7½	28	31	8 : 1	19″	4′-0″
21	9			1 : 1		
22	9	31	34	10 : 1	20″	4′-6″
24	9	36	40	10 : 1	22″	4′-6″
27	9	45	51	10 : 1	24″	4′-6″
30	9	55	63	10 : 1	26″	4′-6″

    10. Joint ring.
    11. Piston rod gland packing ring.
    12. Release valve.
    13. Diaphragm for release valve.
    14. Release valve seating ring.
    15. Insertion joint for release valve.
    16. Hose pipe connection for engine and tender cylinders.

CENTRE of GRAVITY and WEIGHT DISTRIBUTION.

For any engine of large dimensions and conforming closely to the loading gauge, the height of the centre of gravity above rail level can only be controlled within narrow limits, this dimension usually being between 5'-0" and 6'-0" for modern British standard gauge engines, and from 6'-0" to 7'-0" in Continental practice.   A high centre of gravity improves the riding characteristics of the engine, consequently reducing wear of tyres and permanent way; the only point to be observed in connection therewith is that the mass of the engine, acting vertically downwards, shall be sufficient to overcome the greatest tendency to overturn.

Let W = weight of locomotive, lb.,
    M = speed, miles per hour,
    R = radius of curve, feet, and
    C = centrifugal force, lb.

Then, taking g as 32.2 feet per second per second,

$$C = \frac{WM^2}{14.95R} \quad\dots\dots\dots\dots\dots\dots\dots\dots\dots\dots\dots\dots\dots\dots\dots \quad (272)$$

Fig. 62 (a) is a diagram of an engine on a superelevated curve, where

    X = vertical distance from line of action of centrifugal force to top of outer rail, inches, and
    Y = horizontal distance from line of action of weight of locomotive to centre of outer rail, inches.

Then, for equilibrium,

$$\frac{WM^2X}{14.95\,R} = WY$$

$$\text{whence } M = \sqrt{\frac{14.95\,RY}{X}}$$

The state of equilibrium is, however, unstable and, to allow for this, it has been suggested that a factor of safety of 2 be adopted, the safe speed being obtained from

$$M = 0.5 \sqrt{\frac{14.95 \ RY}{X}}$$ .... (273)

Alternatively, the superelevation of the outer rail may be disregarded. Referring to Fig. 62 (b),

Let G = one half the distance between rail centres, inches, and

H = height of centre of gravity of locomotive above common level of rails, inches,

Then

$$M = \sqrt{\frac{14.95 \ RG}{H}}$$ .... (274)

In the transverse plane, the centre of gravity is generally assumed to be symmetrically located, i.e., on the vertical centre line of the engine. Although the disposition of air and

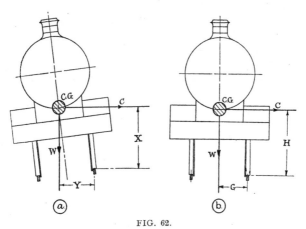

FIG. 62.

feed water pumps, for instance, detract from the accuracy of this assumption, the effect on the engine as a whole is negligible; the only appreciable error likely to arise occurs in the case of two-cylinder compounds. Limitations imposed by the strength of the permanent way demand that, longitudinally, the centre of gravity of the engine shall be located in the vicinity of the line bisecting the total wheelbase. If placed near the trailing end, uneven loads on the coupled wheels result, causing the engine to pitch when running.

The longitudinal position of the centre of gravity is determined, when the loads on, and spacing of, the axles are known, by the principle of moments. Let the total weight of the engine be W, and the loads on the individual axles, w_1, w_2, w_3, w_4 . . . Further, take any convenient datum point, from which W acts at an unknown distance X, and the individual axle loads at distances x_1, x_2, x_3, x_4 . . . . . . respectively.

Then,

$$WX = w_1 x_1 + w_2 x_2 + w_3 x_3 + w_4 x_4$$

whence, as a general expression,

$$X = \frac{\Sigma\, wx}{W} \quad \dots\dots\dots\dots\dots\dots\dots\dots\dots\dots\dots\dots\dots\dots\dots (275)$$

The following method for the approximate determination of the individual axle loads, when the total weight of the engine and the longitudinal position of its centre of gravity are known, is due to Mr. T. H. Sanders. Assume the springs to be of equal strength, i.e., having uniform deflection per unit load, and the spring rigging identical throughout the engine. Let the spring deflection at the leading axle be x, and at the trailing axle, $(x + y)$. The deflection for intermediate axles is assumed to be proportional to their relative position in the total wheelbase, e.g., if the total wheelbase be l, then the deflection for an axle distant n from the leading axle is

$$x + \frac{n}{l}\, y$$

Further, let the known total weight of the engine be W, acting at a distance A from any selected datum point; the individual axle loads act at varying distances B from this point.

Then

$$WA = \Sigma\, (x + y)\, B$$

and $\quad W = \Sigma\, (x + y)$

These equations are solved simultaneously to evaluate x and y. In connection with the foregoing, it should be noted that

(i) y may be either positive or negative in value, and

(ii) the terms " spring deflections " and " weights " are synonymous and interchangeable.

The position of the centre of gravity should be determined on two bases:—

(*i*)   That for the spring borne weight, which affects spring design.

(*ii*)   That for the total weight on rail, in order to comply with permanent way restrictions.

These values are again subdivided, in the case of tank engines, according to whether the engine is in full working order or has the tanks and bunker either empty or partially depleted. In spite of the fact that the total engine weight is reduced in these latter circumstances, it may be found on investigation that the location of the tanks is such that the weights on certain axles, usually at the leading end, are increased to an undesirable extent.

The variation in the longitudinal positions of the centres of gravity for spring borne weight and total weight on rail respectively is small, and will probably be found not to exceed 6″. It is at the same time obvious that the unsprung details, comprising wheels and axles, axleboxes, coupling rods, part of the total mass of the connecting rods and of those motion details which are directly attached to the axles (see Chapter IX, section on balancing), should be minimised in weight; they may represent 20% of the total in modern design. Typical weights of wheels and axles, which may be used for approximations applicable to standard gauge engines, are as follows:—

Pair of carrying wheels and axle .... 1.25—1.5 tons.

,,   ,, coupled wheels, up to 5′-0″ diar.,
and axle .... 2.25—2.5 tons.

,,   ,, coupled wheels, over 5′-0″ diar.,
and axle ....   3 tons.

,,   ,, driving wheels, up to 5′-0″ diar.,
and crank axle ....   3.25 tons.

,,   ,, driving wheels, over 5′-0″ diar.,
and crank axle ....   4 tons.

A fair allowance for a gunmetal axlebox would be 0.1 ton, and for a pair of coupling rods, suitable for a six-coupled engine, 0.5 ton.   These weights, as previously stated, are, although representative, purely approximate, and should be accepted for the present purpose only in the event of more definite data not being available.

The weights on individual axles are mainly determined by the longitudinal position of the centre of gravity; variation of individual axle loads may, however, be effected to a certain extent by the provision of adjustable hangers for the springs or of compensating gear in which the equalising beams have alternative fulcra. It is hardly necessary to add that the utilisation of either of these methods will not change the position of the centre of gravity. In the case of an engine having but two axles (0-4-0), variation of the individual axle loads can only be effected by redistribution of the spring borne components, thereby altering the position of the centre of gravity; adjustment of spring hangers in this particular instance merely disturbs the alignment of the frames.

In general, it is essential that the weights on all the coupled axles of an engine shall be as nearly as possible equal. The weight placed on leading bogies or trucks must be sufficient to enable them effectively to guide the engine when traversing curves under all running conditions; the effects of track depression, the drawbar pull, frontal air pressure and the upward thrust on the slidebars all conspire to reduce the static weight distribution at the leading end when the engine is in motion. The usual practice is to make the static load on leading trucks about one half of that on the adjacent coupled axle; in the case of a bogie, the total weight taken by it is approximately equal to that on the contiguous coupled axle. As a general statement, these proportions should be regarded as minima.

FLEXIBILITY ON CURVES.

Play in Rigid Wheelbase.

Consideration will now be given to the radius of the minimum curve which can be negotiated, but not at speed, by a given engine.

Let R = radius of curve,
B = rigid wheelbase, and
C = total lateral movement of axle.
Then, adopting a uniform unit of length,
$$B^2 = 2\,RC - C^2$$

The value of C^2 is relatively very small, and may therefore be neglected.

Hence,

$$B = \sqrt{2\,RC} \quad\dotfill\quad (276)$$

$$R = \frac{B^2}{2\,C} \quad\dotfill\quad (277)$$

and $C = \dfrac{B^2}{2R}$ .... (278)

The foregoing formulæ apply essentially to four-wheeled vehicles. They may, however, be used in connection with engines having a greater number of axles if the trailing axle, *i.e.*, the last axle to enter the curve, is able, and may therefore be legitimately assumed, to take up a position radial to the curve negotiated by the engine. Should the extent of C be insufficient to justify this assumption, then this radial position will fall at some point within the wheelbase, at a distance X from the trailing axle, given (von Borries) by

$$X = \frac{B}{2} - \frac{RC}{B} \quad .... (279)$$

The engine may then be drawn in position accordingly on the curve to be traversed.

It is customary, in the case of main line engines for the standard gauge in this country, to provide sufficient flexibility to enable them to traverse a minimum curve of 5 chains radius; in certain instances a minimum of 4.5 chains has been stipulated.

Lateral movement of the coupled axles is possible:—

(1) Between the tyre flange and the rail. Thin flanged tyres should be employed only for intermediate coupled wheels, as otherwise the engine will " hunt " on its rigid wheelbase, this latter condition being emphasized should a bogie or truck be adjacent to coupled axles provided with thin flanged tyres.

(2) Between the axlebox flanges and horn guides. This dimension is in some instances, where long rigid wheelbases are unavoidable and occur in conjunction with curves of small radius, increased beyond the normal fitting allowance. This necessitates the adoption of a spherical contour either for the crankpins or the coupling rod brasses of the axles concerned.

(3) Between the axlebox bearings and the axle journals.

(4) By an increase of the rail gauge on curves. This device is commonly employed on the Continent, but not to the same extent in this country.

The most obvious method of ascertaining whether an engine has sufficient flexibility to traverse the stipulated minimum curve is to superpose the wheelbase on a curve drawn to the same scale. The great disparity of the dimensions concerned, however, renders difficult the attainment of a satisfactory degree of accuracy, and the adoption of Roy's method may therefore be recommended. Herein, B, a portion of the curve to radius R, and C are so set out graphically that, if C is drawn full size, then B and R may be to scales of $\dfrac{1}{n}$ and $\dfrac{1}{n^2}$ respectively, the value of n being adjusted to suit the size of drawing sheet available.

Bogies.

The wheelbase of bogies for standard gauge engines usually ranges from about 6'-6" to 8'-0". This dimension should be made as large as possible on account of the marked improvements effected, both in riding and in guiding qualities, as the wheelbase is lengthened. The permitted side play varies approximately from 2" to 5" each way, the lower limit representing British practice of some years ago, and the higher, modern American practice. A definite tendency to increase the side play may now be observed in this country, and displacements of from $3\frac{1}{2}$" to 4" on either side of the central position are becoming common; this is not altogether influenced by the general increase occurring in the length of the total engine wheelbase, and may be in part attributed to recognition of the fact that the provision of flexibility beyond the essential minimum is beneficial generally.

In some cases the bogie centre pin is located excentrically with relation to the wheelbase, and may be about 6" from the line of bisection, i.e., nearer the trailing axle, for wheelbases of the order of 7'-0".By this means the possible lateral movement of the leading axle is increased, and a certain amount of weight at the same time transferred to the trailing axle. It is claimed for this arrangement that the functioning of the bogie generally is improved.

It was pointed out by the late Mr. S. R. M. Porter (Proc. I. Mech. E., 1934) that the flange forces at the wheels of a leading bogie can be reduced, and the side control springs at the same time more than doubled in strength, if:—

> With the bogie pivot remaining at the bisection of the bogie wheelbase, the control springs are moved 6" to 8" to the rear, and the trailing bogie boxes are given at least $\frac{3}{8}$" more side play than the leading boxes.

This procedure, however, impairs the performance of the bogie when trailing, and is therefore applicable only to engines which are turned at the end of each trip.

The swing link type of bogie is rarely adopted in modern practice; there is no doubt that a bogie in which the lateral movement is spring controlled is far superior from the point of view of riding qualities, the tendency to "hunt," for instance, when running on a straight road being almost entirely absent. This point is substantiated by some graphs published in Mr. Dendy Marshall's work, *The Resistance of Express Trains*.

The slot in the stretcher for the bogie centre pin is customarily straight, but in a few instances radial slots have been provided. The centre bearing should be of large diameter in order to improve the transverse stability of the engine. In a few designs, chiefly of Continental origin, part of the weight is taken by widely spaced side bearings. The bogie then oscillates with the main frames, but the stretcher, by reason of the fact that it does not take the whole of the load transmitted to the bogie, may be of lighter construction than is customary.

The side control springs, which may be either helical or laminated, are arranged with an initial compression of from 0.75 to 2 tons, the final compression when under load ranging from 2 to 4 tons. Special attention must be paid to their design and housing as, should one fail, the riding of the engine is unbalanced, and further, these springs, especially if of the laminated type, are frequently inaccessible, thus preventing ready replacement; as regards the actual controlling action, laminated springs are preferable.

Limitations of the available clearances sometimes dictate the use of coiled bearing springs for the axleboxes. They are, however, very sensitive, and their employment usually results in an excessively "lively" bogie as regards movement in the vertical plane. The more usual suspension, typical of British practice, *viz.*, a long inverted laminated spring acting on a cradle, or equalising beam, is decidedly advantageous. The static deflection of such springs varies considerably in practice, in some designs being as small as $1\frac{1}{4}''$, and in others, up to $3''$.

The plate frame bogie offers several advantages when compared with the bar frame construction. The latter comprises a continuous top bar forming the sides and ends of the bogie frame; pedestal bars or castings, connected at their lower extremities by tie bars, are bolted under it, and the centre casting is also bolted to it. With this arrangement:

1. Longitudinal rigidity is mainly in the top bar, and therefore too high above the axle centres.
2. The end cross staying is at the same level, and therefore suffers from the same disability.
3. As with bar type main frames, the bearing surface available for the horn guides is limited and there is no allowance for wear in consequence.

With the plate frame, on the other hand:

1. Rigidity is provided in the frame where most necessary.
2. The location of the transverse staying is sufficiently low to prevent whipping of the horn spaces.
3. Ample bearing area is provided for the boxes in the horn guides.
4. The centre casting is substantial, may be attached well down in the frames and extended towards the frame ends.

Pony Trucks and Radial Axles.

Pony trucks are now almost universally employed, in preference to radial axles, as they enable the desired extent of flexibility to be achieved with greater facility. Cases have occurred in the past in which the arc on which a pony truck or radial axle swings has been struck from the centre of the rigid wheelbase, with the result that the damping effect on the "hunting" of the engine was minimised. Several formulæ have been deduced for the determination of the appropriate radius, and two are given hereunder.

According to von Borries,

$$r = \frac{D^2 - B^2}{2\,D} \qquad\qquad\qquad\qquad\qquad (280)$$

And to J. D. Baldry,

$$r = \tfrac{1}{2}\left(E - \frac{F^2}{E}\right) \qquad\qquad\qquad\qquad (281)$$

In the foregoing,

r = radius for radial axles, or effective length of bar in the case of pony trucks,
D = total wheelbase of engine,
B = rigid wheelbase of engine,

E = distance from axis of truck or radial axle to centre of rigid wheelbase, and

$$F = \frac{B}{2}$$

Uniformity of units employed must of course be observed.

The minimum total lateral movement, G, to be provided may be found (von Borries), for any given curve of radius R, from

$$G = \frac{D^2-B^2}{2R} \quad\dotfill (282)$$

The side movement of trailing trucks is about 4″ or 5″ each way in America, and although this amount is now being approached in European practice, the play at present allowed in some cases is only from 1″ to 1½″ each way.

TANKS, BUNKERS AND TENDERS.

Imperial gallons × 0.1606 = cubic feet.
Cubic feet × 6.227 = Imperial gallons.
1 ton of typical British bituminous coal occupies approximately the same cubic space as 275 Imperial gallons of water.

Tank Engines : Water Tanks.   Saddle tanks are rarely adopted in modern designs as they possess several disadvantages.   The centre of gravity of the engine may be raised to an undesirable extent and the fluctuation of its position, due to the difference between full and empty tanks, is relatively great; for these reasons the application of saddle tanks is usually confined to shunting and other engines which are not intended to run at high speeds.   The enginemen's look-out is also restricted, and the irregular contour of platework tends to increase constructional and maintenance costs alike. Lastly, there is the possibility of sufficient radiant heat being absorbed from the boiler to prevent the ordinary type of injector from picking up.   Pannier tanks are preferable to the saddle type, as most of these objections do not apply to quite the same extent.

With regard to side tanks, insufficient attention is often devoted by British designers to the question of accessibility of the firebox side stays.   When necessary to deal with the latter from the outside, it should not be essential to remove the side tanks in the first instance, and the tanks should, if possible, be located ahead of the firebox. In such cases a cover plate conforming to the general outlines of the tank may be provided, in order to achieve continuity of line, if minimisation of air resistance and the less important question of appearances are being studied.

The actual location of the tanks is usually determined by axle load restrictions, the required position of the centre of gravity of the engine and, to a certain extent, by adhesion. Where necessary to arrange a clearance in the tank, *e.g.*, to permit of access to inside motion, the provision of longitudinal connecting pipes, below the tank, must not be omitted, as otherwise a portion of the tank is isolated and, therefore, ineffectual.

Suitable cross connecting pipes must also be provided to effect uniform discharge of water, and the feed outlets so located that either of the injectors, or the feed pump, as the case may be, is capable of utilising the whole of the available water in the tank. Wash plates must be provided to prevent surge, and also to brace the tanks structurally, and suitable vents arranged to relieve the pressure of air, wherever it may be trapped whilst the tank is being filled.

When the tanks are of large dimensions the tank top at the leading end may be inclined downwards, in order to increase the range of the enginemen's outlook, and also, in those instances where the inner sides of the tanks conform to the outline of a tapered boiler, to distribute uniformly the weight of the water.

The filler must be sufficiently large to act as a manhole, and be provided with a sieve in addition to those fitted over the actual feed outlets. Hand holes should be provided to enable the latter easily to be removed from the outside for periodical cleaning. The filler orifice, except when a condenser is provided, must naturally be at a higher level than that of the top plate of the tank.

Either $\frac{3}{16}''$ or $\frac{1}{4}''$ plate may be used for the tank side sheets, the joints for riveted work being made almost invariably with asbestos millboard.

Bunkers. Care must be taken that no dead space is formed, on either side of the coal door, from which it is difficult or impossible for the fireman to obtain coal, as otherwise the fuel accumulates there and eventually becomes stale. As additional water tanks are in many instances arranged at the bottom of the bunker, the best method of overcoming this difficulty is to make the bunker self-trimming; the provision of this latter characteristic is in any event to be recommended.

The side coal rails, or preferably plates, should be so inclined that the range of vision through the rear spectacles which, incidentally, should be as large as can conveniently be arranged, is not in any way impaired when the bunker is fully loaded with coal. Similarly, the end plates should also be inclined inwards in order to eliminate the risk of injury from falling coal when enginemen or others are manipulating the couplings.

Tenders. The design of axles and axleboxes has already been considered (see Chapter IX), and many of the preceding general remarks on tanks also apply here.

It is important that the water and fuel capacities of the tender, which of course affect its weight, should not exceed the normal maximum requirements by a large margin; the only effect of a heavy tender is to reduce the remunerative load which the locomotive is capable of hauling. The water capacity may be considerably reduced when troughs are available and **water scoops** fitted.

The scoop should preferably be power operated; manually actuated gears, more especially with handwheel control, are slow in action, and the available leverage is not always sufficient to lift the scoop from the trough against heavy resistance. The provision of a large drain pipe having its mouth level with the top of the tank, to mitigate possible flooding of the footplate, is most desirable.

The air release pipe must be of generous cross sectional area, and the hinged scoop must be adjustable, in order that the stipulated dip below the water level in the trough, about 2″, may be constant, irrespective of wear of tyres, etc. Provision should also be made for the positive locking of the scoop in the "up" position for normal running. The angle between the water level and the scoop, when in the "down" position, may be about 25°. Innovations in scoop design on the L.M.S.R., having as dual objects the reduction of water wastage at the troughs and an increase in the quantity picked up by the tender, involve the fitting of a flanged external lip around the body of the scoop and the provision of an independent deflector. The latter, which is placed 1′-4″ in front of the scoop, is of inverted U form, the two side arms or vanes projecting vertically downwards into the trough, the vanes being somewhat closer together at the back than at the front. The effect of the motion of this deflector through the water, in advance of the scoop, is to throw the water inwards, so that it is heaped up at the centre of the trough, the level being coincidentally reduced at the sides.

In the absence of scoops, bogie tenders may be necessary; owing to oscillation, their riding qualities compare unfavourably with those of the six wheeled type usually adopted in British practice.

Tender Frames are usually of $\frac{3}{4}''$ or $\frac{7}{8}''$ plate, tank sides and well plates $\frac{1}{4}''$ thick, with $\frac{5}{16}''$ or $\frac{3}{8}''$ plate for the tank bottom. The front plates are generally stiffened with supplementary plates about $\frac{3}{8}''$ thick. A suitable angle section for tank work is $2\frac{1}{2}'' \times 2\frac{1}{2}'' \times \frac{3}{8}''$ and, unless welding is adopted, $\frac{1}{2}''$ rivets with a pitch of approximately $1\frac{5}{8}''$ may be employed. The top of the main frames is generally about 4'-0" above rail level in British standard gauge practice, and the well has a depth of from 1'-0" to 1'-6".

The filler hole may be about 1'-6" in diameter. On certain tenders of Continental design a rectangular filler lid, equal in length to the tank, is provided, thus allowing considerably more latitude when drawing up to take water. The benefit of this arrangement is especially marked on those occasions when it is necessary to take water at intermediate stations without detaching from the train.

It will be found convenient to provide the tanks with shackles for lifting purposes.

Tool boxes or cupboards and tank water gauges should, for obvious reasons, be so located that access may be had to them at any time without the necessity for negotiating the fuel space arising.

The outlet pipe from fuel oil storage tanks may be extended for a short distance vertically into the tank and the latter provided with a drain cock, so that any water or other foreign matter present in the tank may be discharged from the "dead" space so formed, and not find its way into the burners.

Coal Door and Firing Step. The coal door should be of plate, and should open by sliding across the tender rather than vertically, thereby eliminating unnecessary exertion on the part of the fireman; the runners should be at the top of the door plate, as far removed from the firing step as possible. The use of grilles in place of doors is not to be recommended; they are very liable to jam with anthracite and bituminous grades of coal, and also provide a free passage to the cab for coal dust as the tender becomes partially empty.

The tender firing step should be at a higher level than the bottom of the firehole so that gravity is again utilised to assist the fireman. The longitudinal distance from firing step to firehole must also be determined by purely practical considerations, and must be such that, having loaded his shovel at the firestep, the fireman merely has to pivot on his heels to discharge the coal through the firehole without being obliged to take an additional pace forward; at the same time, sufficient room must be provided for him to swing his shovel back when he wishes to feed the front portion of the grate, and also to permit of free use of the fire irons. An appropriate dimension is from 6'-0" to 7'-0".

$\frac{3}{16}$" or $\frac{1}{4}$" plate is sufficiently robust for the coal door, provided that the edges be reinforced, e.g., with half-round section beading. To allow for wear, the plate forming the firing step itself should be of substantial section and capable of easy replacement without involving any work inside the tank.

The footboard must be at such a height that the fireman is sufficiently above his grate and that at the same time his head is clear of the cab roof. With British loading gauges the firing floor should therefore be from 5'-0" to 5'-6" above rail level. The firing step of the tender may be about 1'-6" or 1'-9" above the firing floor (i.e., engine footplate), and the bottom of the firehole, naturally, somewhat less.

It is most important that the whole of the footboard within the cab should be at one level, and the provision of " steps," at the sides, for instance, is not to be encouraged.

Tender Coal Space. The tender is a very unsatisfactory vehicle from the aerodynamic point of view. Throughout the time it is in motion air currents impinge on the irregular surface presented by the coal, eddying thence into the cab; tender front plates may be observed which encourage this process. A considerable improvement would be effected by roofing in self-trimming coal spaces completely with an easily removed cover of plate, this procedure, in conjunction with the usual coal watering arrangements, having the additional merit of mitigating the evil of coal dust in the cab. This principle has been elaborated and carried into effect, as a patented feature, on certain Beyer-Garratt articulated engines, on which the coal is disposed in rotating, inclined, and therefore self-trimming, hoppers.

SUPERSTRUCTURES.

Although each has its individual function to fulfil, none of the superstructures contributes directly to the fundamental purpose of the locomotive as a generator of power. Such details must therefore be so designed that their weight is a minimum. To this end the thinnest possible plate must be utilised, necessary rigidity being secured by the use of angle, tee and other suitable rolled sections as stiffeners, and advantage may be taken of the wide scope offered for the replacement of riveted work by welded joints.

The only justifiable exception to weight reduction lies in the outside auxiliary frames. These, if well braced, have a considerable, although indeterminate, effect on the structural rigidity of the locomotive as a whole, and assist the main frames in the attainment of this object; their thickness, for standard gauge engines, may be about $\frac{3}{8}''$ or $\frac{1}{2}''$. The actual section of the angle employed in conjunction with the auxiliary frames is necessarily determined to a large extent by individual features of the design under consideration, but in any event the thickness of the metal should not be less than $\frac{1}{2}''$.

As a clumsy device to increase adhesion, although by a negligible amount, it was common practice in the past to cast sandboxes, splashers and other superstructures in iron. It is now generally recognised that a more generously proportioned boiler is a far more profitable method of achieving the same end.

External Footplate or Platform. $\frac{3}{16}''$ mild steel plate is sufficiently strong for this purpose. Although special brackets are necessary in places to secure the plating to the main frames, full use should be made of any outside motion plates, cylinder castings, etc., which may be extended where required for this purpose. A substantial gusset is essential to make a joint with the buffer beam, especially when side buffers are used. The plating should preferably be altogether clear of the coupled wheels, or at least raised to such an extent that free access may be had to the coupling rod and, if outside, connecting rod brasses, when on top centre, and also to the motion. Should splashers be entirely eliminated, it is advisable to make provision, in the form of plate guards, for the localisation of grit thrown up by the wheels.

The footplating must be so arranged that there is no hindrance to the withdrawal of valves from outside cylinders. Further, chiefly for safety reasons, variations in level of the footplate should be avoided and, if feasible, eliminated entirely.

Support for Pipes. All piping attached to the auxiliary frames and footplate should be secured at short intervals with clips. The latter should in all cases be insulated from the platework with hardwood or fibre packing in order to minimise the effects of vibration on the pipe joints.

Cab. Side sheets and weatherboard may be of $\frac{1}{8}$" mild steel plate with $1\frac{3}{4}$" × $1\frac{3}{4}$" × $\frac{1}{8}$" angle; plating forming foundations for seats should be of stiffer section, say, $\frac{3}{16}$" thick. The cab roof may be either of the same material as the side sheets or of fireproofed wood; the metal is ultimately cheaper, more durable and has a neater appearance, but the latter is lighter, forms a more effective insulation against extremes of temperature, and deadens sound. Irrespective of the material adopted for the roof, the incorporation with the latter of some form of adjustable ventilator, in addition to the one frequently provided in the weatherboard, is to be recommended.

Side windows are appreciated by the enginemen, and either one or two, according to the space available, may be provided. One window on each side should be capable of opening, controlled by clamps; the direction of opening should be longitudinal rather than vertical. In locating the side windows, care must be exercised that as much as possible of the aperture is to the rear of the firebox side, as otherwise the reflected glare from the lights of stations, etc., on the lagging plate by night may easily become disconcerting to the driver.

The front windows should be as large as clearances permit, and so arranged that the driver is normally positioned near them, thus counteracting mirror action in darkness. They may be hinged at the side of the window frame for tender engines, unless forming part of a door giving access to the running board. In the case of side tank engines, the hinges should be located on the top edges of the window frames; the fireirons, if stowed on top of the tank, may then be passed through the aperture without undue risk of breaking the glass. In all cases, other than that of the drop light, the provision of a simple catch or lock, to retain the windows in the open position when desired, is advisable.

The cab roof must be so guttered, with angle of about 1" × 1" × $\frac{1}{8}$" section, that there is no likelihood of water obscuring the vision, with especial reference to that ahead. When the cab roof is extended rearwards for the better protection of the enginemen, the extension should either be hinged or so arranged to slide that no additional stripping is involved when it is required to lift the engine at the trailing end.

Footsteps.   In addition to those affording communication between the cab and permanent way, others should be so located as to facilitate the inspection and rapid oiling of all major bearings.   Where two or more steps are required, they should be staggered and not placed on the same vertical centre line; with the latter arrangement negotiation is difficult and comparatively dangerous.

The steps, which may be of $\frac{1}{2}''$ steel plate, should have the ends radiused upwards and their top surfaces chequered to improve the grip.   If roughened by nibbing with a half round chisel, the resulting roughness is so destructive to the boots that enginemen almost invariably file the nibs flush with the plate, thereby defeating the primary object of this procedure.

Splashers.   When fitted, may be built up with $\frac{1}{8}''$ mild steel plate and $1\frac{1}{2}'' \times 1\frac{1}{2}'' \times \frac{1}{4}''$ angle.   The cost of such splashers, and also their weight, may be reduced by the employment of welded joints in place of riveting.

Sandboxes.   May be of $\frac{1}{8}''$ plate, with welded joints and stiffened with $1\frac{1}{2}'' \times 1\frac{1}{2}'' \times \frac{1}{8}''$ angle.   The boxes must be so located that any sand spilled when filling shall not be liable to fall into the motion or axleboxes.   Provision must be made for the total exclusion of both rain water and that used for locomotive purposes.   Where manually operated valves are employed, the valves should be well within arm's length of the filler hole in order that the removal of any possible obstruction may be facilitated; alternatively, a suitable hand hole with cover must be provided.

Trailing sandboxes, when placed in the cab, must have the filling holes located with due regard to the possible entry of rain water through the side windows, or look-out aperture, in the event of the lid not making a watertight joint.

It is practically universal practice in America and on the Continent to place the sandboxes astride the boiler barrel, and advantage is taken of this procedure, in the U.S.A. at least, to replenish the sand supply by means of compressed air mains installed for the purpose at the sheds.   The chief advantage claimed for this location of the sandboxes is that sand is dried by radiant heat from the boiler; unless ventilation is provided, however, and this implies a means of ingress to the box for atmospheric moisture, the sand will tend to " sweat," and consequently cake. Other objections which may be raised to this practice are inaccessibility as regards removal of possible obstructions, as it is rarely possible for the valves to be within reach of the filler hole as previously recommended, inordinate length of the sandpipes, and the greater potential danger of any spilled sand.

Handrails. May be of $1\frac{3}{8}''$ outside diameter steel tube, with a thickness of either 13 or 12 W.G., in preference to rod, thus reducing weight. By using tubes of suitable dimensions, provision is made for the accommodation of the spindle for the regulator (if located in the smokebox), and controls for the blower valve, ash ejector, or any other smokebox detail operated from the cab. The arrangement, where possible, of the handrail such that it is continuous around the engine may be regarded as a safety measure.

APPENDIX.

Ultimate Tensile Strength and other Particulars of Materials for Locomotive Construction, as specified by the British Standards Institution.

The following extracts from the British Standards Specifications are reproduced by kind permission of the British Standards Institution. Official copies of the specifications may be obtained from the Publications Department of the Institution, 28, Victoria Street, London, S.W.1, price 2s. 2d. post free; the reference numbers given below should be quoted.

1. STEELS.

Reference.	Purpose.	Process of Manufacture.	Ultimate Tensile Strength, tons per square inch.	Maximum Content of Sulphur or of Phosphorus.	Remarks.
B.S.S. No. 24. Part 1—1928.	*AXLES.* Crank Axles.	Acid Open Hearth.	28—53.	0.04%	
	Straight Axles.	Acid Open Hearth.	35—40.	0.04%	Yield Point not less than 50% of tensile strength.
	Straight Axles.	Acid or Basic Open Hearth or Acid Bessemer.	35—40.	0.05%, if Basic Open Hearth.	
B.S.S. No. 24. Part 2—1928.	*TYRES.* *Class C.* *Class D.* *Class E.*	Acid Open Hearth.	50—55. 56—62. 63—69.	0.04%	

Reference.	Purpose.	Process of Manufacture.	Ultimate Tensile Strength, tons per square inch.	Maximum Content of Sulphur or of Phosphorus.	Remarks.
B.S.S. No. 24. Part 4—1930.	FORGINGS. Class A. Special Forgings which will be case hardened.	Acid or Basic Open Hearth or Electric.	24—28.	0.05%	Maximum Manganese content, 0.07%
	Class B. Ordinary and boiler forgings.	Acid or Basic Open Hearth or Electric.	26—32.	0.05%	
	Class C. Special forgings without wearing surfaces, also rolled bars.	Acid Open Hearth or Electric.	32—38.	0.05%	
	Class D. Special forgings with wearing surfaces, also rolled bars.	Acid Open Hearth or Electric.	40—45.	0.05%	Yield Point not less than 50% of tensile strength.
	CASTINGS. Castings with wearing surfaces.	An approved process.	35—40.	0.06%	
			Over 40.	0.06%	
	Other General Castings and Wheel Centres.	An approved process.	26.	0.06%	
B.S.S. No. 24. Part 6—1929.	BOILER WORK. PLATES.	Acid or Basic Open Hearth.	26—30.	0.05%	
	SECTIONS, FLATS and BARS, other than Rivet Bars.	Acid or Basic Open Hearth.	26—32.	0.05%	
	RIVET BARS.	Acid or Basic Open Hearth.	24—28.	0.05%	

Reference.	Purpose.	Process of Manufacture.	Ultimate Tensile Strength, tons per square inch.	Maximum Content of Sulphur or of Phosphorus.	Remarks.
B.S.S. No. 53—1927.	BOILER WORK—continued. COLD DRAWN WELD-LESS TUBES (including superheater smoke and element tubes).	Open Hearth	20—26.	Sulphur, 0.035% Phosphorus, 0.030%	With minimum elongation of 28% on 8" length of tube. Standard sizes:— 1⅝" o.d., 13, 12 & 11 S.W.G. 1¾", 1⅞" & 2" o.d., 12, 11 & 10 S.W.G. 2¼" o.d., 11 & 10 S.W.G.
B.S.S. No. 5009—1924.	HIGH CARBON NICKEL STEEL TUBES.		45.	0.05%	Minimum Yield Point, 38 tons per square inch. Carbon, 0.3—0.4%. Nickel, 2.75—3.5%. Manganese, 0.35—0.65%.
B.S.S. No. 24. Part 6—1929.	PLATES, SECTIONS, BARS and RIVETS, NOT APPLIC-ABLE TO BOILER WORK. (Strengths given apply only to thicknesses or diameters of 5/16" or over). PLATES. For other than cold flanging or pressing.	Acid or Basic Open Hearth.	26—32.	0.06%	
	For cold flanging or pressing.	Acid or Basic Open Hearth.	24—28.	0.06%	

429

Reference.	Purpose.	Process of Manufacture.	Ultimate Tensile Strength, tons per square inch.	Maximum Content of Sulphur or of Phosphorus.	Remarks.
B.S.S. No. 24. Part 6—1929.	PLATES, SECTIONS, BARS and RIVETS, NOT APPLICABLE TO BOILER WORK—continued.				
	SECTIONS and FLATS.				
	For other than welding or cold working.	Acid or Basic Open Hearth.	26—32.	0.06%	
	For welding or cold working.	Acid or Basic Open Hearth.	24—28.	0.06%	
	ROUND and SQUARE BARS.				
	For other than welding or cold working.	Acid or Basic Open Hearth.	26—32.	0.06%	
	For welding or cold working	Acid or Basic Open Hearth.	24—28.	0.06%	
	RIVET BARS.	Acid or Basic Open Hearth.	24—28.	0.06%	
B.S.S. No. 32—1935.	STEEL BARS FOR AUTOMATIC, SEMI-AUTOMATIC AND TURRET LATHES.				
	Grade 1. Grade 2. Grade 3.		Cold drawn and rolled — Min. 35/28/28; Other finishes — Min. 35/28/26	0.06% 0.06% From 0.08% to 0.15%	Grade 3 will not withstand shock loads.

2. IRON (" Best Yorkshire "). B.S.S. No. 51—1929.

Form in which manufactured.	Ultimate Tensile Strength, tons per square inch.
PLATES.	
With Grain.	
¼" and under 1" in thickness.	21—24.
Over 1" in thickness.	20—24.
Across Grain.	
¼" and under 1" in thickness	20 (minimum).
Over 1" in thickness	20—24.
ROUNDS AND SQUARES.	
⅜" to $\frac{9}{16}$" diameter or side	22—25.
¾" diameter or side	21—24.
1" and upwards, diameter or side.	21—23½.
FLATS, ANGLE AND TEE SECTIONS. ...	21—24.

3. COPPER. B.S.S. No. 24 Part 5—1925.

Analysis:—
Copper ... ... 99.2% (minimum).
Arsenic ... ... From 0.30% to 0.50%.
Antimony ... ... 0.05% (maximum).
Bismuth ... ... 0.01% (maximum).

Purpose.	Minimum Ultimate Tensile Strength, tons per square inch.	Remarks.
PLATES for fireboxes.	14.	
RODS, either rolled or extruded, for STAY BOLTS, RIVETS, etc.	14.5.	
TUBES	14.5.	With minimum elongation of 50% on 2″ when portion of tube used as test piece.
SEAMLESS PIPES.	14.5.	With minimum elongation of 50% on 2″ when portion of pipe used as test piece.

LIST OF PLATES.

INDEX

438 LOCOMOTIVE DESIGN: DATA & FORMULÆ

Printed in Great Britain by Richard Tilling, 106 Great Dover Street, London, S.E.1.

Bombay Baroda and Central India Railway Company

Telephone No. .... Office

....

No. ....

Dated .... 19 ....